MECHANICAL VIBRATIONS

BERNARD MORRILL

ASSOCIATE PROFESSOR OF MECHANICAL ENGINEERING
SWARTHMORE COLLEGE

THE RONALD PRESS COMPANY · NEW YORK

Copyright, ©, 1957, by

THE RONALD PRESS COMPANY

All Rights Reserved

Library of Congress Catalog Card Number: 57-8293

PRINTED IN THE UNITED STATES OF AMERICA

To my wife
BERNICE

PREFACE

The teaching of mechanical vibrations to senior mechanical engineering students at Swarthmore College has been the stimulation necessary to encourage the writing of this text. The material presented in this book is intended to serve for a first course in mechanical vibrations for undergraduate or graduate students. The ultimate aim is to present the basic elementary vibration theory in a manner sufficiently rigorous so that the student will extend himself to master the mathematical techniques which will serve him as a useful tool in his further studies.

The theory of mechanical vibrations has its roots firmly embedded in mathematics and, in particular, in the field of differential equations, both of the ordinary and the partial differential type. Of necessity, an introductory text must be limited to linear differential equations and, as a result, to linear systems of vibrations. The question of how far the mathematical treatment can be pushed in an introductory text must arise in every teacher's mind. The answer to this question must be dependent upon the prior mathematical preparation of the student. This text assumes that the student is adequately grounded in integral calculus. Therefore, a rather full treatment of the solution of a second order linear differential equation is contained in Chapter 2. Mastering the techniques of the second order linear differential equation will serve as the necessary mathematical tool for the next three chapters.

In order to prepare the student adequately for further study or research in the literature of the field of mechanical vibrations, however, a minimum coverage in the field of partial derivatives and partial differential equations must be given. The introductory section of Chapter 6 deals with partial derivatives. A sufficient discussion of partial derivatives has been given so that the Lagrange equations can be developed. By using the Lagrange equations as a tool, a new vista of the solution of problems in mechanical vibrations is opened. The introduction of the solution of partial differential equations in Chapter 7 by means of the method of the separation of variables again extends the area of solution of problems in the field of mechanical vibrations; namely, vibrations in a continuous medium. The last chapter, entitled "Miscellaneous Topics," introduces the electrical analogy, the mobility method, and an elementary discussion of the analogue computer.

v

The influences that have fostered this text are many. The texts of Timoshenko, Den Hartog, and Hansen and Chenea have been of particular influence. However, the author must also acknowledge the effect of all other texts listed in the bibliography, for they have played no small part in his education. He is especially grateful to his colleagues, Dr. David Rosen and Professor Carl Barus, who have read and critically commented upon several chapters.

BERNARD MORRILL

Swarthmore, Pennsylvania
   February, 1957

CONTENTS

MECHANICAL
VIBRATIONS

CHAPTER 1

DYNAMICS OF A PARTICLE

1-1. Introduction. The study of vibrations covers a vast field. Vibrations are not only a part of many scientific areas; they are also a part of our daily lives. Seismic recordings thousands of miles from the center of an earthquake give evidence of the part vibrations play in seismology. Vibrations are the input and output of our radio. The disastrous finale of the Tacoma Narrows bridge resulted from the building up of the amplitude of vibration caused by the aerodynamic forces of the wind. The vibrations of an automobile passing over a rough road are well known to all of us. These are only a small sampling of the examples of vibrations that might be given.

It is because vibrations play such an intimate part in our daily lives that the study of vibrations has such importance. To make a complete study of vibrations is well beyond the scope of this text. This text, therefore, will deal with the limited field of mechanical vibrations. In fact, it is written to serve as an introductory text to the subject of mechanical vibrations.

The question may arise in the reader's mind why so much study should go into this limited field. The answer in part lies in the fact that in studying mechanical vibrations we deal primarily with detrimental vibrations and that it is very important that those vibrations be analyzed, thereby making possible the first steps in controlling them. While washing machines have been known, in the past, to shear their bolt fastenings because of excessive vibrations, new types remain firm on the floor without fastenings because their vibrations have been controlled. It is incumbent, therefore, upon the design engineer today not only to design a machine but to be able to control the design so that mechanical vibrations neither destroy the machine itself nor make the machine obnoxious.

Mechanical vibrations are a part of the study of dynamics. It is necessary, therefore, to be conversant with the field of kinematics and kinetics to be properly prepared to study mechanical vibrations. The equations of motion for a vibratory system stem directly from a study of the force system acting upon the body which is in motion. It is necessary, therefore, to understand the nature of the displacement, velocity, and accelera-

3

tion of the body under study. This text will accent three different approaches in determining the equations of motion. For relatively simple systems, the Newtonian and energy approaches will be used; for complex systems, the Lagrangian approach.

The Newtonian method is based upon the well-known second law of Newton which states that the sum of the forces is equal to the mass times the acceleration $(F = ma)$.* The mass in problems of mechanical vibrations is usually a constant, and the Newtonian approach may be considered dependent upon a study of the acceleration of the mass.

The energy method will be used to complement the Newtonian approach. There are types of simple vibratory problems that are more readily solved by an energy balance than by force determination. The energy method, as it will be used in this text, will be applied only to systems in which the energy level is constant at all times; that is, the sum of the potential energy and the kinetic energy remains constant.

The Lagrangian method is not as readily defined as the Newtonian. This difficulty is primarily due to the fact that the Lagrangian method is not introduced in elementary dynamics. It will suffice to say that energy, both potential and kinetic, is fundamentally involved. In the case of potential energy, a study of displacements is necessary; in the case of kinetic energy, the prime concern is with the velocity.

In each of the three approaches to the problem of mechanical vibrations an analysis of one or more of the kinematic properties of displacement, velocity, and acceleration must be made. It is therefore necessary to devote a portion of this chapter to a study or review of kinematics.

1-2. Kinematics of a Particle. Let us first define a particle. A body which is so small that its position in space may be determined by the coordinates of a single point may be defined as a particle. We may extend this definition to cover bodies which are relatively large as long as we deal with the center of mass of the body as defining the body. This device will be used in this text as long as the body may be classed as a rigid body. A rigid body will be defined as one not possessing elastic properties.

The motion of any particle may be considered to consist of two parts: (1) translation and (2) rotation. No matter how complex the motion of a particle is at any given instant, the motion may be defined by translation superposed on a pure rotation. It is therefore necessary to study these two components of motion. Let us consider a particle in pure translation first. Fig. 1-1 shows a particle, A, moving in a straight line in the x-y plane. At any time t it is ρ distance away from the origin O. The broken line represents the path of motion with time. We may at any time t define the position of A by a coordinate system. Two coordinate

---

* This is not the statement made by Newton. See the Section 1-4 on Kinetics for a clarification of this statement.

systems lend themselves very nicely to defining the position of A: polar coordinates and Cartesian coordinates.

In the polar coordinate system, A is uniquely defined by ρ and θ, where ρ is a function of time and θ is a constant. In the Cartesian coordinate system, both x and y, where x and y are each functions of time, also define the particle A. However, we must also know the relationship between x and y. This relationship is readily determined by the slope of the path of motion. The polar coordinate system is usually a simpler system than the Cartesian system for defining the above path of motion. Since either system defines the motion of A, then there must be some connecting link between the two systems. That link is

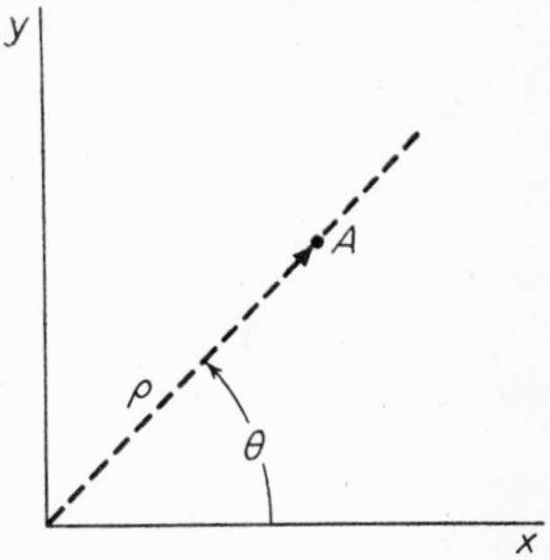

$$x = \rho \cos \theta$$

and $\qquad\qquad\qquad\qquad\qquad\qquad\qquad$ (1–1)

$$y = \rho \sin \theta$$

Fig. 1–1.

Eqs. (1–1) permit one to move from the polar coordinate to the Cartesian coordinate system and vice versa. All of the above can be readily extended to a three-dimensional system when the polar coordinate system is replaced by cylindrical coordinates.

Now that we have defined the position of particle A we can proceed to find its velocity and acceleration. In general, if we define s as the displacement of a particle then

$$v = \frac{ds}{dt}$$

and $\qquad\qquad\qquad\qquad\qquad\qquad\qquad$ (1–2)

$$a = \frac{dv}{dt} = \frac{d^2s}{dt^2}$$

where v = velocity
$\qquad a$ = acceleration

Since s is equal to the vector addition of x and y, then

$$v = \frac{ds}{dt} = \frac{dx}{dt} + \frac{dy}{dt}$$

and $\qquad\qquad\qquad\qquad\qquad\qquad\qquad$ (1–3)

$$a = \frac{d^2x}{dt^2} + \frac{d^2y}{dt^2}$$

Applying Eqs. (1–3) to Eqs. (1–1) we get

$$v = \frac{d\rho}{dt} \cos \theta + \frac{d\rho}{dt} \sin \theta = \frac{d\boldsymbol{\rho}}{dt}$$

and

$$a = \frac{d^2\rho}{dt^2} \cos \theta + \frac{d^2\rho}{dt^2} \sin \theta = \frac{d^2\boldsymbol{\rho}}{dt^2}$$

(1–4)

To simplify the notation for derivatives with respect to time, let us use the Newtonian time derivative notation of a dot above the dependent variables, that is,

$$\frac{dx}{dt} = \dot{x} \qquad \frac{dy}{dt} = \dot{y}$$

$$\frac{d^2x}{dt^2} = \ddot{x} \qquad \frac{d^2y}{dt^2} = \ddot{y}, \quad \text{etc.}$$

Then Eqs. (1–4) may be written as

$$v = \dot{\boldsymbol{\rho}}$$

and

$$a = \ddot{\boldsymbol{\rho}}$$

(1–5)

It can be seen from Eqs. (1–4) or (1–5) that the velocity and acceleration are independent of θ. This result, of course, is to be expected since θ is independent of time; in fact, θ is a constant. Eqs. (1–5) lead us to another, a simpler, way of getting the velocity and acceleration. Let us consider the particle A to be defined in the polar coordinate system. A single vector, which we shall call a position vector, will define particle A. A vector is defined by three properties: (1) magnitude, in our case ρ, (2) inclination, θ, (3) sense, the arrowhead as depicted in Fig. 1–1.

In our case, since θ is a constant, we can see that $v = \dot{\boldsymbol{\rho}}$ and $a = \ddot{\boldsymbol{\rho}}$ can be directly obtained by differentiating the magnitude of the vector. It will be seen later on that the derivative of a vector is composed of two components: the derivative of the magnitude, and the magnitude times the derivative of the inclination. In our case the inclination is constant, and therefore its derivative has vanished. The sense of the new vector is dependent upon whether ρ is increasing or decreasing. An increasing ρ gives $\dot{\boldsymbol{\rho}}$ an outward sense, while a decreasing ρ gives $\dot{\boldsymbol{\rho}}$ an inward sense.

The same treatment may be repeated for $\dot{\boldsymbol{\rho}}$, which is now a velocity vector. The acceleration is the derivative of the vector $\dot{\boldsymbol{\rho}}$ and it is $\ddot{\boldsymbol{\rho}}$. Its inclination is still θ and its sense depends upon whether $\dot{\boldsymbol{\rho}}$ is increasing or decreasing.

Let us now consider a particle which is in rotation. For a start, let us consider a particle which is moving in a circular orbit in the x-y plane,

Fig. 1–2. Furthermore, let the angular velocity ω be constant; then

$$\rho = R = \text{constant}$$

and (1–6)

$$\theta = \omega t$$

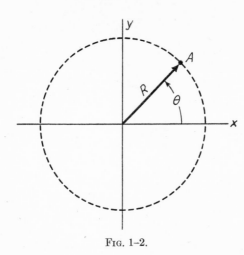

Fig. 1–2.

Again we may define A by a position vector R, where the magnitude is constant and the inclination, θ, is a function of time, or we may define A by Eq. (1–1), which now becomes

$$x = R \cos \theta$$
$$y = R \sin \theta$$

(1–7)

We find the velocity and acceleration of A by applying the general Eq. (1–3)

$$v = \dot{x} + \dot{y} = -R (\sin \theta)\dot{\theta} + R (\cos \theta)\dot{\theta}$$

and (1–8)

$$a = \ddot{x} + \ddot{y} = -R(\cos \theta)\dot{\theta}^2 - R(\sin \theta)\ddot{\theta} - R(\sin \theta)\dot{\theta}^2 + R(\cos \theta)\ddot{\theta}$$

Since $\dot{\theta} = \omega$ and $\ddot{\theta} = 0$, we may rewrite Eq. (1–8) as

$$v = R\omega(\cos \theta - \sin \theta)$$

and (1–9)

$$a = -R\omega^2(\cos \theta + \sin \theta)$$

Let us plot the velocity vectors of Eq. (1–9). First we must define a sign convention for θ. Let us take θ positive if it is increasing clockwise and θ negative if it is increasing counterclockwise. Then θ in Fig. 1–2 is negative. Fig. 1–3 shows the component velocity vectors and their resultant plotted.

We can see that a single vector $R\omega$ represents the velocity of particle A. Moreover, $R\omega$ is perpendicular to R, the position vector, which can be

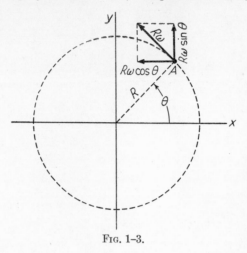

FIG. 1–3.

readily shown by similar triangles. This means that the velocity vector is out of phase with the position vector by 90°. The sense of the velocity vector is in the direction of increasing θ.

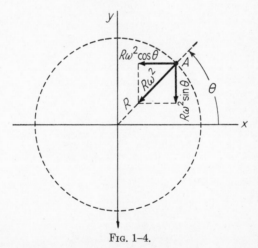

FIG. 1–4.

The acceleration components as governed by Eq. (1–9) are sketched in Fig. 1–4. Note that the resultant acceleration vector is always inward since it is not dependent upon whether θ is positive or negative, since ω is always a squared term.

Let us pause at this point to draw some conclusions concerning the velocity and acceleration vectors of the above restricted case of particle motion. To recapitulate the restrictions of the motion, these restrictions are: (1) the particle is traveling in a circular orbit, namely, R is constant at all times; (2) the angular velocity ω is also constant. Under these restrictions we can draw the conclusion that the velocity vector is 90° out of phase with the position vector R, and its sense is in the direction of the angular displacement. The acceleration vector is 180° out of phase with the position vector, and its sense is always radially inward toward O.

Direct differentiation of the position vector R with respect to time is possible. The derivative of the magnitude, which is constant, is zero. The magnitude times the derivative of the inclination therefore gives us the required result; that is,

$$\frac{d\boldsymbol{R}}{dt} = R\frac{d\theta}{dt} = \boldsymbol{R}\boldsymbol{\omega} \qquad (1\text{--}10)$$

The direction is perpendicular to $\boldsymbol{R}$ and is in the sense of increasing θ. A more general situation may be obtained by discussing the case where there are no restrictions placed upon ρ and θ.

Let us, then, consider the general case of motion where no restrictions are placed on ρ and θ. This means that ρ and θ are each functions of time, and the first and second derivatives of ρ and θ with respect to time are assumed to exist. The previous relations of Eq. (1–1) still hold. To determine the velocity and acceleration, we need only apply the relations of Eq. (1–3). The unrestricted vector is shown in Fig. 1–5.

Then

$$\boldsymbol{v} = \boldsymbol{v}_x + \boldsymbol{v}_y = \dot{\boldsymbol{x}} + \dot{\boldsymbol{y}} \qquad (1\text{--}11)$$

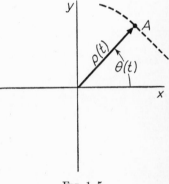

FIG. 1–5.

To find $\dot{\boldsymbol{x}}$ and $\dot{\boldsymbol{y}}$ we must recognize that each is the product of two dependent variables of time; that is, they have the form of $\dfrac{d}{dt}(uv) = \dot{u}v + u\dot{v}$; $x = \rho\cos\theta$, $y = \rho\sin\theta$, $\dot{x} = \dot{\rho}\cos\theta - \rho\dot{\theta}\sin\theta$, $\dot{y} = \dot{\rho}\sin\theta + \rho\dot{\theta}\cos\theta$. Eq. (1–11) then becomes

$$\boldsymbol{v} = \dot{\rho}\cos\theta - \rho\dot{\theta}\sin\theta + \dot{\rho}\sin\theta + \rho\dot{\theta}\cos\theta \qquad (1\text{--}12)$$

The four components of $\boldsymbol{v}$ are plotted in Fig. 1–6a. The four components are combined so that a radial and tangential component defines $\boldsymbol{v}$.

We now can note that the $\boldsymbol{\rho}\dot{\boldsymbol{\theta}}$ component is the same as the $\boldsymbol{R}\dot{\boldsymbol{\theta}}$ component in the case of circular motion or pure rotation and that the $\dot{\boldsymbol{\rho}}$ component is the same as the case of translation. Either of the previous cases of translation and circular motion can be derived from the general case by setting θ = constant in the case of the former and ρ = constant in the case of the latter. The velocity of an unrestricted vector ρ, which is confined to a plane, then can be determined, if so desired, by the superposition of a rotation upon a translation.

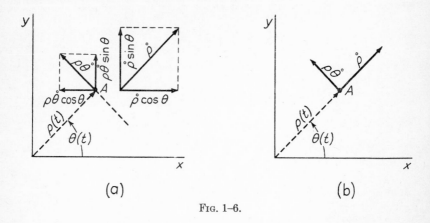

Fig. 1–6.

Let us look at this velocity derivation from another point of view. Let us consider the position vector ρ at inclination, sense, and magnitude as shown in Fig. 1–5. Then the differentiation of this position vector with respect to time yields two resulting components $\dot{\rho}$ and $\rho\dot{\theta}$ as shown in Fig. 1–5. We see that $\dot{\rho}$ is the derivative of the magnitude of the position vector and has the sense and inclination of the original vector. Now $\rho\dot{\theta}$ is the product of the magnitude of the position vector times the derivative of the inclination (angle θ) of the position vector and has the inclination of $90° + \theta$ and has the sense of increasing θ.

Keeping the above in mind, we can derive the components of acceleration from the components of the velocity in the same manner. Differentiation of each of the two velocity components with respect to time will yield two acceleration components for each of the velocity components, or four acceleration components in all. Let us first differentiate the $\dot{\rho}$ component. This differentiation is done in Fig. 1–7a, with the original position vector ρ shown by a dotted arrow and $\dot{\rho}$ by a broken line arrow. We need only apply the rules of the preceding paragraph. Now we differentiate the $\rho\dot{\theta}$ component, which is shown in Fig. 1–7b. Note that the differentiation of $\rho\dot{\theta}$ results in two vectors, one of which has two terms.

Fig. 1–7c combines the vector components of Figs. 1–7a and 1–7b. The two $\rho\dot{\theta}$ components have been combined into a single vector component. The combination of the two $\rho\dot{\theta}$ components is known as Coriolis's component of acceleration.

In the above case, we cannot say that the acceleration of a point moving in a plane can be found by the superposition of the accelerations of a point in translation on a point in rotation. Now $\ddot{\rho}$ is found directly from translation and $\rho\dot{\theta}^2$ is found by a rotation about O with a constant angular velocity. We surmise that $\rho\ddot{\theta}$ would occur if the case of circular motion which we have analyzed were not restricted to constant angular velocity. Coriolis's term of $2\dot{\rho}\dot{\theta}$ would not have been anticipated if we used a superposition method. Therefore, a superposition of translation and rotation accelerations does not apply as does the like superposition for velocity.

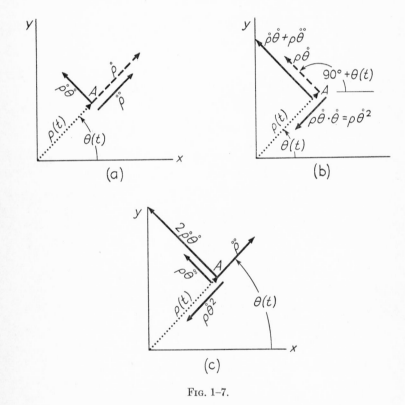

FIG. 1–7.

A few words should be said about Coriolis's component. The existence of this component can be shown to depend upon ρ only. The component will exist when ρ is a function of time. It will not exist when ρ is a constant. Of course $\dot{\theta}$ must exist, otherwise we have a translation, but $\ddot{\theta}$ does not have to exist.

In summation we may say that there are three acceleration components for the general case of plane acceleration:

1. Radial component

$$a_r = \pm\ddot{\rho} - \rho\dot{\theta}^2$$

2. Tangential component

$$a_t = \rho\ddot{\theta} \tag{1-13}$$

3. Coriolis's component

$$a_c = 2\dot{\rho}\dot{\theta}$$

To help the student correlate the Newtonian time derivative notations with the symbols usually used, the following table is given:

$\dot{\theta} = \omega$ Angular velocity

$\ddot{\theta} = \dot{\omega} = \alpha$ Angular acceleration

$\dot{\rho} = v_r$ Radial velocity

$\ddot{\rho} = \dfrac{dv_r}{dt}$ Time rate of change of radial velocity

This text will for the most part use the Newtonian notation, since the accelerations and velocities will invariably become part of the differential equation of motion, and when they are written in the time derivative form they tend to simplify the solution of the differential equation.

For the sake of completeness, Eq. (1–12) should be differentiated so that the acceleration can be determined. In doing so, it soon becomes apparent that the vector differentiation method has many advantages over the direct differentiation method. Differentiation of Eq. (1–12) yields:

$$\begin{aligned}
a = \ &\ddot{\rho}\cos\theta - \dot{\rho}\dot{\theta}\sin\theta - \dot{\rho}\dot{\theta}\sin\theta - \rho\ddot{\theta}\sin\theta \\
&- \rho\dot{\theta}^2\cos\theta + \ddot{\rho}\sin\theta + \dot{\rho}\dot{\theta}\cos\theta + \dot{\rho}\dot{\theta}\cos\theta \\
&+ \rho\ddot{\theta}\cos\theta - \rho\dot{\theta}^2\sin\theta
\end{aligned} \tag{1-14}$$

In the preceding discussion of the kinematics of a particle, the particle had a fixed point as a frame of reference. Supposing, however, that the kinematic properties of a particle A may be determined with reference to another particle B which is not fixed in space. Then the properties found in the preceding discussion are not absolute, but relative to point B. The gap between relative properties and absolute properties, however, is fairly easy to close. Consider three points: A, B, and O (Fig. 1–8), where only O is a fixed point. If the properties of A are known relative to B, that is, with reference to the coordinate axes x'-y', and the properties of B are known relative to fixed point O, that is, the relative properties of B are known with reference to the coordinate axes x-y, then we can determine the absolute properties of A (that is, with reference to the axes x-y) in the following manner. The absolute properties at A equal the absolute properties at B plus the properties of A relative to B. These relations may be expressed in equation form for the displacement, velocity, and acceleration as follows:

$$s_A = s_B + s_{A/B}$$

$$v_A = v_B + v_{A/B} \qquad (1\text{--}15)$$

$$a_A = a_B + a_{A/B}$$

FIG. 1–8.

The subscripts A and B refer to the absolute properties at A and B, and A/B refers to the relative properties of A with respect to B. B/A refers to the relative properties of B with respect to A.

One last point should be made before closing the discussion of kinematic properties. In any rigid kinematic body (we define a rigid kinematic body as one whose particles remain constantly at the same distance from each other) there lies a point whose absolute velocity is zero at a given time t, and there also lies another point whose absolute acceleration at a given time t, is zero. These are known as instant centers of velocity and acceleration. The two instant centers do not necessarily act at the same point.

The use of instant centers for determining kinematic properties can be very helpful when the properties are wanted at a specific time t. However, in the study of mechanical vibrations, the kinematic properties usually must be defined at all values of t so that the solution will be a general one. Therefore it is beyond the scope of this text to discuss the use of instant centers to determine the velocity and acceleration of a body.

Example. A quick return mechanism, Fig. 1–9a, consists of a crank (AB) with a slide attached which in turn controls the rod (BC). If the crank has a length of 2 in. and is rotated counterclockwise at a constant angular velocity of 1 radian per sec., determine the angular acceleration of the rod BC at the moment when AB makes an angle of 30° with the horizontal as shown.

SOLUTION. By means of the law of cosines we find that

$$\rho^2 = (BC)^2 = 2^2 + 4^2 + 2(2 \times 4) \cos 120°$$

$$\rho = 5.291 \text{ in.}$$

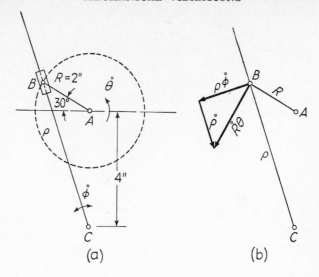

Fig. 1–9.

Then by means of the law of signs

$$\sin \angle CBA = \frac{4(\sin 120°)}{5.291} = \frac{4 \times 0.866}{5.291}$$

$$\sin \angle CBA = 0.6547$$

$$\angle CBA = 40.9°$$

The velocity of point B on AB, Fig. 1–9b, is

$$V_{B \text{ on } AB} = R\dot\theta = 2 \times 1 = 2.0 \text{ in. per sec.}$$

There will be two components of velocity of B on BC which will be the orthogonal components of $V_{B \text{ on } AB}$ taken tangential to and collinear with the rod BC. The tangential component is $\rho\dot{\phi}$ and the collinear component is $\dot{\rho}$.

$$\rho\dot{\phi} = R\dot{\theta} \cos 40.9° = 2 \times 0.7559$$

$$\rho\dot{\phi} = 1.512 \text{ in. per sec.}$$

$$\dot{\phi} = \frac{1.512}{5.291} = 0.286 \text{ radians per sec.}$$

$$\dot{\rho} = R\dot{\theta} \sin 40.9° = 1.309 \text{ in. per sec.}$$

It should be noted that $\dot{\rho}$ is the velocity of the slide on the rod. Actually it is the velocity of B on AB relative to the velocity of B on BC.

Since $\dot{\theta}$ is a constant there is only one component of acceleration, Fig. 1–9c, for the crank AB. That is,

$$R\dot{\theta}^2 = 2 \times 1^2 = 2 \text{ in. per sec. per sec.}$$

Now $R\dot{\theta}^2$ will have a component perpendicular to BC. This orthogonal component is also an orthogonal component of the acceleration of B on BC. Since the orthogonal component is tangential to BC, it must be equal to $\rho\ddot{\phi}$ plus $2\dot{\rho}\dot{\phi}$.

$$2\dot{\rho}\dot{\phi} = 2 \times 1.309 \times 0.286$$

$$2\dot{\rho}\dot{\phi} = 0.749 \text{ in. per sec. per sec.}$$

Then

$$\rho\ddot{\phi} = R\dot{\theta}^2 \times \sin 40.9° - 2\dot{\rho}\dot{\phi}$$

$$\ddot{\phi} = \frac{2 \times 0.6547 - 0.749}{5.291}$$

$$\ddot{\phi} = 0.106 \text{ radians per sec. per sec., clockwise}$$

1–3. Simple Harmonic Motion. During the study of mechanical vibrations, we shall encounter periodic motion as the most common of all motions that we shall analyze. We therefore define periodic motion as one in which the pattern of the motion repeats itself during a fixed interval of time. The interval of time is called a period.

Simple harmonic motion is a frequent type of periodic motion that continuously appears in the study of simple vibratory systems. It is the basis for all periodic motions since any given periodic motion may be expressed as the sum of a series of harmonic motions. We will define simple harmonic motion as the motion of a point moving back and forth along a straight line, the point having an acceleration which is always proportional to its displacement. Expressed mathematically

$$\ddot{x} = -Ax \tag{1-16}$$

where A is a constant of proportionality. The negative sign indicates that the sense of acceleration is always opposite to that of displacement.

Let us look at a displacement which is defined by a trigonometric function; say

$$x = X \cos \omega t \tag{1-17}$$

where X is the amplitude. The angular frequency or angular velocity is denoted by ω, which we will deem a constant. Differentiation of Eq. (1–17) twice with respect to time yields:

$$\ddot{x} = -X\omega^2 \cos \omega t = -\omega^2 x \tag{1-18}$$

By our definition, then, Eq. (1–17) defines simple harmonic motion. Had we used a sine term in Eq. (1–17) in place of the cosine, the result would have been the same, except that the motion would have been 90° out of phase for the $\cos \omega t = \sin (\omega t + 90°)$.

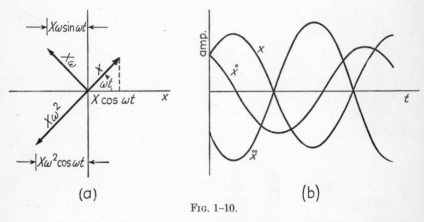

(a)   (b)

Fig. 1–10.

We can extend our concept of a position vector to cover our definition of simple harmonic motion. If a position vector of constant magnitude is rotating at constant angular velocity, ω, then the trace of the rotating vector on either the x or y axis yields simple harmonic motion. The trace of the rotating vector X on the x axis is $X \cos \omega t$ and we have demonstrated that $x = X \cos \omega t$ is simple harmonic motion. The derivatives of Eq. (1–17) may also be plotted as rotating vectors. These are shown in Fig. 1–10a. Fig. 1–10b shows the displacement, velocity, and acceleration plotted against time. They are governed by the equations

$$x = X \cos \omega t$$

$$\dot{x} = -X\omega \sin \omega t \tag{1-19}$$

and

$$\ddot{x} = -X\omega^2 \cos \omega t$$

The phase relationships can be readily seen in either Fig. 1–10a or Fig. 1–10b. The acceleration may be thought of as leading the displacements by 180° and the velocity as leading the displacement by 90°. The angle between the two vectors rotating with the same angular frequency is known as the phase angle. Measuring from the displacement vector X, we can see from Fig. 1–10a that the phase angle between the velocity vector and the displacement vector is 90° and that the phase angle between the acceleration and the displacement is 180°.

The rotating vector makes a complete revolution in 2π radians. The period, τ, which is the time required to complete one cycle, is

$$\tau = \frac{2\pi}{\omega} \quad \text{sec.} \tag{1–20}$$

since $\omega t = 2\pi$ and $t = \tau$. The frequency, which is the number of cycles or periods per second, is the reciprocal of the period or

$$f = \frac{1}{\tau} = \frac{\omega}{2\pi} \quad \text{cycles per sec.} \tag{1–21}$$

If a motion is defined by two or more simple harmonic motions each of which has the same angular frequency ω, but all of which are out of phase with each other, then the harmonic motions may be combined into a single vector representation. Let

$$x = x_1 + x_2$$

where

$$x_1 = A \cos \omega t$$

and

$$x_2 = B \cos (\omega t + \phi)$$

then

$$x = A \cos \omega t + B \cos (\omega t + \phi)$$
$$= C \cos (\omega t + \psi) \tag{1–22}$$

This vector addition is shown in Fig. 1–11.

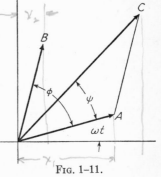

Fig. 1–11.

1–4. Kinetics. The science of dynamics is divided into two parts. In one, kinematics, the geometry of the motion is considered apart from the physical causes of the motion. In the other, kinetics, or, as it is often called, dynamics, the manner in which the motion is produced by the acting forces is investigated. In this section on kinetics the aim will be to derive the differential equation of motion which results from the forces acting on a body. The solution of the differential equation of motion will be considered in Chapters 2 and 3.

Newton's second law of motion may in substance be stated to be that the net force acting on a particle is proportional to the time rate of change of the momentum. Mathematically, the above statement may be expressed as

$$F = \frac{d}{dt}(mv) \qquad (1\text{-}23)$$

The type of problem that we shall attempt to solve in this text will be so restricted that we shall be able to say that the mass is at all times a constant. Under this assumption, then, Eq. (1–23) becomes

$$F = m\frac{dv}{dt} = ma \qquad (1\text{-}24)$$

If the motion of the mass is rotational, then Eq. (1–24) is replaced by

$$T = I\alpha \qquad (1\text{-}25)$$

where T is the external torque, I the moment of inertia about the center of rotation, and α the angular acceleration. Eq. (1–25) is readily derived from Eq. (1–23).

Consider a force acting on a particle at a distance r from the center of rotation. The force times the distance r constitutes a torque about the center of rotation. Then

$$T = Fr = \frac{d}{dt}(mv)r$$

But

$$v = \omega r$$

Hence

$$T = \frac{d}{dt}(m\omega r)r$$

Since m and r are considered to be constant, we get upon differentiation

$$T = mr^2\alpha$$

The term mr^2 is defined as the mass moment of inertia of the particle about the center of rotation, and as a consequence

$$T = I\alpha$$

Of course it is understood that I is a constant.

If the center of rotation coincides with the center of gravity, then we obtain the moment of inertia of the mass in the usual manner with reference to the center of gravity. However, if the two centers do not coincide, we can relate the two moments of inertia by the following relationship:

$$I_{\text{C.R.}} = I_{\text{C.G.}} + m\rho^2 \tag{1-26}$$

where ρ is the distance from the center of gravity to the center of rotation.

By way of demonstrating the application of Eq. (1-24), let us consider a mass supported by a spring which is massless and linear. If the mass is initially displaced and released, it will then oscillate. What we desire to find is the equation of motion of that oscillation. Fig. 1-12a shows the

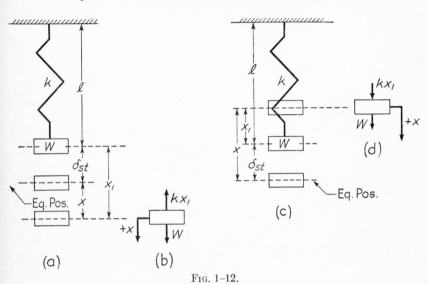

Fig. 1-12.

vibratory system under question. Originally the spring has a length l which we measure to the center of the mass for convenience. When the mass whose weight is W is attached to the spring, the spring will elongate a distance marked δ_{st}, delta static. Since the spring is linear, $W = kx$. Then W/k is defined as δ_{st} and it is a constant. Let us call the position $l + \delta_{st}$ the equilibrium position, inasmuch as this is the position of static equilibrium. The body is now displaced and allowed to oscillate. At any time t, the displacement from the original length is x_1. Let us take a free body of the mass (Fig. 1-12b). There will be a force kx_1 acting upward because of the elongation of the spring and a force W acting downward because of the weight. Taking the downward displacement as positive, so that the acceleration is positive, Eq. (1-24) is now applied.

$$F = ma \tag{1-24}$$

$$-kx_1 + W = \frac{W}{g}\ddot{x}_1 \tag{1-27}$$

Rearranging we get

$$\frac{W}{g}\ddot{x}_1 + kx_1 - W = 0 \qquad (1\text{--}28)$$

From Fig. 1–12a we can see that

$$x_1 = \delta_{st} + x \qquad (1\text{--}29)$$

$$\delta_{st} = \frac{W}{k} \qquad (1\text{--}30)$$

Substituting Eq. (1–29) and then Eq. (1–30) into Eq. (1–28) we get

$$\frac{W}{g}\ddot{x}_1 + k\left(\frac{W}{k} + x\right) - W = 0$$

or

$$\frac{W}{g}\ddot{x}_1 + kx = 0 \qquad (1\text{--}31)$$

We now differentiate Eq. (1–29) twice with respect to time, noting that δ_{st} = constant. We get as a result

$$\ddot{x}_1 = \ddot{x} \qquad (1\text{--}32)$$

Substituting Eq. (1–32) into Eq. (1–31) yields the required equation of motion

$$\frac{W}{g}\ddot{x} + kx = 0 \qquad (1\text{--}33)$$

It is important to note that the resulting equation of motion (1–33) now has its displacements measured from the equilibrium position of the spring, not from the position of the spring when not loaded. Recognizing this fact, we can always neglect $k\delta_{st}$ and the weight of the mass, since these cancel each other. We should, however, be cognizant of the fact that kx is the change of spring force due to a displacement x from the equilibrium position and not the total spring force.

Let us straighten out in our minds the question of sign. The above derivation was made as the mass was moving downward. We will define the displacement and the acceleration as being positive on the downward side of the equilibrium position. The reactive spring force is negative, since the spring is in tension and is opposing motion. Now let us consider the mass as it moves upward. It is still on the positive side of the equilibrium position, so that the displacement is still positive. Fig. 1–12a may also be used to represent this configuration. The acceleration is positive even though it is decreasing. It is important to note this fact, since many students mistake a decreasing acceleration for a negative acceleration.

The spring is still in tension, therefore the spring force is still negative. Eq. (1–33) is valid for this position of analysis.

Now let the mass pass through the equilibrium position on its way upward, Fig. 1–12c. The displacement and acceleration are now negative, but the spring is now in compression and the spring force is now positive, Fig. 1–12d. The equation governing this position is now

$$kx_1 + W = -\frac{W}{g}\ddot{x}_1 \tag{1–34}$$

but now

$$x_1 = x - \delta_{st} \tag{1–35}$$

Then

$$k\left(x - \frac{W}{k}\right) + W = -\frac{W}{g}\ddot{x}_1 \tag{1–36}$$

and since

$$\ddot{x} = \ddot{x}_1$$

$$\frac{W}{g}\ddot{x} + kx = 0 \tag{1–37}$$

which is the same equation of motion as Eq. (1–33).

The last position to be analyzed occurs when the mass is moving downward but still remains on the negative side of the equilibrium position. Fig. 1–12c can still be used for this analysis. The displacement and the acceleration are still negative; the spring force is positive and Eq. (1–37) or Eq. (1–33) still applies. Thus we have seen that for any position of the mass, the single result of Eq. (1–33) is valid.

Let us now consider the problem of a simple oscillating pendulum (Fig. 1–13). The acceleration is tangential to the motion and is $l\ddot{\theta}$. For our analysis we take the position of θ moving outward. This is the direction for positive displacement and acceleration. The force in the tangential direction is $W \sin \theta$ and is opposite to the acceleration. Then by applying Eq. (1–24) we get

$$-W \sin \theta = \frac{W}{g}l\ddot{\theta}$$

Simplifying we get

$$\frac{l}{g}\ddot{\theta} + \sin \theta = 0 \tag{1–38}$$

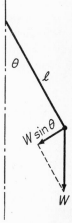

Fig. 1–13.

which is the equation of motion for the pendulum.

We can derive Eq. (1–38) by using Eq. (1–25) instead of Eq. (1–24).

$$T = I\alpha \tag{1–25}$$

We must remember that I is calculated about the center of rotation; then

$$I_{\text{C.R.}} = I_{\text{C.G.}} + m\rho^2 \tag{1-26}$$

The $I_{\text{C.G.}}$ is a negligible quantity in this case since ml^2 ($\rho = l$) is very much larger than the $I_{\text{C.G.}}$. To verify this fact, assume that the pendulum bob is a small cylinder of radius r. The moment of inertia of a cylinder is $mr^2/2$. It can be readily shown that $ml^2 \gg mr^2/2$, since we have defined r to be a small quantity. Then

$$I_{\text{C.R.}} = \frac{W}{g} l^2$$

Applying Eq. (1–25), that is, taking moments about the pivot point, we get, since $\alpha = \ddot{\theta}$,

$$-(W \sin \theta)l = \frac{W}{g} l^2 \ddot{\theta}$$

or

$$\frac{l}{g}\ddot{\theta} + \sin \theta = 0 \tag{1-39}$$

which is the same as Eq. (1–38).

It is interesting to note that the mass of the pendulum plays no part in the equation of motion.

In either the case of the mass and the spring or that of the simple pendulum, a single equation completely defines the motion. This fact is not surprising since in either case a single coordinate x or θ defines the position of the mass. We call such motion a single degree of freedom. In nature, where mass possesses elasticity and each infinitesimal quantity of mass is free to move relative to the other infinitesimal quantities of mass, there exists an infinite number of degrees of freedom. We can think of such a system as a series of small masses, each attached to a spring which represents the elasticity of the mass. A single mass would then consist of an infinite number of masses and springs so interlinked as to represent the total mass and its elasticity. The equations of motion for this case are expressed by an infinite number of equations. In general we can say that the number of degrees of freedom will depend on the number of independent coordinates necessary to define the position of the mass. More will be said about this subject in Chapter 6 in a discussion of generalized coordinates. For the time being we will confine our studies to systems of a single degree of freedom.

1-5. Integration of the Equation of Motion. Let us consider a particle moving in a straight line under the action of several forces F_1, F_2, F_3, etc. The equation of motion is

$$m\ddot{x} = F_1 + F_2 + F_3 + \cdots \tag{1-40}$$

Eq. (1–40) may be rewritten in two different forms:

a.
$$m \frac{dv}{dt} = F_1 + F_2 + F_3 + \cdots \tag{1–41}$$

b.
$$m \frac{dv}{dt} \cdot \frac{ds}{ds} = mv \frac{dv}{ds} = F_1 + F_2 + F_3 + \cdots \tag{1–42}$$

The integration of Eqs. (1–41) and (1–42) yields

$$m(v_2 - v_1) = (F_1 + F_2 + \cdots)(t_2 - t_1) \tag{1–43}$$

and

$$\frac{mv^2}{2} = \int F_1 ds + \int F_2 ds + \cdots \tag{1–44}$$

Eq. (1–43) is the impulse-momentum relationship. In this text we shall make no further use of this relationship, and therefore no additional comments need be made. However, Eq. (1–44) is of particular interest to us. We recognize that $mv^2/2$ is the kinetic energy of the mass and that the integral of the force times a distance is the external work. We can draw the conclusion that the kinetic energy of a system is equal to the external work.

Let us apply this energy concept to the spring and mass problem of the preceding section.

$$F_1 = -kx$$

$$F_2 = F_3 = 0 \tag{1–45}$$

and

$$ds = dx$$

Substituting this into Eq. (1–44) we get

$$\frac{mv^2}{2} = \int -kx \, dx \tag{1–46}$$

Integration yields

$$\frac{mv^2}{2} = -\frac{kx^2}{2} + C \tag{1–47}$$

where C is a constant of integration.

The change of potential energy from the equilibrium position is $kx^2/2$. In fact this change of potential energy is the entire change of potential energy of the system. We denote this quantity as an energy change, for there is a locked-in amount of potential energy when the system is at rest at the equilibrium position. In order to simplify our notational system we shall hereafter refer to the change of potential energy as the potential energy. We can now write that

$$T + V = \text{constant} \tag{1–48}$$

where

$$T = \text{kinetic energy}$$

and

$$V = \text{potential energy}$$

It must be pointed out that Eq. (1–48) was derived for a conservative system. We define a conservative system as one in which the total energy level remains the same; that is, no energy is dissipated or added during its action. In the case of the spring and the mass, we assume that there is no hysteresis loss in the spring.

There are times when it is advantageous to derive the equation of motion from Eq. (1–48). Often it is easier to determine the potential and kinetic energy of a system than to obtain forces and acceleration. This procedure is usually called the energy method for deriving the equation of motion. We can readily demonstrate the energy method by determining the equation of motion for the simple pendulum of Fig. 1–13. The velocity of the pendulum is $l\dot\theta$, and therefore the kinetic energy is

$$T = \frac{W}{2g} (l\dot\theta)^2$$

The easiest way to determine the potential energy of a system is to select a standard position, usually the equilibrium position, and then calculate the change of elevation from that standard position. We select, in this case, the equilibrium position (when $\theta = 0$) as the standard position. Then, in the displaced position, the change of elevation is $l - l \cos\theta$. Consequently $V = Wl(1 - \cos\theta)$. Substituting T and V into Eq. (1–48) we get

$$\frac{W}{2g} (l\dot\theta)^2 + Wl(1 - \cos\theta) = C \tag{1–49}$$

We now differentiate Eq. (1–49) with respect to time. We get

$$\frac{W}{2g} \cdot 2l^2\dot\theta\ddot\theta + Wl (\sin\theta)\dot\theta = 0$$

Simplifying, we get

$$\frac{l}{g} \ddot\theta + \sin\theta = 0 \tag{1–50}$$

which is the same as Eq. (1–38).

We can formalize the above procedure for the energy method by writing

$$\frac{d}{dt} (T + V) = 0 \tag{1–51}$$

as the equation of motion.

We must remember that Eq. (1–51) can be applied only to a conservative system.

Example. A cylinder of radius r and weight W is placed upon a concave cylindrical surface of radius R. When oscillating, the cylinder rolls on the concave surface without slipping. Determine the equation of motion (1) by the direct method, (2) by the energy method.

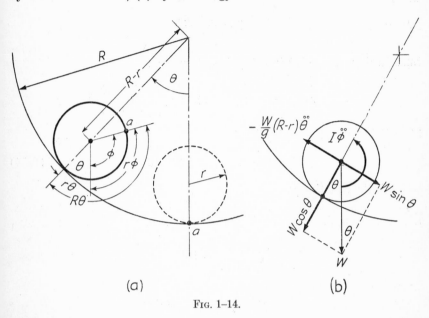

(a)   (b)

FIG. 1–14.

1. *Direct Method.* The broken-line circle in Fig. 1–14a represents the cylinder in the position of equilibrium. The solid-line circle represents the cylinder in the displaced position, having taken positive θ moving clockwise from the equilibrium position. The cylinder will have two components of acceleration, a rotational one and a translational one. Point a originally was the point of contact in the equilibrium position. After displacement, a is located as shown. The absolute rotation of the cylinder is ϕ. Then the angular acceleration is $\ddot{\phi}$. The translational acceleration is $(R - r)\ddot{\theta}$. The mass times these accelerations is shown in Fig. 1–14b along with the weight W and its two components. We take moments about the point of contact in the displaced position, thereby eliminating the need to find the forces at the point of contact.

$$-Wr\sin\theta - \frac{W}{g}r(R - r)\ddot{\theta} = \frac{Wr^2}{2g}\ddot{\phi} \qquad (1\text{–}52)$$

From Fig. 1–14a we can see that due to rolling contact the following relations hold:

$$R\theta = r\theta + r\phi$$

and

$$\phi = \frac{R - r}{r} \theta \qquad (1\text{-}53)$$

Then

$$\ddot{\phi} = \frac{R - r}{r} \ddot{\theta}$$

Substituting Eq. (1-53) into Eq. (1-52), we get:

$$- Wr \sin \theta - \frac{W}{g} r (R - r) \ddot{\theta} = \frac{Wr^2}{2g} \left(\frac{R - r}{r} \right) \ddot{\theta}$$

Simplifying and rearranging yields

$$\tfrac{3}{2}(R - r)\ddot{\theta} + g \sin \theta = 0 \qquad (1\text{-}54)$$

which is the equation of motion.

2. *Energy Method.* The velocity consists of a translation, $(R - r)\dot{\theta}$, and a rotation, $\dot{\phi}$. From the rolling contact relation we have seen that

$$\dot{\phi} = \frac{R - r}{r} \dot{\theta}$$

Then

$$T = \tfrac{1}{2}mv^2 + \tfrac{1}{2}I\omega^2$$

where $mv^2/2$ is the kinetic energy due to translation and $I\omega^2/2$ the kinetic energy due to rotation.

$$T = \frac{1}{2} \frac{W}{g} (R - r)^2 \dot{\theta}^2 + \frac{1}{2} \frac{Wr^2}{2g} \left(\frac{R - r}{r} \right)^2 \dot{\theta}^2$$

$$T = \frac{3}{4} \frac{W}{g} (R - r)^2 \dot{\theta}^2$$

Taking the equilibrium position as the standard position, we get

$$V = W(R - r)(1 - \cos \theta)$$

Applying the equation

$$\frac{d}{dt} (T + V) = 0 \qquad (1\text{-}51)$$

we get

$$\frac{d}{dt} \left[\frac{3}{4} \frac{W}{g} (R - r)^2 \dot{\theta}^2 + W(R - r)(1 - \cos \theta) \right] = 0$$

and

$$\frac{3}{4}\frac{W}{g}(R-r)^2 \cdot 2\dot\theta\ddot\theta + W(R-r)\sin\theta\,\dot\theta = 0$$

Simplifying yields

$$\tfrac{3}{2}(R-r)\ddot\theta + g\sin\theta = 0 \qquad (1\text{--}55)$$

which is the same as Eq. (1–54).

Before we attempt to solve the differential equations of motion, we must pay some attention to the form of the equations. The Eq. (1–33) of motion for the spring and mass is a linear second-order differential equation with constant coefficients. Solution of this type of equation presents no particular problems and will be discussed in Chapter 2. Eq. (1–38), representing the equation of motion of the pendulum, is nonlinear, and its solution does present a problem. There are two approaches to dealing with nonlinear equations: (1) to solve them exactly and (2) to linearize the equation and find an approximate solution. The second system will be employed in this text. The exact solution of Eq. (1–38) can be effected by a change of variable and by employing elliptic functions. If, however, we linearize the equation by assuming that θ is small and that as a first order approximation the $\sin\theta \doteq \theta$, then the linearized equation may be solved by introducing a small error. The amount of the error is less than 1 percent, for $\theta = 30°$.

We shall not try to solve any of the differential equations of motion which we have developed in this chapter. To solve each equation as a separate case can be readily accomplished. However, it will better serve our purpose to solve in general form a single differential equation, the solution of which will be applicable to every case which concerns itself with a single degree of freedom. Therefore, Chapter 2 will be devoted to the general solution for a vibratory system limited to a single degree of freedom.

BIBLIOGRAPHY

BEGGS, JOSEPH S. *Mechanism*. New York: McGraw-Hill Book Co., Inc., 1955.

DOUGHTIE, V. L., and JAMES, W. H. *Elements of Mechanism*. New York: John Wiley & Sons, Inc., 1954.

PLETTA, D. H. *Engineering Statics and Dynamics*. New York: The Ronald Press Co., 1951.

ROUTH, EDWARD JOHN. *A Treatise on Dynamics of a Particle*. New York: G. E. Stechert & Co., [1898].

SLOANE, ALVIN. *Engineering Kinematics*. New York: The Macmillan Co., 1945.

SMART, E. HOWARD. *Advanced Dynamics*. 2 vols. London: Macmillan & Co., Ltd., 1951.

TIMOSHENKO, S., and YOUNG, D. H. *Engineering Mechanics Dynamics*. New York: McGraw-Hill Book Co., Inc., 1937.

PROBLEMS

1-1. A particle moving along a straight line is governed by the equations

$$x = 5t^2 \cos 30° \text{ ft.}$$

$$y = 5t^2 \sin 30° \text{ ft.}$$

Determine the value of the velocity and acceleration at the end of the fourth second.

1-2. A particle moving along a straight line is controlled by the equations

$$x = \rho \cos \theta \text{ in.}$$

$$y = \rho \sin \theta \text{ in.}$$

If $\theta = 37°$ and $\rho = 2t + 4t^3$, determine the velocity and acceleration at the end of the second second.

1-3. A particle is moving along a circle whose radius is 3 ft. If at any time t the magnitude of the velocity is $4t^2$ ft. per sec., determine the angular velocity and angular acceleration at time $t = 2$ sec.

1-4. A cylinder of $r = 1$ ft. rolls on a plane with a uniform angular velocity of 3 radians per sec. Determine the magnitude of the velocity and acceleration of a point on the circumference of the cylinder when the angle of rotation is 60°.

1-5. A particle moving in a plane is governed by the equations

$$x = \rho \cos \theta$$

$$y = \rho \sin \theta$$

Lay out to scale the components of acceleration when $\rho = 2.0$ in., if

$$\rho = 1 + 2t^2 \text{ in.}$$

and

$$\theta = 4t^3 \text{ radians.}$$

Fig. P1–6.

1-6. Two rods which have been hinged together are free to swing as a compound pendulum, as sketched in Fig. P1–6. Determine the velocity of the mid-point of the lower of the two rods.

1-7. Sketch the vector components of the acceleration of the mid-point of the lower rod, Fig. P1–6. [*Hint:* Determine the relative acceleration of the lower rod with respect to the upper rod and apply Eq. (1–15).]

1-8. Show that the equation

$$x = A \cos kt + B \sin kt$$

represents simple harmonic motion.

1-9. Demonstrate that the displacement given by

$$x = A \cos (kt + \phi)$$

where A is a constant and ϕ is a constant phase angle, is simple harmonic motion.

1-10. What is the period of the simple harmonic motion of Problem 1-9?

1-11. At a certain point on the coast the difference between high and low tide is 12 ft. If high tide occurs at 1:30 P.M. and the next high tide is at 2 A.M., determine the height of water above the low level mark at 3:30 A.M., if we may assume that the tide motion is simple harmonic.

1-12. The motion of a particle governed by simple harmonic motion may be expressed by

$$x = 10 \sin (\omega t + 30°)$$

If one of the components is

$$x = 2 \sin (\omega t + 45°)$$

determine the other component of the harmonic motion.

1-13. Determine the differential equation of motion of the mass supported by two springs as shown in Fig. P1-13 if each spring has a spring constant of k.

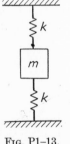

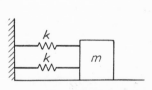

FIG. P1-13.   FIG. P1-14.

1-14. Determine the differential equation of motion of the mass attached to two springs as shown in Fig. P1-14, if each spring has a spring constant of k. The plane upon which the mass slides may be considered to be frictionless.

1-15. By integrating the differential equation obtained for Problem 1-14, determine the kinetic energy of the system if the initial displacement of the mass is x_0.

1-16. Assuming that the solution to the D.E. found for Problem 1-14 may be expressed as simple harmonic motion, so that for an initial displacement of x_0,

$$x = x_0 \cos 2kt$$

determine the impulse-momentum relationship of the system by integrating the differential equation.

1–17. Assuming that the angular displacements of the pendulum (Fig. P1–17) are small so that the displacements of the spring are small, write the expression for the differential equation of motion. Assume that the bar is rigid and weightless.

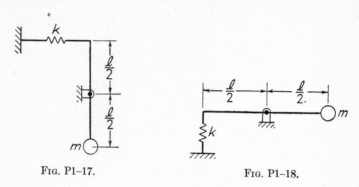

FIG. P1–17. FIG. P1–18.

1–18. Assuming that the angular displacements of the pendulum (Fig. P1–18) are small so that the displacements of the spring are small, write the expression for the differential equation of motion. Assume that the bar is rigid and weightless.

1–19. A bar whose moment of inertia about its own center of gravity is I_G is pivoted on a knife edge at one end and is supported by a spring, as shown in Fig. P1–19. Determine the equation of motion for small displacements of the spring.

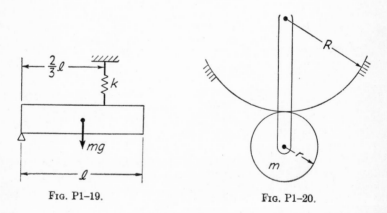

FIG. P1–19. FIG. P1–20.

1–20. A cylinder supported by a weightless arm, as shown in Fig. P1–20, is free to oscillate as it rolls without slipping over a fixed cylindrical surface. Determine by means of the Newtonian approach, and then by the energy method, the equation of motion for the system.

1-21. A pulley, supported by a rod whose torsional spring constant is k_t, is subjected to a tug from a rope. Determine the D.E. equation of motion if the effect of the rope on the oscillations is neglected.

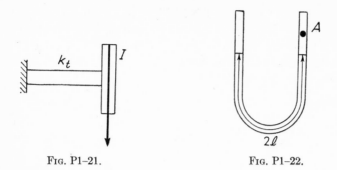

FIG. P1-21.   FIG. P1-22.

1-22. A U-tube manometer has been filled with mercury. The total tube length of the mercury is $2l$ and the cross sectional area is A. The tube is initially disturbed so that the mercury oscillates in the tube. Determine the differential equation of motion of the oscillation.

CHAPTER 2

MATHEMATICS OF A SYSTEM OF A
SINGLE DEGREE OF FREEDOM

2-1. Differential Equation. The differential equation of a system of a single degree of freedom is readily derived by using the Newtonian approach. Let us consider a system that takes in all of the elements of a simple but forced vibratory system. Such a system can be represented by a single mass coupled with a spring and a viscous damper. The spring represents the elasticity of the system; the damper, the energy dissipation of the system. We shall assume that the spring is linear; that is, the force acting on the spring is proportional to the deflection of the spring. This proportionality constant will be denoted by k. The viscous damper, representing the energy dissipation, may be assumed to be a conventional

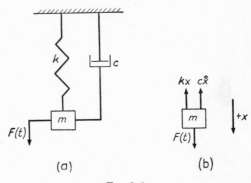

(a)   (b)

Fig. 2-1.

dashpot, and the forces acting on the dashpot shall be assumed to be proportional to the velocity of the piston of the dashpot. This proportionality constant shall be denoted by c. In order to complete the mathematical picture of this system, a forcing function dependent upon time will be added and such a force denoted by $F(t)$. This system is assembled diagrammatically in Fig. 2-1a.

Now if we consider the mass, m, to be displaced downward from its equilibrium position, we can sketch a free body diagram of the mass, Fig.

2-1b. Because of the assumption of the displacement, x will be positive in the downward direction and the general statement of

$$\text{force} = \text{mass} \times \text{acceleration}$$

yields the equation

$$F(t) - kx - c\dot{x} = m\ddot{x}$$

Rearranging this equation, there results:

$$m\ddot{x} + c\dot{x} + kx = F(t) \tag{2-1}$$

This is the differential equation of motion for the above described system. In a more general sense this equation may be written as:

$$A_0\ddot{x} + A_1\dot{x} + A_2x = F(t) \tag{2-2}$$

Eq. (2–2) is a linear differential equation of the second order with constant coefficients.

It should be noted that A_1 and $F(t)$ vanish respectively for the case of no damping and/or no forcing function.

2-2. Solution of the Homogeneous Equation. The standard procedure for solving Eq. (2–2) is first to consider the equation as being homogeneous; that is, to set the right-hand side (R.H.S.) of the equation equal to zero and, secondly, to find a solution that will satisfy the R.H.S. in particular. The solution of the homogeneous equation yields a solution that is called the complementary solution; the solution satisfying the R.H.S., the particular solution. The sum of these two solutions is the complete solution desired.

For those who have been exposed to the second-order differential equation, the complementary solution may often be found by inspection. Intuitively one would know that since the nature of the problem is vibratory, a sine and/or cosine function should satisfy the homogeneous equation. However, even though such a guess might be correct, this approach is not a satisfactory one. It will be demonstrated that Eq. (2–2) represents a nonvibratory system as well as a vibratory one. Even though the system being analyzed usually concerns itself with an oscillatory motion, greater insight into the oscillatory motion can be gained by a complete understanding of all the systems Eq. (2–2) can represent.

Consider now the homogeneous equation:

$$A_0\ddot{x} + A_1\dot{x} + A_2x = 0 \tag{2-3}$$

and particularly note that the coefficients A_0, A_1, and A_2 are constants. Therefore, we should look for a solution in terms of some function that does not change its form when continuously differentiated.

The equation:

$$x = Ce^{rt} \tag{2-4}$$

where C and r are arbitrary coefficients, will obviously satisfy the above requirement. Differentiating Eq. (2–4) with respect to t the proper number of times and substituting these derivatives into Eq. (2–3) yields:

$$A_0 C r^2 e^{rt} + A_1 C r e^{rt} + A_2 C e^{rt} = 0 \qquad (2\text{--}5)$$

or

$$A_0 r^2 + A_1 r + A_2 = 0 \qquad (2\text{--}6)$$

Eq. (2–6) may be considered to be the auxiliary algebraic equation to Eq. (2–5). Solving for the roots of Eq. (2–6), we get:

$$r = \frac{-A_1 \pm \sqrt{A_1^2 - 4A_0 A_2}}{2A_0} \qquad (2\text{--}7)$$

Note that r has two roots or a double root. This duality is to be expected and is required for a second-order equation.

The solution to Eq. (2–3) may now be written as:

$$x = C_1 e^{r_1 t} + C_2 e^{r_2 t} \qquad (2\text{--}8)$$

providing the values of r_1 and r_2 are not equal. We must investigate the original coefficients m, c, and k to determine whether r_1 and r_2 are real or imaginary. A third case might also arise—the one when r_1 equals r_2.

If $A_1^2 > 4A_0 A_2$, then the roots are real and Eq. (2–8) need not be altered. If $A_1^2 < 4A_0 A_2$, then the roots are imaginary and Eq. (2–8) should be rewritten in complex form:

$$x = C_1 e^{(a+bi)t} + C_2 e^{(a-bi)t} \qquad (2\text{--}9)$$

where $i = \sqrt{-1}$, $r_1 = a + bi$, and $r_2 = a - bi$. If $A_1^2 = 4A_0 A_2$, then the quantity under the radical of Eq. (2–7) vanishes and the solution appears to take the form of

$$x = (C_1 + C_2) e^{at} \qquad (2\text{--}10)$$

We cannot admit the above equation as a solution to the differential equation of motion. Since we can combine the constants C_1 and C_2 to form a single constant C, we violate the requirement that a second-order differential equation have two independent arbitrary constants in its solution. It is necessary, therefore, to multiply one of the constants, say C_2, by the independent variable t. The introduction of t into Eq. (2–10) yields a proper solution in the form of

$$x = (C_1 + C_2 t) e^{at} \qquad (2\text{--}11)$$

The validity of Eq. (2–11) may be ascertained by substituting Eq. (2–11) and its required time derivatives into Eq. (2–3).

Let us consider the physical significance of Eq. (2–8). Since r has been identified as being real, Eq. (2–8) then is of hyperbolic form and cannot represent a vibratory system. For those who are not familiar with hyperbolic functions, let us consider the hyperbolic cosine and sine (cosh and sinh) which are defined as:

$$\cosh u = \frac{e^u + e^{-u}}{2} \qquad \sinh u = \frac{e^u - e^{-u}}{2} \qquad (2\text{--}12)$$

We merely require that u be real to satisfy the cosh and sinh definitions. Eqs. (2–12) can be combined so that the relationship

$$e^u = \cosh u + \sinh u \qquad (2\text{--}13)$$

is obtained.

Eq. (2–8) may now be rewritten, using the relationship in Eq. (2–13), in the form of

$$x = C_1(\cosh r_1 t + \sinh r_1 t) + C_2(\cosh r_2 t + \sinh r_2 t) \qquad (2\text{--}14)$$

Eq. (2–14) clearly demonstrates that the displacement x is of hyperbolic form and cannot be vibratory. For our immediate purpose, this solution is not of great interest in the study of vibratory systems.

However, it must be mentioned at this point that r, though real, can be either positive or negative. The sign of r is governed by the value of the damping constant, c. By nature, m is always positive and k is nearly always positive (there is a concept of a negative spring). Therefore, if c is positive, r is negative; if c is negative, r is positive. The sign of r, when r is real, may be determined from Eq. (2–7) if one notes that

$$|A_1| > \sqrt{A_1{}^2 - 4A_0A_2} \qquad \text{for } A_2 > 0$$

or

$$|c| > \sqrt{c^2 - 4mk} \qquad \text{for } k > 0$$

When r is real, whether it be positive or negative, the system is said to be overdamped; that is, the system does not oscillate. However, when r is negative ($c > o$), the displacement is decremental with time and would seek the equilibrium position if not prevented by the strong damping action. This is not so for the case of negative damping when r is positive. The displacement is incremental with time. As a consequence of negative damping, any disturbance, no matter how small, will cause the mass to move away from the equilibrium position and the displacement will increase with time until the system destroys itself. This latter case is one of dynamic instability and is beyond the scope of this discussion.

Eq. (2–9) represents the case when r_1 and r_2 are complex. The form of Eq. (2–9) does not lend itself readily to physical interpretation. Rearranging Eq. (2–9), we get:

$$x = e^{at}[C_1 e^{ibt} + C_2 e^{-ibt}] \qquad (2\text{--}15)$$

Let us for the moment consider the expansion of e^{nu} into a Maclaurin series, where n is a constant coefficient and u is the variable. Then:

$$e^{nu} = 1 + nu + \frac{n^2 u^2}{2!} + \frac{n^3 u^3}{3!} + \frac{n^4 u^4}{4!} + \cdots \qquad (2\text{--}16)$$

By substituting $u = t$ and $n = ib$ first, then $n = -ib$, we get:

$$e^{ibt} = 1 + ibt - \frac{b^2 t^2}{2!} - \frac{ib^3 t^3}{3!} + \frac{b^4 t^4}{4!} + \cdots \qquad (2\text{--}17)$$

$$e^{-ibt} = 1 - ibt - \frac{b^2 t^2}{2!} + \frac{ib^3 t^3}{3!} + \frac{b^4 t^4}{4!} - \cdots \qquad (2\text{--}18)$$

Adding Eqs. (2–17) and (2–18) and rearranging, we get:

$$\frac{e^{ibt} + e^{-ibt}}{2} = 1 - \frac{b^2 t^2}{2!} + \frac{b^4 t^4}{4!} - \cdots \qquad (2\text{--}19)$$

Subtracting Eq. (2–18) from Eq. (2–17) and rearranging, we get

$$\frac{e^{ibt} - e^{-ibt}}{2} = i\left[bt - \frac{b^3 t^3}{3!} + \frac{b^5 t^5}{5!} - \cdots \right] \qquad (2\text{--}20)$$

The R.H.S. of Eqs. (2–19) and (2–20) are the well-known trigonometric series equivalents of $\cos bt$ and $i \sin bt$, respectively.

Eqs. (2–19) and (2–20) become:

$$e^{ibt} + e^{-ibt} = 2 \cos bt \qquad (2\text{--}21)$$

$$e^{ibt} - e^{-ibt} = 2i \sin bt \qquad (2\text{--}22)$$

Eqs. (2–21) and (2–22) may be combined first by addition and then by subtraction to yield:

$$e^{ibt} = \cos bt + i \sin bt \qquad (2\text{--}23)$$

$$e^{-ibt} = \cos bt - i \sin bt \qquad (2\text{--}24)$$

The above equations are known as Euler's relations. These relations may be substituted into Eq. (2–15) so that, in simplified form, Eq. (2–15) becomes:

$$x = e^{at}[A \cos bt + B \sin bt] \qquad (2\text{--}25)$$

where $A = C_1 + C_2$ and $B = i(C_1 - C_2)$.

For the evaluation of a and b, we must refer to Eqs. (2–1) and (2–3). By dividing Eq. (2–1) by m, it can be shown that

$$a = -\frac{c}{2m} \qquad \text{and} \qquad b = \sqrt{\frac{k}{m} - \left(\frac{c}{2m}\right)^2}$$

Often, b is referred to as the natural damped circular frequency. We shall, therefore, let

$$\omega_{nd} = \sqrt{\frac{k}{m} - \left(\frac{c}{2m}\right)^2} \quad \text{radians per sec.} \tag{2-26}$$

The natural damped frequency is, therefore

$$f_{nd} = \frac{\omega_{nd}}{2\pi} \quad \text{cycles per sec.} \tag{2-27}$$

The solution for Eq. (2–15), the case where

$$A_1{}^2 < 4A_0A_2 \quad \text{or} \quad \left(\frac{c}{2m}\right)^2 < \frac{k}{m}$$

becomes

$$x = e^{-(c/2m)t}[A \cos \omega_{nd}t + B \sin \omega_{nd}t] \tag{2-28}$$

The term $[A \cos \omega_{nd}t + B \sin \omega_{nd}t]$ can be combined into a single trigonometric term which will be identified by a phase angle with respect to the angular displacement $\omega_{nd}t$.

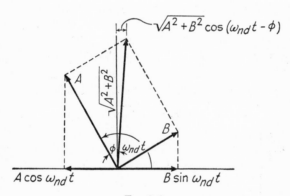

FIG. 2–2.

$A \cos \omega_{nd}t$ and $B \sin \omega_{nd}t$ may each be represented by vectors. The cosine vector leads the sine vector by 90°. At any time t, these vectors may be plotted as in Fig. 2–2 and the resultant vector substituted in their stead. The resultant vector has an amplitude of $\sqrt{A^2 + B^2}$ and the vector lags the cosine vector by the angle ϕ, where

$$\phi = \tan^{-1} \frac{B}{A}$$

Now Eq. (2–28) can be rewritten in its simplest form:

$$x = \sqrt{A^2 + B^2} \, e^{-(c/2m)t} \cos (\omega_{nd}t - \phi) \tag{2-29}$$

Eq. (2–29) yields a vibratory motion, the amplitude of which will either decrease or increase with time. If the damping constant c is positive, then the amplitude of vibration will decrease with time and eventually nearly vanish. However, if c is negative, the amplitude increases with time and eventually will destroy the mechanical system. This case is known as negative damping and results in an unstable vibratory system.

Eq. (2–8) represents the case of an overdamped nonvibratory system and Eq. (2–9) that of a damped vibratory system. As might be suspected, Eq. (2–11) represents the transition between the overdamped and the damped systems. Eq. (2–11) may therefore be referred to as the critically damped system. This occurs when

$$\left(\frac{c}{2m}\right)^2 = \frac{k}{m} \tag{2–30}$$

It is assumed that Eq. (2–11) represents a stable system; that is to say that c is positive. By using the original constants, Eq. (2–11) may be rewritten as:

$$x = (C_1 + C_2 t)e^{-(c/2m)t} \tag{2–31}$$

It is quite apparent that this equation is nonvibratory and that for large values of t, $e^{-(c/2m)t}$ approaches zero as a limit. Therefore, with increasing time, Eq. (2–31) approaches the equilibrium position. The importance of Eq. (2–31) rests on the fact that the value of the damping constant c becomes a limiting value of the damper for vibratory motion. This critical value c_c can be determined from Eq. (2–30) and it is

$$c_c = \sqrt{4km} \tag{2–32}$$

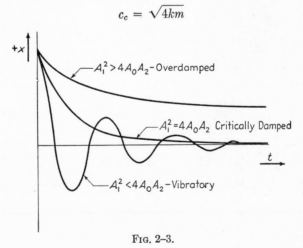

FIG. 2–3.

Fig. 2–3 represents the plot of the three conditions covered by the mathematics of the second-order homogeneous differential Eq. (2–3) when

c is considered to be a positive quantity. These conditions show the nature of the overdamped, critically damped, and vibratory systems.

The above discussion was based on the homogeneous equation and the influence of the particular solution has been completely neglected. Therefore, all of the above will be valid without modification for any free system, that is, when no forcing function exists. Under the above circumstance, it is possible to evaluate the constants of the equation. These constants can be evaluated from the time boundary conditions which are usually known. One such condition is the initial displacement, another the initial velocity or acceleration. Since there are two constants to be evaluated, two boundary conditions are required for their evaluation.

By way of example, let us consider the evaluation of the constants of Eq. (2–28). Note that Eq. (2–28) is easier to handle than Eq. (2–29). Let us assume that the initial conditions are:

$$x = x_0 \quad \text{when} \quad t = 0$$

$$\dot{x} = 0 \quad \text{when} \quad t = 0$$

That is, we have an initial displacement x_0 and the mass is at rest initially. Since

$$x = e^{-(c/2m)t}[A \cos \omega_{nd}t + B \sin \omega_{nd}t] \tag{2–28}$$

then

$$\dot{x} = -\frac{c}{2m} e^{-(c/2m)t}[A \cos \omega_{nd}t + B \sin \omega_{nd}t]$$

$$- e^{-(c/2m)t}[A\omega_{nd} \sin \omega_{nd}t - B\omega_{nd} \cos \omega_{nd}t]$$

Substituting the initial conditions, we get:

$$x_0 = A$$

and

$$0 = -\frac{c}{2m} A + \omega_{nd}B$$

Then

$$B = \frac{cx_0}{2m\omega_{nd}}$$

The constants having been evaluated, Eq. (2–28) now becomes:

$$x = x_0 e^{-(c/2m)t} \left[\cos \omega_{nd}t + \frac{c}{2m\omega_{nd}} \sin \omega_{nd}t \right] \tag{2–33}$$

or

$$x = x_0 \sqrt{1 + \left(\frac{c}{2m\omega_{nd}}\right)^2}\, e^{-(c/2m)t} \cos(\omega_{nd}t - \phi) \tag{2–34}$$

where

$$\phi = \tan^{-1} \frac{c}{2m\omega_{nd}}$$

2-3. Particular Solution. To find the particular solution, $F(t)$ must be expressed in explicit form. Since the forcing function in many cases can be considered to be of trigonometric form, let the forcing function be $F \cos vt$, where v is the circular forcing frequency.

The usual method for solving the particular solution is to differentiate continuously the forcing function until all the derivatives are obtained. The assumed solution is then taken in the form of the forcing function and its derivatives. Only terms in $\cos vt$ and $\sin vt$ will be obtained when the forcing function is represented by $F \cos vt$. We can, therefore, assume the particular solution to be

$$X = D \sin vt + E \cos vt \tag{2-35}$$

where D and E are arbitrary constants to be evaluated by satisfying Eq. (2–2), that is,

$$A_0 \ddot{x} + A_1 \dot{x} + A_2 x = F \cos vt \tag{2-36}$$

Eq. (2–35) is now differentiated with respect to time to get the first and second derivatives.

$$\dot{X} = Dv \cos vt - Ev \sin vt \tag{2-37}$$

$$\ddot{X} = -Dv^2 \sin vt - Ev^2 \cos vt \tag{2-38}$$

These derivatives are substituted into Eq. (2–36), yielding:

$$-A_0 v^2 [D \sin vt + E \cos vt] + A_1 v [D \cos vt - E \sin vt]$$

$$+ A_2 [D \sin vt + E \cos vt] = F \cos vt \tag{2-39}$$

Now the coefficients of the sine and cosine terms of the L.H.S. must equal the coefficients of the sine and cosine terms of the R.H.S., respectively. That is:

$$-A_0 v^2 D - A_1 v E + A_2 D = 0$$

$$-A_0 v^2 E + A_1 v D + A_2 E = F \tag{2-40}$$

Rearranging these equations to facilitate solution by means of determinants, we get

$$(A_2 - A_0 v^2)D - A_1 v E = 0$$

$$A_1 v D + (A_2 - A_0 v^2)E = F \tag{2-41}$$

Then

$$D = \frac{FA_1\nu}{(A_2 - A_0\nu^2)^2 + A_1{}^2\nu^2}$$

$$E = \frac{F(A_2 - A_0\nu^2)}{(A_2 - A_0\nu^2)^2 + A_1{}^2\nu^2} \qquad (2\text{-}42)$$

The particular solution then becomes:

$$X = \frac{F}{(A_2 - A_0\nu^2)^2 + A_1{}^2\nu^2} [A_1\nu \sin \nu t + (A_2 - A_0\nu^2) \cos \nu t] \quad (2\text{-}43)$$

or

$$X = \frac{F}{\sqrt{(A_2 - A_0\nu^2)^2 + A_1{}^2\nu^2}} \cos(\nu t - \psi) \qquad (2\text{-}44)$$

where

$$\psi = \tan^{-1} \frac{A_1\nu}{A_2 - A_0\nu^2}$$

When the original parameters m, k, and c are substituted, Eqs. (2–43) and (2–44), respectively, become:

$$X = \frac{F}{(k - m\nu^2)^2 + c^2\nu^2} [c\nu \sin \nu t + (k - m\nu^2) \cos \nu t] \qquad (2\text{-}45)$$

and

$$X = \frac{F}{\sqrt{(k - m\nu^2)^2 + c^2\nu^2}} \cos(\nu t - \psi) \qquad (2\text{-}46)$$

where

$$\psi = \tan^{-1} \frac{c\nu}{k - m\nu^2}$$

If we define $\sqrt{k/m}$ as being the natural circular frequency, ω_n, and remembering that $c_c = \sqrt{4km}$, Eq. (2–46) may be rewritten as:

$$X = \frac{F}{k} \frac{\cos(\nu t - \psi)}{\sqrt{\left[1 - \dfrac{\nu^2}{\omega_n{}^2}\right]^2 + \left[2 \dfrac{c\nu}{c_c\omega_n}\right]^2}} \qquad (2\text{-}47)$$

where

$$\psi = \tan^{-1} \frac{2 \dfrac{c\nu}{c_c\omega_n}}{1 - \dfrac{\nu^2}{\omega_n{}^2}}$$

2-4. Complete Solution. The combination of the complementary and particular solutions yields the complete solution of Eq. (2–1) when this equation represents a vibratory system. The complementary portion is called the transient solution since it vanishes with time. We shall denote the transient solution by the symbol x_λ. The steady state condition is given by the particular solution. The steady state solution is so called because if given a sufficient period of time, it will represent the motion of a forced vibratory system. Let x_μ represent the steady state solution; then the complete solution may now be written as

$$x = x_\lambda + x_\mu \tag{2–48}$$

where

$$x_\lambda = e^{-(c/2m)t} [A \cos \omega_{nd}t + B \sin \omega_{nd}t] \tag{2–28a}$$

and

$$x_\mu = \frac{F}{(k - m\nu^2)^2 + c^2\nu^2} [c\nu \sin \nu t + (k - m\nu^2) \cos \nu t] \tag{2–45a}$$

In many mechanical vibration problems, the steady state condition alone is of interest. If that be the case, Eq. (2–45) holds the complete solution to the motion of the vibratory system. However, there are occasions when the engineer is interested in the motion of a system during the time interval in the neighborhood of time equal to zero. The maximum displacements and stresses will occur during this short period. The complete solution will have to be utilized if we are to probe into the vibrations during this interval. The evaluation of the constants A and B will be necessary if the complete solution is to be utilized. The constants will be determined in Chapter 3 by applying a set of boundary conditions to Eq. (2–48).

BIBLIOGRAPHY

JOHNSON, WALTER C. *Mathematical and Physical Principles of Engineering Analysis.* New York: McGraw-Hill Book Co., Inc., 1944.

KÁRMÁN, THEODORE VON, and BIOT, MAURICE A. *Mathematical Methods in Engineering.* New York: McGraw-Hill Book Co., Inc., 1940.

OLDENBURGER, RUFUS. *Mathematical Engineering Analysis.* New York: The Macmillan Co., 1950.

PHILLIPS, H. B. *Differential Equations.* 3d ed. New York: John Wiley & Sons, Inc., 1934.

REDDICK, HARRY W. *Differential Equations.* New York: John Wiley & Sons, Inc., 1943.

REDDICK, H. W., and MILLER, F. H. *Advanced Mathematics for Engineers.* 3d ed. New York: John Wiley & Sons, Inc., 1955.

YATES, ROBERT C. *Differential Equations.* New York: McGraw-Hill Book Co., Inc., 1952.

PROBLEMS

2–1. Evaluate the constants of Eq. (2–28) when the initial conditions at $t = 0$ are $x = 0$ and $\dot{x} = v_0$.

2-2. Evaluate the constants for the critically damped Eq. (2–31) when the initial conditions are at $t = 0$; $x = x_0$ and $\dot{x} = 0$.

2-3. Solve the differential equation derived in Problem 1–17 for small angles of oscillation. Evaluate the constants when the pendulum is activated by an initial displacement of θ_0.

2-4. Solve the differential equation derived in Problem 1–17 and evaluate the constants when the pendulum is activated by an initial velocity v_0.

2-5. Solve the differential equation obtained in Problem 1–20, if the arm supporting the cylinder is limited to small angles of oscillation. If the system starts from the equilibrium position by imparting to the arm an angular velocity of Ω, determine the value of the constants.

2-6. Solve the differential equation of motion obtained in Problem 1–22, and evaluate the constants when the initial disturbance causes the mercury to move $\pm\frac{1}{2}$ in. from the equilibrium position.

2-7. In Section 2–3, the forcing function was selected as $F \cos \nu t$. Substitute $F \sin \nu t$ for $F \cos \nu t$ in Eq. (2–36) and solve. Compare the results with Eq. (2–43) and explain the difference.

CHAPTER 3

SINGLE DEGREE OF FREEDOM

3–1. Free, Undamped Systems. Chapter 2 introduced the mathematical tools for solving the equation of motion for a system with a single degree of freedom. It is now possible to complete the solutions of the problems discussed in Chapter 1. The systems discussed in this introductory chapter were all free, undamped systems.

Eq. (1–33) is the equation of motion of a mass attached to a spring. This system is free and undamped; free, for there is no external forcing function acting upon it, and undamped, for there is no mechanism by which the energy in the system can be dissipated. Since the system is free, the solution of

$$m\ddot{x} + kx = 0 \tag{1–33}$$

is found in the complementary solution, x_λ, Eq. (2–28a). However, there is no damping and $c = 0$. As a result the exponential becomes equal to unity and $\omega_{nd} = \omega_n = \sqrt{k/m}$. The solution of Eq. (1–33) then becomes

$$x = A \cos \sqrt{\frac{k}{m}}\, t + B \sin \sqrt{\frac{k}{m}}\, t \tag{3–1}$$

The constants A and B must be determined from the time boundary conditions of the problem. To induce motion we initially displace the mass from its equilibrium position. Let this initial displacement be x_0. Then the boundary conditions are:

when $t = 0$ $\qquad x = x_0 \qquad$ and $\qquad \dot{x} = 0$ $\tag{3–2}$

The boundary or initial conditions are now applied to Eq. (3–1) with two resulting equations:

$$x_0 = A\,(1) + B\,(0)$$

$$0 = A \sqrt{\frac{k}{m}}\,(0) + B \sqrt{\frac{k}{m}}\,(1) \tag{3–3}$$

Whence

$$A = x_0 \qquad \text{and} \qquad B = 0 \tag{3–4}$$

44

The solution to Eq. (1-33) then is

$$x = x_0 \cos \sqrt{\frac{k}{m}}\, t \qquad (3-5)$$

This motion is clearly simple harmonic motion. The circular frequency is $\sqrt{k/m}$ radians per sec. The natural frequency, ω_n, is the term used to denote the circular frequency of a free undamped oscillation. Since $m = W/g$ and $k = W/\delta_{st}$, the natural frequency may be expressed in another manner:

$$\omega_n = \sqrt{\frac{k}{m}} = \sqrt{\frac{g}{\delta_{st}}} \qquad (3-6)$$

From the relations of Eq. (3-6) we can see that the natural frequency of a system is a physical property of that system and is dependent upon the δ_{st} of the system, assuming that g is constant.

Fig. 3-1 is a chart showing the relation between δ_{st} and ω_n. If the static deflection of a spring and mass system is known, the natural frequency may be found directly from this chart. It is also obvious that we have two parameters which may be altered to change the natural frequency, k and m. This fact is often important in design work. To decrease the natural frequency, we can soften the spring (lower the k value) or increase the mass. To increase the natural frequency, we can stiffen the spring (raise the k value) or decrease the mass. The choice of whether the spring or the mass is altered depends usually upon the design problem.

The natural frequency can be determined immediately from the equation of motion without obtaining its formal solution. By dividing Eq. (1-33) by m, we get

$$\ddot{x} + \frac{k}{m} x = 0 \qquad (3-7)$$

Since $k/m = \omega_n{}^2$, then Eq. (1-33) becomes

$$\ddot{x} + \omega_n{}^2 x = 0 \qquad (3-8)$$

This is the standard form of the equation of motion for a free, undamped system with a single degree of freedom. The constant coefficient modifying the motion x will always be the squared natural frequency of the system.

By way of examples let us complete the other problems for which the equations of motion were found in Chapter 1.

a. *Simple Pendulum.* Eq. (1-38) represents the equation of motion for a simple pendulum:

$$\frac{l}{g}\ddot{\theta} + \sin\theta = 0 \qquad (1-38)$$

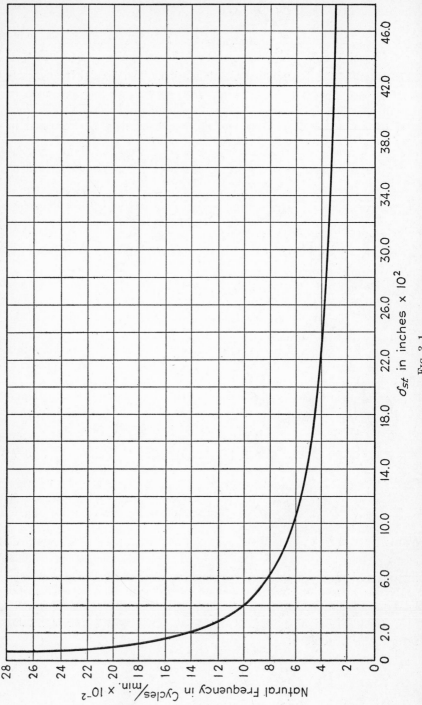

FIG. 3-1.

In accordance with the discussion of nonlinear equations in Chapter 1, we recite that θ is restricted to be a small angle, thereby linearizing Eq. (1–38). Rewriting the linearized equation as

$$\ddot{\theta} + \frac{g}{l}\theta = 0 \tag{3–9}$$

we find that it has the same form as Eq. (3–7). If we assume the same type of initial conditions as we did for Eq. (3–7) (that is, let the initial displacement be θ_0), then the solution to Eq. (3–9) is

$$\theta = \theta_0 \cos \sqrt{\frac{g}{l}}\, t \tag{3–10}$$

and

$$\omega_n = \sqrt{\frac{g}{l}} \tag{3–11}$$

We may draw the conclusion that the standard form of the differential equation of motion for a pendulum or torsional system is

$$\ddot{\theta} + \omega_n{}^2 \theta = 0 \tag{3–12}$$

b. Cylinder Oscillating on Concave Cylindrical Surface. The standard linearized form of Eq. (1–54) is

$$\ddot{\theta} + \frac{2g}{3(R-r)}\theta = 0 \tag{3–13}$$

For an initial displacement of θ_0, the solution for Eq. (3–13) is

$$\theta = \theta_0 \cos \sqrt{\frac{2g}{3(R-r)}}\, t \tag{3–14}$$

and

$$\omega_n = \sqrt{\frac{2g}{3(R-r)}} \tag{3–15}$$

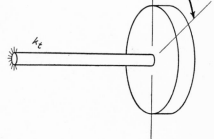

Fig. 3–2.

Another type of pendulum which is used as a schematic representation of machine elements is the torsional pendulum. Consider a disc attached to a rod as shown in Fig. 3–2. Let the torsional spring constant be denoted by k_t. The torsional spring constant is the constant of proportionality relating the torque to the angular displacement. In general

$$T = k_t \theta$$

If the disc, which has a mass moment of inertia I, is allowed to oscillate, the D.E. of motion becomes

$$-k_t\theta = I\ddot{\theta}$$

or

$$\ddot{\theta} + \frac{k_t}{I}\theta = 0 \tag{3-16}$$

The solution, for an initial angular displacement of θ_0, is

$$\theta = \theta_0 \cos\sqrt{\frac{k_t}{I}}\, t \tag{3-17}$$

The importance of the preceding discussions lies not in our ability to solve the equation of motion for the simple systems investigated, but in

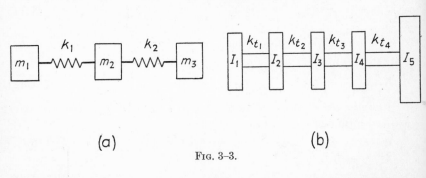

(a)   (b)

Fig. 3–3.

using simple systems to represent vibratory systems. The spring and mass, the simple pendulum, and the torsional pendulum can be employed to represent schematically complicated pieces of equipment. The solutions of the schematic representations often serve as excellent first-order approximate solutions to relatively complicated problems. A train may be represented by a series of masses and springs (Fig. 3–3a), where the engine and cars are the masses and the couplings are the springs. An internal combustion engine may be reduced to a series of discs and torsional springs. Fig. 3–3b is a schematic representation of a four-cylinder engine and its flywheel. The discs are schemata of the masses, both rotating and oscillating, of the piston and crank assemblies, and the torsional springs represent the elasticity apportioned to each cylinder assembly. The spring, the mass, the torsional spring, the inertial disc, and the pendulum are the tools for visualizing and solving vibration problems of relatively complicated systems.

Example. A cam follower may be represented by a spring-loaded pendulum, Fig. 3–4a. Derive the D.E. of motion and the natural frequency of the pendulum system.

SOLUTION. Fig. 3–4b is a free body of the pendulum. Taking moments about the pivot, we get for small oscillations

$$-kxa = ml^2\ddot{\theta}$$

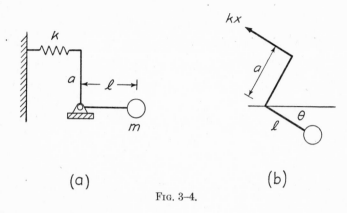

(a)   (b)

FIG. 3–4.

For small displacements of the spring

$$x = a\theta$$

Then

$$ml^2\ddot{\theta} + ka^2\theta = 0$$

or

$$\ddot{\theta} + \frac{ka^2}{ml^2}\theta = 0$$

The above expression is the desired D.E. of motion, from which we can deduce that

$$\omega_n = \sqrt{\frac{ka^2}{ml^2}}$$

3–2. Springs. The spring constant has been previously defined for both the helical spring and the torsional spring. The respective relationships are repeated.

$$k = \frac{F}{x} \quad \text{lbs./in.}$$

$$k_t = \frac{T}{\theta} \quad \text{in.-lbs./radian}$$

In a general sense, a spring represents the elasticity of a system. Let us determine the spring constants for springs as we see them in their original state. A helical spring is nothing more than a wire or rod wound into a coil. The determination of the deflection of a helical spring is extremely complicated. One of the finest treatises published in this country on mechanical springs is by A. M. Wahl.[1] In our case, however, we will use the approximate solution found in elementary texts on strength of materials.[2]

$$x = \frac{8FD^3n}{Gd^4} \tag{3-18}$$

where F = the applied force in lbs.
d = diameter of the wire in inches
D = mean diameter of coil in inches
G = shear modulus in psi.
n = number of turns of wire

Then

$$k = \frac{F}{x} = \frac{Gd^4}{8D^3n} \quad \text{lbs./in.} \tag{3-19}$$

The total angle of twist for a rod of diameter d subject to a torque is

$$\theta = \frac{32lT}{\pi d^4 G} \quad \text{radians} \tag{3-20}$$

where l = length of rod in inches.
Then

$$k_t = \frac{T}{\theta} = \frac{\pi d^4 G}{32l} \quad \text{in.-lbs./radian} \tag{3-21}$$

Often beams are used to support machinery and the beams act as springs. The two most common types are the simply supported beam and the cantilever beam. If a simply supported beam is loaded at the center the deflection is

$$x = \frac{Fl^3}{48EI} \tag{3-22}$$

where E = Young's modulus in psi.
I = area moment of inertia of beam section in inches[4]
l = length of beam in inches[4]

Then

$$k = \frac{F}{x} = \frac{48EI}{l^3} \quad \text{lbs./in.} \tag{3-23}$$

We can interpret Eq. (3–23) to mean that if a mass is centrally supported on a free beam (Fig. 3–5a), its equivalent system is a mass and a spring

[1] A. M. Wahl, *Mechanical Springs* (Cleveland: Penton Publishing Co., 1944).
[2] S. Timoshenko, *Strength of Materials*, Part I (Princeton, N. J.: D. Van Nostrand Co., Inc., 1940).

(Fig. 3–5*b*). By the same procedure, the spring constant of a cantilever beam is

$$k = \frac{3EI}{l^3} \qquad (3\text{–}24)$$

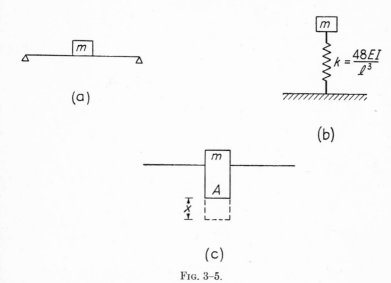

(a)

(b)

(c)

Fig. 3–5.

Other mediums may serve as springs. A body which floats in a fluid is supported by a spring. Consider a mass floating in a fluid (Fig. 3–5*c*) whose specific weight is γ lbs. per cu. in. If A is the cross section of the body, inches squared, wetted by the fluid, then the force opposing a displacement x is

$$F = \gamma A x \qquad (3\text{–}25)$$

and

$$k = \gamma A \qquad (3\text{–}26)$$

The natural frequency of the above system is found to be

$$\omega_n = \sqrt{\frac{k}{m}} = \sqrt{\frac{\gamma A}{m}} \quad \text{radians/sec.} \qquad (3\text{–}27)$$

Springs may be combined in several different ways: in parallel, in series, or in a combination of series and parallel. Fig. 3–6 shows these combinations.

Springs which are in parallel may be defined as such if the displacement for each spring is the same, Fig. 3–6*a*.

$$F_1 = k_1 x \qquad \text{and} \qquad F_2 = k_2 x \qquad (3\text{–}28)$$

The total force F must be equal to the sum of the forces, F_1, F_2, F_3; and the equivalent spring constant k_e must be equal to the total force divided by the displacement x.

Then, for the system described by Fig. 3–6a,

$$F = F_1 + F_2 = (k_1 + k_2)x \qquad (3\text{–}29)$$

and

$$k_e = \frac{F}{x} \qquad (3\text{–}30)$$

Substituting Eq. (3–29) for F into Eq. (3–30), we get

$$k_e = k_1 + k_2 \qquad (3\text{–}31)$$

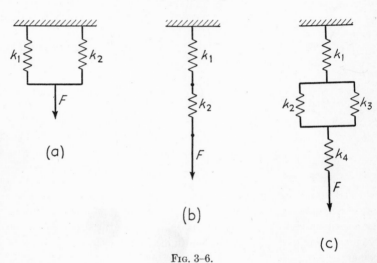

(a)

(b)

(c)

Fig. 3–6.

In general we may say that when springs are combined in parallel, the spring constant for the entire spring system is the sum of the individual spring constants. Reduced to a mathematical statement,

$$k_{e \text{ parallel}} = \sum_{i=1}^{n} k_i \qquad (3\text{–}32)$$

where n = number of springs in parallel.

Springs in series are defined by the fact that the force is the same on each individual spring. Referring to Fig. 3–6b, we find that

$$F = k_1 x_1 \qquad\qquad F = k_2 x_2$$

and

$$x = x_1 + x_2 = F\left(\frac{1}{k_1} + \frac{1}{k_2}\right)$$

Then

$$\frac{F}{k_e} = F\left(\frac{1}{k_1} + \frac{1}{k_2}\right) \qquad (3\text{-}33)$$

and

$$\frac{1}{k_e} = \frac{1}{k_1} + \frac{1}{k_2} \qquad (3\text{-}34)$$

Generalizing Eq. (3–34), we can draw the conclusion that the combined effect of springs in series is that of a single spring whose spring constant is the reciprocal of the sum of the reciprocals of the individual spring constants. Expressed mathematically,

$$k_e \text{ series} = \frac{1}{\displaystyle\sum_{i=1}^{n} \frac{1}{k_i}} \qquad (3\text{-}35)$$

When the spring system is a combination of springs in parallel and in series, as in Fig. 3–6c, there is no fixed pattern of mathematical expression to represent all cases. We combine each group of springs in parallel to find an equivalent spring for each group and then combine the equivalent springs with the other springs in a series combination. For the case of Fig. 3–6c, the equivalent spring constant is

$$\frac{1}{k_e} = \frac{1}{k_1} + \frac{1}{k_2 + k_3} + \frac{1}{k_4} \qquad (3\text{-}36)$$

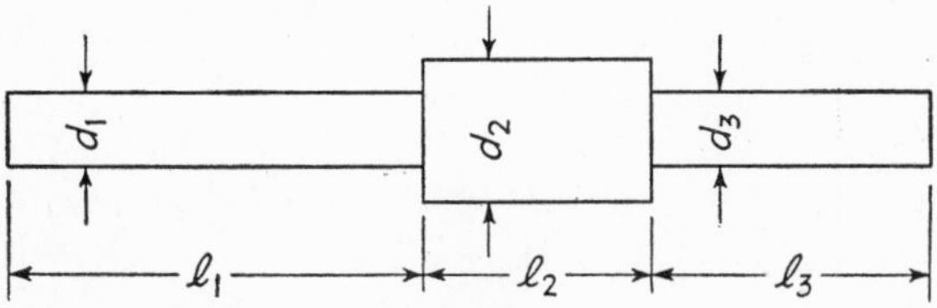

FIG. 3–7.

Stepped shafts are fairly common machine elements. There are many reasons why shafts are made with sections of different diameters. Consider such a shaft, Fig. 3–7. It consists of three sections of different lengths and diameters. Each section will have a torsional spring constant of the form

$$k_t = \frac{\pi d^4 G}{32l} \qquad (3\text{-}21)$$

The shaft may be considered to be made up from three separate shafts in series. Then

$$\frac{1}{k_{te}} = \frac{1}{k_{t1}} + \frac{1}{k_{t2}} + \frac{1}{k_{t3}}$$

or

$$k_{te} = \frac{\pi G}{32} \left[\frac{1}{\dfrac{l_1}{d_1{}^4} + \dfrac{l_2}{d_2{}^4} + \dfrac{l_3}{d_3{}^4}} \right] \tag{3-37}$$

Another way, perhaps simpler, is to reduce each section to a single diameter, but having a new length. We need only to preserve the relation in Eq. (3–21). We can write

$$k_t = \frac{\pi d^4 G}{32l} = \frac{\pi d_e{}^4 G}{32l_e} \tag{3-38}$$

It is most convenient to let the equivalent diameter be 1 in. Then

$$l_e = \frac{l}{d^4} \tag{3-39}$$

We can do this for the entire stepped shaft; then

$$l_e = \frac{l_1}{d_1{}^4} + \frac{l_2}{d_2{}^4} + \frac{l_3}{d_3{}^4} \tag{3-40}$$

The torsional spring constant for the shaft in Fig. 3–7 is

$$k_{te} = \frac{\pi G}{32l_e} = \frac{\pi G}{32} \left[\frac{1}{\dfrac{l_1}{d_1{}^4} + \dfrac{l_2}{d_2{}^4} + \dfrac{l_3}{d_3{}^4}} \right] \tag{3-41}$$

which is the same as Eq. (3–37).

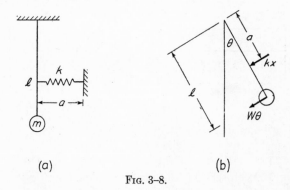

(a)   (b)

Fig. 3–8.

Example. Determine the spring constant of a simple pendulum which is restrained by a spring as shown in Fig. 3–8a.

SOLUTION. Perhaps the easiest way of determining the spring constant is first to write the D.E. of motion of the system. By drawing a free body diagram, Fig. 3–8b, we can see that, for small displacements of the spring,

$$-kxa - Wl\theta = ml^2 \ddot{\theta}$$

Since
$$x \doteq a\theta$$
then
$$ml^2\ddot{\theta} + (ka^2 + Wl)\theta = 0$$
By inspection of the D.E., we see that
$$k_e = ka^2 + Wl$$

3–3. The Effect of the Spring Mass. Heretofore, we have assumed that the springs of the various systems studied were massless. A massless spring really means that the mass of the spring is negligible in comparison with the mass vibrated. There are, however, times when the mass of a spring cannot be neglected. Let us, therefore, see what the effect of the spring mass on a vibrating system is.

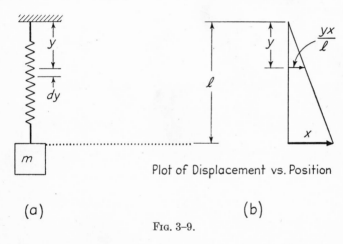

Plot of Displacement vs. Position

(a)   (b)

FIG. 3–9.

Fig. 3–9 depicts a mass on a spring when the mass has been displaced from its equilibrium position. We will assume that the displacement of any point on the spring is linearly proportional to the distance the point is from one end of the spring. This qualification does not allow for surge or wave motion in the spring and is a reasonable assumption. Let y be any position on the spring and dy a differential length. When the mass is at x distance from the equilibrium position, then point y will have moved xy/l distance from its equilibrium position, Fig. 3–9b. It appears that the energy method is perhaps a simpler approach than the direct method. The velocity at point y will be proportional to $\dot{x}$ and is $\dot{x}y/l$. The kinetic energy of the entire spring is found by integrating over the length of the spring. Then

$$T_s = \int_0^l \frac{m_s'}{2}\left(\frac{y\dot{x}}{l}\right)^2 dy = \frac{m_s'l\dot{x}^2}{2\cdot 3} = \frac{m_s\dot{x}^2}{6}$$

where $m_s' = $ mass per unit length of spring and $m_s = $ total mass of spring. The total kinetic energy of the system is

$$T = T_m + T_s = \frac{1}{2}\left(m + \frac{m_s}{3}\right)\dot{x}^2 \tag{3-42}$$

The potential energy of the system is the energy which is stored in the spring. This energy is independent of the spring mass.

$$V = \frac{kx^2}{2} \tag{3-43}$$

The energy equation relationship is

$$\frac{d}{dt}(T + V) = 0 \tag{1-51}$$

Substituting, we get

$$\frac{d}{dt}\left[\frac{1}{2}\left(m + \frac{m_s}{3}\right)\dot{x}^2 + \frac{kx^2}{2}\right] = 0 \tag{3-44}$$

Then

$$\left(m + \frac{m_s}{3}\right)\ddot{x} + kx = 0 \tag{3-45}$$

and

$$\omega_n = \sqrt{\frac{k}{m + \dfrac{m_s}{3}}} \quad \text{radians/sec.} \tag{3-46}$$

The conclusion that can be drawn then is that the effect of the distributed spring mass is to increase the mass of the system by one-third of the mass of the spring.

In the same manner it can be shown that the effect of a torsional spring on a torsional pendulum system is of the same character, namely,

$$\omega_n = \sqrt{\frac{k_t}{I + \dfrac{I_s}{3}}} \quad \text{radians/sec.} \tag{3-47}$$

Proof of Eq. (3-47) is left to the student, to do as an exercise.

Example. A motor weighing 1000 lbs. is fastened to the free end of a steel cantilever beam, 6×6 WF, 5 ft. long. Determine the natural frequency of the system, taking into account the weight of the beam. Calculate the percentage of error when the weight of the beam is neglected.

SOLUTION. A 6×6 WF beam has the following properties: weight per foot = 20 lbs.; area moment of inertia = 41.7 in.[4] We can calculate the spring constant to be

$$k = \frac{3EI}{l^3} = \frac{3 \times 30 \times 10^6 \times 41.7}{5^3 \times 12^3} = 1.74 \times 10^4 \text{ lbs./in.}$$

$$W = 1000 + \frac{100}{3} = 1033 \text{ lbs.}$$

$$\omega_n = \sqrt{\frac{k}{m}} = \sqrt{\frac{386 \times 1.74 \times 10^4}{1033}} = 80.6 \text{ radians/sec.}$$

$$f = \frac{\omega_n \times 60}{2\pi} = 770 \text{ cpm}$$

When we neglect the weight of the beam we get

$$\omega_n = \sqrt{\frac{386 \times 1.74 \times 10^4}{1000}} = 82.0 \text{ radians/sec.}$$

$$\text{Error} = \frac{1.4}{80.6} \times 100 = 1.73\%$$

Note that the error is not very great, considering that the spring weighs 10 percent of the weight of the mass.

3–4. Free, Damped Systems. In Chapter 2 the homogeneous equation of motion which includes damping was discussed. This equation represents a free, damped system as diagramed by Fig. 3–10. The mathematical solution to the equation of motion is given by

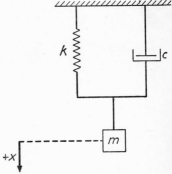

$$x_\lambda = e^{-(c/2m)t}[A \cos \omega_{nd}t + B \sin \omega_{nd}t] \quad (2\text{--}28a)$$

and

$$\omega_{nd} = \sqrt{\frac{k}{m} - \left(\frac{c}{2m}\right)^2} \quad (2\text{--}26)$$

An analysis of Eq. (2–28a) points out two effects of damping: one, that the vibration vanishes with time (a transient vibration); the other, that the frequency of the system is lowered by damping.

Fig. 3–10.

As the damping constant is increased, that is, made stronger, the natural (damped) frequency diminishes until the natural frequency is zero. When this occurs, as was pointed out in Chapter 2, the system ceases to be vibratory and

$$c = c_c = \sqrt{4km} \quad (2\text{--}32)$$

Let us look at

$$\left(\frac{c}{2m}\right)^2 = \left(\frac{cc_c}{2mc_c}\right)^2 = \frac{c^2{\omega_n}^2}{{c_c}^2} = \zeta^2{\omega_n}^2 \tag{3-48}$$

where we now define $\zeta = c/c_c$, the damping ratio or factor.

If we substitute ${\omega_n}^2 = k/m$ in Eq. (2-26), we get

$$\omega_{nd} = \omega_n \sqrt{1 - \left(\frac{c}{c_c}\right)^2} = \omega_n\sqrt{1 - \zeta^2} \tag{3-49}$$

The constants A and B are evaluated from the time boundary conditions. Taking the case when $t = 0$; $x = x_0$ and $\dot{x} = 0$, we get

$$A = x_0 \qquad B = \frac{x_0\zeta}{\sqrt{1 - \zeta^2}}$$

Then Eq. (2-28a) becomes

$$x = x_0 e^{-\zeta\omega_n t}\left[\cos \omega_n\sqrt{1 - \zeta^2}\,t + \frac{\zeta}{\sqrt{1 - \zeta^2}}\sin \omega_n\sqrt{1 - \zeta^2}\,t\right] \tag{3-50}$$

or

$$x = \frac{x_0}{1 - \zeta^2}\,e^{-\zeta\omega_n t}[\cos (\omega_n\sqrt{1 - \zeta^2}\,t - \phi)] \tag{3-51}$$

where

$$\phi = \tan^{-1}\frac{\zeta}{\sqrt{1 - \zeta^2}}$$

The amplitude for Eq. (3-51) will be denoted by X_0, where

$$X_0 = \frac{x_0}{1 - \zeta^2}$$

Eq. (3-51) may now be written as

$$x = X_0 e^{-\zeta\omega_n t}\cos (\omega_{nd}t - \phi) \tag{3-52}$$

valid only for the initial conditions when $t = 0$, $x = x_0$, and $\dot{x} = 0$.

Example. Determine the equation of motion for a spring-dashpot-mass system when such a system starts from rest at the equilibrium position with an initial velocity v_0.

SOLUTION. In general,

$$x = e^{-\zeta\omega_n t}[A \cos \omega_{nd}t + B \sin \omega_{nd}t]$$

Then

$$\dot{x} = -\zeta\omega_n e^{-\zeta\omega_n t}[A \cos \omega_{nd}t + B \sin \omega_{nd}t]$$
$$-\omega_{nd}e^{-\zeta\omega_n t}[A \sin \omega_{nd}t - B \cos \omega_{nd}t]$$

The initial conditions are: when $t = 0$, $x = 0$, and $\dot{x} = v_0$.

Then

$$A = 0 \qquad \text{and} \qquad B = \frac{v_0}{\omega_n \sqrt{1 - \zeta^2}}$$

Consequently

$$x = \frac{v_0}{\omega_n \sqrt{1 - \zeta^2}} e^{-\zeta \omega_n t} \sin \omega_n \sqrt{1 - \zeta^2}\, t$$

which is the required equation of motion.

It is instructive to rework the above problem starting with the following equation:

$$x = e^{-\zeta \omega_n t} \sqrt{A^2 + B^2} \cos (\omega_{nd} t - \phi)$$

where

$$\phi = \tan^{-1} \frac{B}{A}$$

Then

$$\dot{x} = -\zeta \omega_n e^{-\zeta \omega_n t} \sqrt{A^2 + B^2} \cos (\omega_{nd} t - \phi)$$
$$-e^{-\zeta \omega_n t} \sqrt{A^2 + B^2}\, \omega_{nd} \sin (\omega_{nd} t - \phi)$$

From the initial conditions we see that

$$0 = \sqrt{A^2 + B^2} \cos \phi$$

(since $\sqrt{A^2 + B^2}$ cannot be equal to zero, then the $\cos \phi = 0$ and $\phi = 90°$ and the phase shift is therefore $90°$)
and

$$v_0 = -\zeta \omega_n \sqrt{A^2 + B^2} \cos \phi + \sqrt{A^2 + B^2}\, \omega_{nd} \sin \phi$$

We now evaluate the amplitude to be:

$$\sqrt{A^2 + B^2} = \frac{v_0}{\omega_{nd}} = \frac{v_0}{\omega_n \sqrt{1 - \zeta^2}}$$

Substituting, we get

$$x = \frac{v_0}{\omega_n \sqrt{1 - \zeta^2}} e^{-\zeta \omega_n t} \cos (\omega_n \sqrt{1 - \zeta^2}\, t - 90°)$$

The above is equal to

$$x = \frac{v_0}{\omega_n \sqrt{1 - \zeta^2}} e^{-\zeta \omega_n t} \sin (\omega_n \sqrt{1 - \zeta^2}\, t)$$

which is the same result previously obtained.

3–5. Logarithmic Decrement. It is possible to determine the value of the damping constant c from a study of Eq. (3–52). The time-displacement curve for Eq. (3–52) may be thought of as consisting of two elements, a

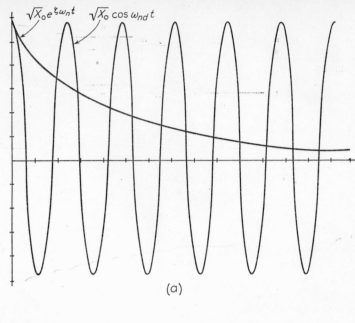

$\sqrt{X_o} e^{\zeta \omega_n t}$ $\sqrt{X_o} \cos \omega_{nd} t$

(a)

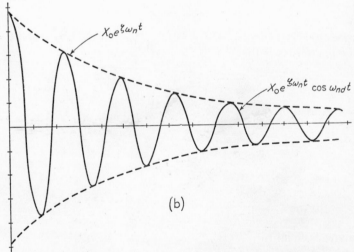

$X_o e^{\zeta \omega_n t}$

$X_o e^{\zeta \omega_n t} \cos \omega_{nd} t$

(b)

Fig. 3–11.

negative exponential curve which is asymptotic to the time ordinate and a harmonic curve, the frequency of which is ω_{nd}. The time-displacement curves of these two elements are shown in Fig. 3–11a. The resultant displacement curve is the product of these curves, and it is shown in Fig. 3–11b. The curve $X_0 e^{-\zeta \omega_n t}$, when plotted positively and as a mirror image, becomes the envelope of the resultant curve. The decay of the resultant curve is emphasized by the envelope and may be considered to be a function of $e^{-\zeta \omega_n t}$.

Let us define a time t_1 when the cos $(\omega_{nd} t - \phi)$ has the value of unity. The envelope will be tangent to the displacement curve at this point. The displacement x_1, at time t_1, is

$$x_1 = X_0 e^{-\zeta \omega_n t_1} \tag{3-53}$$

We now define a time t_2 equal to t_1 plus n times the period of the vibration, where n is an integer. At the time t_2, the value of cos $(\omega_{nd} t - \phi)$ will also be unity and the exponential envelope will be tangent at the point x_2. We see that

$$x_2 = X_0 e^{-\zeta \omega_n t_2} \tag{3-54}$$

and both x_1 and x_2 lie on the curve $X_0 e^{-\zeta \omega_n t}$. Since

$$t_2 = t_1 + n\tau = t_1 + \frac{2\pi n}{\omega_{nd}} \tag{3-55}$$

then

$$x_2 = X_0 e^{-\zeta \omega_n \left(t_1 + \frac{2\pi n}{\omega_{nd}} \right)} \tag{3-56}$$

Dividing x_1 by x_2, we get

$$\frac{x_1}{x_2} = e^{\frac{2\pi n \zeta \omega_n}{\omega_{nd}}} = e^{\frac{2\pi n \zeta}{\sqrt{1-\zeta^2}}} = e^{n\delta} \tag{3-57}$$

or

$$\ln \frac{x_1}{x_2} = \frac{2\pi n \zeta}{\sqrt{1-\zeta^2}} = n\delta \tag{3-58}$$

where δ is called the logarithmic decrement.

A record, similar to that of Fig. 3–11b, of the time-displacement chart of a free, damped system can be obtained directly from the vibrating body if suitable instrumentation is used. The recorded peak amplitudes very nearly coincide with the points of tangency of the envelope. Therefore, as a first-order approximation, we can say that the natural logarithm of the ratio of two peak amplitudes, a period apart, yields the logarithmic decrement as defined by Eq. (3–58).

Example. An analysis of a recorded free vibration shows that the amplitude at the start of the second cycle is 0.210 in. and the amplitude at the start of the fourth cycle is 0.033 in. If the mass weighs 6 lbs. and the spring constant is 40 lbs./in., what is the value of the damping constant?

SOLUTION:

$$n\delta = \ln \frac{0.210}{0.033} = \ln 6.364 = 1.8506$$

$$n = 2$$

$$\delta = 0.9253$$

$$\delta^2 = \frac{(2\pi\zeta)^2}{1 - \zeta^2}$$

$$\zeta = \frac{\delta}{\sqrt{\delta^2 + 4\pi^2}}$$

$$\zeta = \frac{0.9253}{\sqrt{(0.9253)^2 + 4\pi^2}} = 0.1457$$

Now

$$c = \zeta c_c = \zeta\sqrt{4km}$$

$$c = 0.1457 \sqrt{\frac{4 \times 40 \times 6}{386}}$$

$$c = 0.230 \text{ lb.-sec./in.}$$

Note: The reader will find it worth while to compare the natural frequency of the system with the natural damped frequency. Even though the damping constant is more than moderate, the difference between the two frequencies is small.

3–6. Damped, Forced Systems. The differential equation of motion for a forced, damped system may be expressed as

$$m\ddot{x} + c\dot{x} + kx = F \cos \nu t \qquad (3\text{–}59)$$

The solution to Eq. (3–59), which has been given by Eq. (2–48), consists of two terms, a transient state and a steady state. If we introduce a new term defining the frequency ratio, ν/ω_n, Eq. (2–48) may be expressed as

$$\overset{\textit{Transient State}}{x = \sqrt{A^2 + B^2}\, e^{-\zeta\omega_n t} \cos(\omega_{nd} t - \phi)} + \overset{\textit{Steady State}}{\frac{F}{k} \frac{\cos(\nu t - \psi)}{\sqrt{(1 - \beta^2)^2 + (2\zeta\beta)^2}}} \qquad (3\text{–}60)$$

where

$$\beta = \frac{\nu}{\omega_n}, \qquad \zeta = \frac{c}{c_c}, \qquad \phi = \tan^{-1}\frac{B}{A}, \qquad \text{and} \qquad \psi = \tan^{-1}\frac{2\zeta\beta}{1 - \beta^2}$$

It has been pointed out in Chapter 2 that the transient state vanishes with time. The time required for the transient very nearly to vanish . pendent upon the damping constant and the mass size. The larger value of c/m or $\zeta\omega_n$, the sooner will the transient state damp out.

In most mechanical problems the interest in the transient state is very slight, for the amplitude resulting from the transient is only appreciable when the system under study is first put into operation. In other words, only when t is in the neighborhood of zero is the transient-state solution of some importance. Therefore this discussion concerning damped, forced vibrations will center itself primarily upon the steady-state vibration.

The maximum amplitude of the steady-state condition is

$$x_{\text{max}} = \frac{F}{k}\frac{1}{\sqrt{(1-\beta^2)^2 + (2\zeta\beta)^2}} \qquad (3\text{--}61)$$

The above equation may be thought of as the product of two distinct parts. One part, F/k, can be considered to be the static deflection of the magnitude of the force. The other, a modifying term of the static deflection, can be defined as a magnification factor or

$$\mu = \frac{1}{\sqrt{(1-\beta^2)^2 + (2\zeta\beta)^2}} \qquad (3\text{--}62)$$

Eq. (3–61) may be written as

$$x_{\text{max}} = \frac{F}{k}\mu \qquad (3\text{--}63)$$

The magnitude of Eq. (3–61) is dependent upon two parameters, ζ and β. Unless damping is specifically introduced into a system, the damping ratio ζ is a very small quantity. Consider the values that can be taken by the μ, when $\zeta = 0$. When the forcing frequency, ν, is very low, μ is very nearly one and the deflection is approximately F/k. As ν is increased, the deflection increases rapidly. When $\nu = \omega_n$, we have a resonance condition and μ becomes infinite. Increasing ν beyond the resonance frequency starts to diminish the amplitude. Note that beyond resonance the term $1 - \beta^2$ becomes negative. The displacement is now negative; that is, the displacement will oppose the direction of the force. As the frequency ratio increases to the value of $\beta = \sqrt{2}$, the amplitude diminishes to the value of $-F/k$. Any further increase of the frequency ratio diminishes the absolute amplitude and in the limit approaches a zero displacement.

If a small amount of damping is present, as is always the case, the amplitude follows the same pattern as the amplitude of the undamped instance but at a slightly lower absolute value. In particular, the influence of a small amount of damping is seen at resonance, where the amplitude is

12 is a graph of the absolute value of μ versus β for The limiting case occurs when $\zeta = 1$. It must be se in the damping ratio always decreases μ for all cy ratio. Marked reductions are obtained in the onance frequency ratio when damping is introduced.

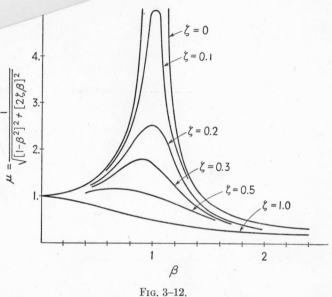

FIG. 3–12.

The maximum amplitude of the damped vibration does not occur exactly at the value of the frequency ratio of 1. However, for small amounts of damping it occurs so close to this value that it may be assumed that the maximum amplitude does occur at $\beta = 1$. The maximum amplitude will occur when the term under the radical in the μ is a minimum. This minimum value is found by taking the derivative of the term under the radical with respect to β and setting it equal to zero.

$$\frac{d}{d\beta}[(1 - \beta^2)^2 + (2\zeta\beta)^2] = 0 \qquad (3\text{–}64)$$

Carrying out the operation as indicated in Eq. (3–64) yields

$$\beta^2 = 1 - 2\zeta^2 \qquad (3\text{–}65)$$

We note that Eq. (3–65) is valid only for value of $\zeta \leq \sqrt{0.5}$. When ζ is greater than $\sqrt{0.5}$, the roots of the equation are imaginary. The physical interpretation we can place on Eq. (3–65) when $\zeta > \sqrt{0.5}$ is that there is no definable zero slope on the amplitude-frequency ratio curve. However, for any amount of damping, no matter how small, the maximum amplitude will always occur below the resonance frequency ratio, $\beta = 1$. It may be of interest to note that in many recording instruments a damping ratio value in the neighborhood of 0.707 is introduced to prevent the recorder from overshooting the true measurement.

Eq. (3–60) defines the phase angle of the steady-state vibration;

$$\psi = \tan^{-1} \frac{2\zeta\beta}{1 - \beta^2} \qquad (3\text{–}63)$$

It is obvious that ψ will vary with the frequency ratio if the damping ratio is kept constant. For a fixed value of ζ, let us see what happens to ψ as β is varied. Below the value of $\beta = 1$, ψ is less than 90°. When β is 1, then $\tan \psi = \infty$ and $\psi = 90°$. When $\beta > 1$, then $\tan \psi$ has a negative

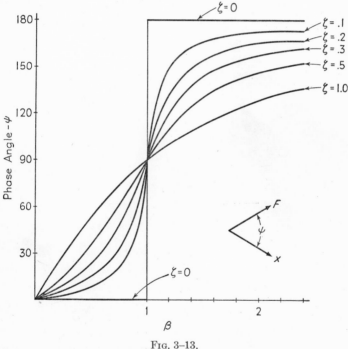

Fig. 3–13.

value. In the limit as β becomes very large, ψ approaches 180°. For the case of no damping when β is less than 1, $\psi = 0$. At $\beta = 1$, $\tan \psi = 0/0$, which is indeterminate. However, if we take the case of a very small amount of damping and $\beta > 1$, then $\tan \psi$ is negative and ψ is very nearly equal to 180°. Then for the case of no damping there is a phase change at the point when $\beta = 1$. The phase angle goes from 0° to 180° at the resonance point when no damping occurs. A plot of phase angle versus β is shown in Fig. 3–13.

The phase angle relates the displacement vector to the forcing vector. When $\beta = 1$, the displacement vector will then lag the forcing vector by 90° for all values of ζ other than zero. For values of β, other than 1, Fig. 3–13, which is a plot of phase angle versus the ratio β for various

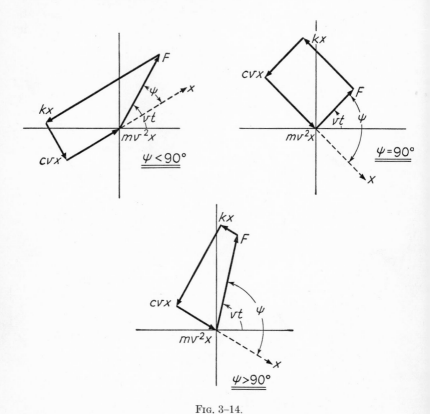

Fig. 3–14.

values of ζ, may be used to determine ψ. Special note should be made to observe that the slopes of the curves are quite steep in the vicinity of resonance. Fig. 3–14 shows the vector diagram of the force system with respect to displacement for various values of ψ. It should be noted that the force polygon must be closed, since the system is in dynamic equilibrium.

Example. A mass weighing 386 lbs. is connected to a spring ($k = 200$ lbs./in.) and a damper ($c = 3$ lbs.-sec./in.) in the conventional manner. If the mass is acted upon by a harmonic force whose amplitude is 10 lbs. and whose frequency is 150 cpm, determine, if the system starts from rest: (1) the equation of motion, (2) the displacement at $t = 0.05$ sec., (3) the maximum displacement under steady-state conditions.

SOLUTION. Let us first evaluate the constants A and B. This evaluation can be simplified if we write Eq. (3–60) in the following form:

$$x = e^{-\zeta \omega_n t}[A \cos \omega_{nd} t + B \sin \omega_{nd} t]$$
$$+ \frac{F}{k} \mu[(1 - \beta^2) \cos \nu t + 2\zeta \beta \sin \nu t]$$

The time boundary conditions are: when $t = 0$, $x = 0$, and $\dot{x} = 0$. By differentiation with respect to time, we get:

$$\dot{x} = -\zeta \omega_n e^{-\zeta \omega_n t}[A \cos \omega_{nd} t + B \sin \omega_{nd} t]$$
$$- \omega_{nd} e^{-\zeta \omega_n t}[A \sin \omega_{nd} t - B \cos \omega_{nd} t]$$
$$- \frac{F}{k} \mu \nu[(1 - \beta^2) \sin \nu t - 2\zeta \beta \cos \nu t]$$

Applying the boundary conditions yields

$$0 = A + \frac{F}{k} \mu(1 - \beta^2)$$

and
$$0 = -\zeta \omega_n A + \omega_{nd} B + \frac{F}{k} \mu(2\zeta \beta \nu)$$

Whence
$$A = -\frac{F}{k} \mu (1 - \beta^2)$$

and
$$B = -\frac{F}{k} \mu \left[\frac{(1 + \beta^2)}{\sqrt{1 - \zeta^2}} \right]$$

where
$$\omega_{nd} = \omega_n \sqrt{1 - \zeta^2}.$$

Then

$$\sqrt{A^2 + B^2} = \frac{F\mu}{k\sqrt{1 - \zeta^2}} \sqrt{(1 - \beta^2)^2 + 4\zeta^2 \beta^2}$$

At any time, t,

(1)
$$x = \frac{F\mu}{k\sqrt{1 - \zeta^2}} \sqrt{(1 - \beta^2)^2 + 4\zeta^2 \beta^2} \, e^{-\zeta \omega_n t} \cos (\omega_{nd} t - \phi)$$
$$+ \frac{F}{k} \mu \cos (\nu t - \psi)$$

where
$$\phi = \tan^{-1} \frac{-\zeta(1 + \beta^2)}{-\sqrt{1 - \zeta^2}(1 - \beta^2)}$$

and

$$\psi = \tan^{-1} \frac{2\zeta\beta}{1 - \beta^2}$$

Let us now evaluate the constants.

$$\omega_n = \sqrt{\frac{k}{m}} = \sqrt{200} = 14.14 \text{ radians/sec.}$$

$$\nu = \frac{f \times 2\pi}{60} = \frac{150 \times 2\pi}{60} = 15.70 \text{ radians/sec.}$$

$$\beta = \frac{\nu}{\omega_n} = 1.110 \qquad 1 - \beta^2 = -0.232$$

$$(1 - \beta^2)^2 = 0.0538 \qquad 1 + \beta^2 = 2.232$$

$$\zeta = \frac{c}{\sqrt{4km}} = 0.1061 \qquad \zeta^2 = 0.01126$$

$$1 - \zeta^2 = 0.996 \qquad \sqrt{1 - \zeta^2} = 0.998$$

$$\omega_{nd} = \omega_n\sqrt{1 - \zeta^2} = 14.11 \text{ radians/sec.}$$

$$2\zeta\beta = 0.236 \qquad (2\zeta\beta)^2 = 0.0555$$

$$\mu = \frac{1}{\sqrt{(1 - \beta)^2 + (2\zeta\beta)^2}} = 3.03$$

$$\phi = \tan^{-1} \frac{-\zeta(1 + \beta^2)}{-\sqrt{1 - \zeta^2}(1 - \beta^2)} = \frac{-0.237}{0.232}$$

$$\phi = \tan^{-1} - 1.023$$

$$\phi = 314.4° = 5.49 \text{ radians}$$

$$\psi = \tan^{-1} \frac{2\zeta\beta}{1 - \beta^2} = \tan^{-1} \frac{0.236}{-0.232} = \tan^{-1} - 1.0172$$

$$\psi = 134.5° = 2.35 \text{ radians}$$

Evaluating the equation of motion at $t = 0.05$ sec., we get

$$x_\lambda = \frac{10}{200} \times \frac{3.03}{0.998} \sqrt{0.0538 + 0.0555} \times$$

$$e^{-0.1061 \times 14.14 \times 0.05} \cos (14.11 \times 0.05 - 5.49)$$

$$x_\lambda = 0.00295 \text{ in.} \tag{3-66a}$$

and

$$x_\mu = \frac{10}{200} \times 3.03 \cos (14.11 \times 0.05 - 2.35) = -0.0106 \text{ in.}$$

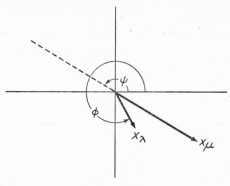

Fig. 3–15.

The two components of displacement are now combined vectorially. Fig. 3–15 shows the two components. Then

(2) $$x = 0.0135 \text{ in.}$$ (3–66b)

The maximum displacement under steady-state conditions is

(3) $$x_{\mu \max} = \frac{10}{200} \times 3.03 = 0.1515 \text{ in.}$$ (3–66c)

3–7. **Negligible Damping.** Some distinction between no damping and negligible damping must be made at this point. By referring to Eq. (3–60), it can be seen that if no damping exists then the transient-state portion of Eq. (3–60) is no longer transient. In nature, this condition is not possible, for c is never zero. With time, the amplitude of an undamped vibration that is not forced will always vanish. Therefore the concept of negligible damping must be used when we discuss an undamped condition. The inference of negligible damping is that the transient nature of the first part of Eq. (3–60) exists even if there is no damping, and that, given a sufficient period of time, only the steady-state portion of the equation remains.

When we use the concept of negligible damping for a short period of time, the undamped forced solution is valid. From Chapter 2 we can piece together this solution:

$$x = A \cos \omega_n t + B \sin \omega_n t + \frac{F}{k} \frac{1}{(1 - \beta^2)} \cos \nu t$$ (3–67)

is the equation for an undamped forced vibration and is valid only in the neighborhood of $t = 0$. Eq. (3–67) is obtained by combining Eqs. (2–28) and (2–47) after c has been set to zero.

To evaluate the constants A and B, the boundary condition must be known. Let us assume that the vibration starts from the equilibrium position and that both the initial displacement and the velocity are zero. Then, when $t = 0$; $x = 0$, and $\dot{x} = 0$. Applying the boundary conditions, we get

$$0 = A(1) + B(0) + \frac{F}{k}\left(\frac{1}{1 - \beta^2}\right)(1)$$

$$0 = A\omega_n(0) + B\omega_n(1) - \frac{F}{k}\nu\left(\frac{1}{1 - \beta^2}\right)(0) \tag{3–68}$$

Then

$$A = -\frac{F}{k}\left(\frac{1}{1 - \beta^2}\right) \qquad \text{and} \qquad B = 0 \tag{3–69}$$

Substituting the results of Eq. (3–69) into Eq. (3–67) yields

$$x = \frac{F}{k}\left(\frac{1}{1 - \beta^2}\right)(\cos \nu t - \cos \omega_n t) \tag{3–70}$$

Since the angular frequencies of the two vectors, represented by Eq. (3–70), are different, the vectors will at times combine to double the amplitude and at other times to negate the amplitude of each other. The increase of amplitude may be of some importance in the design of a machine, and one should be cognizant of this fact.

Of particular interest in this discussion is the case when ν is nearly equal to ω_n, but not exactly equal. The phase angle between the two vectors will change slowly, and as a result, nearly harmonic motion will occur. Let us plot the case when ν is nearly equal to ω_n, as shown in Fig 3–16. It can be readily seen that there is a building up and that there is a vanishing of the vibration which can be contained in a harmonic envelope. This phenomenon is known as "beating" and is the result of the two frequencies being nearly equal. Let us make an analysis which will give us some insight into this phenomenon. Eq. (3–70) may be written as

$$x = 2D \sin \frac{\nu - \omega_n}{2} t \cdot \sin \frac{\nu + \omega_n}{2} t \tag{3–71}$$

where

$$D = -\frac{F}{k}\left(\frac{1}{1 - \beta^2}\right)$$

The motion can be thought of as a sine wave of $\sin\left(\dfrac{\nu + \omega_n}{2}t\right)$ with a varying amplitude of $2D\sin\left(\dfrac{\nu - \omega_n}{2}t\right)$. The envelope will be formed by the harmonic curve of $\sin\left(\dfrac{\nu + \omega_n}{2}t\right)$ and its amplitude will be $2D$.

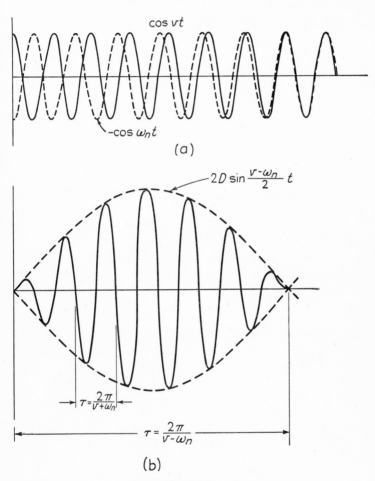

Fig. 3–16.

We now consider the case when $\nu = \omega_n$. Eq. (3–67) is no longer valid for this case of resonance, for when the above conditions are substituted, the displacement is an indeterminate. We therefore must go back and resolve the differential equation for this case. The D.E. is

$$m\ddot{x} + kx = F\cos\omega_n t \qquad (3\text{–}72)$$

The complementary solution is

$$x_c = A \cos \omega_n t + B \sin \omega_n t \qquad (3\text{-}73)$$

The particular solution must be independent of the complementary solution. Since $\nu = \omega_n$, we get our particular solution by multiplying the constants by t. The particular solution is taken in the form of

$$x_p = Dt \cos \omega_n t + Et \sin \omega_n t \qquad (3\text{-}74)$$

Differentiating Eq. (3-74) with respect to time yields:

$$\dot{x}_p = D \cos \omega_n t - D\omega_n t \sin \omega_n t + E \sin \omega_n t + E\omega_n t \cos \omega_n t \qquad (3\text{-}75)$$

$$\ddot{x}_p = -D\omega_n \sin \omega_n t - D\omega_n \sin \omega_n t - D\omega_n^2 t \cos \omega_n t$$
$$+ E\omega_n \cos \omega_n t + E\omega_n \cos \omega_n t - E\omega_n^2 t \sin \omega_n t$$

Substituting x_p and $\ddot{x}_p$ into Eq. (3-72) yields:

$$m(-2D\omega_n \sin \omega_n t - D\omega_n^2 t \cos \omega_n t + 2E\omega_n \cos \omega_n t - E\omega_n^2 \sin \omega_n t)$$
$$+ k(Dt \cos \omega_n t + Et \sin \omega_n t) = F \cos \omega_n t \qquad (3\text{-}76)$$

Since the coefficients on the R.H.S. must equal those of the L.H.S., we get

$$-m2D\omega_n - mE\omega_n^2 t + kEt = 0$$

$$-mD\omega_n^2 t + m2E\omega_n + kDt = F \qquad (3\text{-}77)$$

Simplifying,

$$-2m\omega_n D + (kt - kt)E = 0$$

$$(-kt + kt)D + 2m\omega_n E = F \qquad (3\text{-}78)$$

Then

$$D = 0 \qquad \text{and} \qquad E = \frac{F}{2m\omega_n} \qquad (3\text{-}79)$$

The complete solution becomes

$$x = A \cos \omega_n t + B \sin \omega_n t + \frac{Ft}{2m\omega_n} \sin \omega_n t \qquad (3\text{-}80)$$

Eq. (3-80) represents the displacement of the mass at resonance with negligible damping.

To evaluate A and B, we use the time boundary conditions when $t = 0$; $x = 0$, and $\dot{x} = 0$, and as a result, $A = B = 0$. Then

$$x = \frac{F}{2m\omega_n} t \sin \omega_n t = \frac{F}{c_c} t \sin \omega_n t \qquad (3\text{-}81)$$

The amplitude of the resonance condition increases with time and in the limit approaches infinity. Eq. (3-81) demonstrates that not only does the amplitude become infinite as was demonstrated in Section 3-6, but it also requires a period of time to build the amplitude to appreciable magnitude. The amplitude build-up is a function of the critical damping as well as of the time. The larger the critical damping, the longer it will take for the amplitude to build up. Fig. 3–17 is a sketch of the resonant amplitude increasing with time.

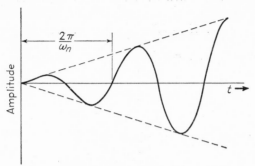

Fig. 3–17.

It is this building up of amplitude that makes it possible to operate at frequencies above the resonance. As a machine is brought up to speed, it will pass through resonance. Usually a machine will attain its operating speed in a very short time so that it passes through the resonance speed quite rapidly and there is not sufficient time for the large resonance amplitudes to build up. Difficulty is sometimes experienced because of the large amplitudes which develop after the power of the machine has been cut off. If the slowing-down process is gradual, the machine may be caught in the resonance region, and dangerous amplitudes may result. It is often necessary to introduce a braking device which will slow the machine down rapidly after the power has been cut off.

Example. A limit switch is set to cut off the power to the motor of a machine when the amplitude of vibration reaches 0.15 in. Since this machine operates above resonance conditions, determine how long a period of time is available for the machine to pass through resonance if the physical parameters of the machine are a mass weighing 50 lbs., an over-all spring constant of 100 lbs./in., and the amplitude of the external harmonic force of 20 lbs. Assume that the boundary conditions of Eq. (3–81) are valid.

SOLUTION:

$$x = \frac{F}{2m\omega_n} t \sin \omega_n t$$

$$\omega_n = \sqrt{\frac{k}{m}} = \sqrt{\frac{100 \times 386}{50}} = 27.8$$

$$x = \frac{20 \times 386}{2 \times 50 \times 27.8} \, t \sin (27.8t)$$

$$x = 2.78t \sin (27.8t)$$

By the trial-and-error method we find $t = 0.054$ sec. This is shown by a checking method.

$$0.15 = 2.78 \times 0.054 \times 0.998$$

$$0.15 = 0.1498$$

The assumed time of 0.054 sec. checks out quite closely. Care must be taken in applying the trial-and-error method to make certain that we are reaching the limiting amplitude for the first time.

3–8. Spring-mounted Rotating Machinery. Spring mounting of rotating machinery is a very common practice. The purpose of such a mounting is to diminish the force which is transmitted to the foundation. Before we investigate this transmission of force, let us determine the displacement of a machine mounted on springs. In order to make the discussion more general let a damper also be included in the system. Such a system is diagrammatically presented in Fig. 3–18. The machine is mounted so that rollers restrict all motion except in the x direction. This restriction insures that only a single degree of freedom will exist. Let the mass of the machine be m, the total spring constant k, and the damping constant c. We will assume that an unbalance exists. Let it be m_1, which acts at a distance e inches away from the center of gravity of the machine. The assumption of an unbalance is a realistic one. Unless a machine has been dynamically balanced with great care, such an unbalance will exist. The unbalance will cause a forcing function due to the centrifugal force of the unbalance. This force is $m_1 e\nu^2 \cos \nu t$, where ν is the circular frequency of the rotating machine. The differential equation governing this system is seen to be

$$m\ddot{x} + c\dot{x} + kx = m_1 e\nu^2 \cos \nu t \qquad (3\text{--}82)$$

The Eq. (3–82) is the same form as Eq. (3–59) when $F = m_1 e\nu^2$. Then the steady-state solution is found by substituting $m_1 e\nu^2$ for F in the steady-state portion of Eq. (3–60).

$$x = \frac{m_1 e\nu^2}{k} \cdot \frac{\cos (\nu t - \psi)}{\sqrt{(1 - \beta^2)^2 + (2\zeta\beta)^2}} \qquad (3\text{--}83)$$

Example. A motor operating at 1750 rpm weighs 50 lbs. and is mounted on four springs, each having a spring constant of 40 lbs./in. If the steady-state amplitude is not to exceed 0.275 in., determine the maximum allowable unbalance.

SOLUTION:

$$\nu = \frac{1750 \times 2\pi}{60} = 183.2 \text{ radians/sec.}$$

$$\omega_n = \sqrt{\frac{160 \times 386}{50}} = 35.2 \text{ radians/sec.}$$

$$\beta = \frac{183.2}{35.2} = 5.21$$

$$\zeta = 0$$

$$\mu = \frac{1}{1 - \beta^2} = 0.0382$$

Since

$$x_{max} = \frac{(m_1 e)\nu^2}{k} \mu$$

then

$$W_1 e = \frac{k x_{max} g}{\nu^2 \mu} = \frac{160 \times 0.275 \times 386}{183.2^2 \times 0.0382}$$

$$W_1 e = 13.33 \text{ lb.-in.} = 213.3 \text{ oz.-in. unbalance}$$

It is interesting to rework this problem with a change in the spring constant. If the spring constant is doubled, the allowable unbalance is diminished approximately tenfold.

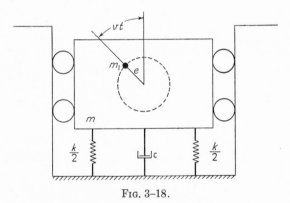

FIG. 3-18.

3-9. Transmissibility. If we now focus our attention on the foundation under the machine in Fig. 3-18, it can be noted that the only avenue by which force can be transmitted to the foundation is through the springs and the damper. Then

$$F_{TR} = F_k + F_c \qquad (3\text{-}84)$$

where F_{TR} is the force transmitted to the foundation. The magnitude of F_k is kx_{max} and that of F_c is cvx_{max}. F_c leads F_k by $90°$. Eq. (3–84) is shown in Fig. 3–19a.

$$F_{TR\,max} = \sqrt{(kx_{max})^2 + (cvx_{max})^2} = kx_{max}\sqrt{1 + (2\zeta\beta)^2} \quad (3\text{–}85)$$

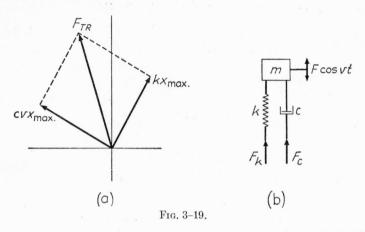

(a)

(b)

Fig. 3–19.

Fig. 3–19b schematically represents the general case of the system under discussion. The ratio of the transmitted force to the impressed force is defined as transmissibility, TR. This ratio is a measure of the isolation which exists between the mass and the ground.

$$TR = \frac{F_{TR}}{F} = \frac{kx_{max}\sqrt{1 + (2\zeta\beta)^2}}{F} \quad (3\text{–}86)$$

Since

$$x_{max} = \frac{F}{k}\,\mu \quad (3\text{–}87)$$

then

$$TR = \sqrt{1 + (2\zeta\beta)^2}\,\mu \quad (3\text{–}88)$$

Fig. 3–20 is a plot of Eq. (3–88) with the absolute value of TR and the frequency ratio as ordinates. Since all curves of varying values of ζ intersect at $TR = 1$ and $\beta = \sqrt{2}$, it is apparent that damping is an aid in limiting TR when $\beta < \sqrt{2}$. Above the ratio of $\beta = \sqrt{2}$, damping is detrimental rather than advantageous. The greatest aid to vibration isolation is to operate the equipment beyond the $\sqrt{2}$ frequency ratio value. Negligible damping, then, is more beneficial than introduced damping. To get a frequency ratio above the value of $\beta = \sqrt{2}$, it is only necessary to use soft enough springs. The springs used for mounting can be suitably selected by the designer.

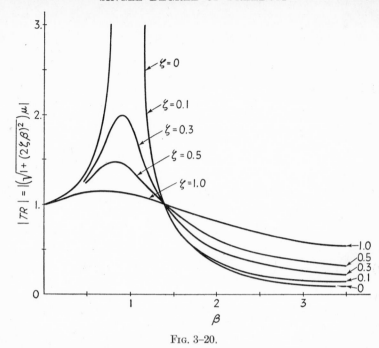

FIG. 3–20.

Example. A small single-cylinder diesel engine operates at a constant speed of 1200 rpm. The engine weighs 850 lbs. In order to isolate the engine from the foundation, it is proposed that the engine be mounted on springs. Let us consider four different mountings: (*a*) on springs only, having a spring constant of 60,000 lbs./in.; (*b*) on the same springs as (*a*) but introducing a damper, $\zeta = 0.13$; (*c*) on springs only having a spring constant of 10,000 lbs./in.; (*d*) on the same springs as (*c*) but using a damper, $\zeta = 0.13$. Compare these mountings by comparing the transmissibility.

SOLUTION:

$$\nu = \frac{1200 \times 2\pi}{60} = 125.7 \text{ radians/sec.}$$

(*a*) $$\omega_n = \sqrt{\frac{60,000 \times 386}{850}} = 165.1 \text{ radians/sec.}$$

$$\beta = \frac{125.7}{165.1} = 0.761$$

$$\zeta = 0$$

$$\mu = \frac{1}{1 - \beta^2} = \frac{1}{0.421} = 2.375$$

$$TR = 2.375$$

(b) From the calculations of (a):

$$\omega_n = 165.1 \qquad \text{and} \qquad \beta = 0.761$$

$$\zeta = 0.13$$

$$\mu = \frac{1}{\sqrt{(1 - \beta^2)^2 + (2\zeta\beta)^2}} = 2.15$$

$$TR = \sqrt{1 + (2\zeta\beta)^2}\,\mu = 0.102 \times 2.15$$

$$TR = 2.19$$

(c)

$$\omega_n = \sqrt{\frac{10,000 \times 386}{850}} = 67.4 \text{ radians/sec.}$$

$$\beta = \frac{125.7}{67.4} = 1.864$$

$$\zeta = 0$$

$$\mu = \frac{1}{1 - \beta^2} = -0.404$$

$$TR = 0.404$$

(d) From the calculations of (c):

$$\omega_n = 67.4 \text{ radians/sec.} \qquad \text{and} \qquad \beta = 1.864$$

$$\zeta = 0.13$$

$$\mu = \frac{1}{\sqrt{(1 - \beta^2)^2 + (2\zeta\beta)^2}} = 0.397$$

$$TR = \sqrt{1 + (2\zeta\beta)^2}\,\mu = 1.111 \times 0.397$$

$$TR = 0.441$$

Of the four mountings, (c) is the best. We note that the introduction of damping for the case above resonance (d) increases the TR. Case (b) is better than (a), for the introduction of damping is beneficial for systems operating below resonance. Even case (c) is not a good design. A very much lower TR can be achieved by using a softer spring system. If we use a spring system in which $k = 2000$ lbs./in., then the $TR = 0.0608$.

3-1?. Vibrating Systems Attached to Moving Supports. Consider the system schematically represented in Fig. 3-21a. The external force is appl\ ?d to the support rather than to the mass, and, as a result, the support is moving with harmonic motion. Such a system occurs frequently as a result of machine installation. A machine may be supported by a beam

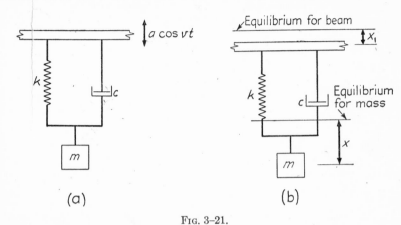

(a)   (b)

FIG. 3-21.

which itself is being excited by a harmonic force. A first approximation of the solution of an automobile being driven over a rough road may be represented by Fig. 3-21a. In order to obtain the equation of motion, let us displace the system of Fig. 3-21a downward. This displacement is shown in Fig. 3-21b. The support has moved from its equilibrium position to x_1, and the mass has moved from its equilibrium position a distance x. The spring force and the damping forces are now functions of the relative displacement and relative velocity, $(x - x_1)$ and $(\dot{x} - \dot{x}_1)$, respectively. Summing the forces acting on the mass we get

$$-k(x - x_1) - c(\dot{x} - \dot{x}_1) = m\ddot{x} \qquad (3\text{-}89)$$

Rearranging, we get

$$m\ddot{x} + c\dot{x} + kx = c\dot{x}_1 + kx_1 \qquad (3\text{-}90)$$

Now

$$x_1 = a \cos \nu t$$

and

$$\dot{x}_1 = -a\nu \sin \nu t \qquad (3\text{-}91)$$

Then

$$m\ddot{x} + c\dot{x} + kx = a\sqrt{k^2 + c^2\nu^2} \cos(\nu t + \psi_1) \qquad (3\text{-}92)$$

where

$$\psi_1 = \tan^{-1}\frac{c\nu}{k}$$

Differential Eq. (3–92) is of the same general form as Eq. (3–59), where $F = a\sqrt{k^2 + c^2\nu^2}$. In addition we have a plus phase angle, ψ_1, tacked on. The sign of the phase angle is a result of the negative sin νt term. Inasmuch as we are interested only in the steady-state solution, the equation for the displacement of the mass is given by the latter half of Eq. (3–60). Making the proper substitution for F, we get

$$x = \frac{a\sqrt{k^2 + c^2\nu^2}}{k} \mu \cos(\nu t - \psi_2) \qquad (3\text{–}93)$$

where

$$\psi_2 = \psi - \psi_1$$

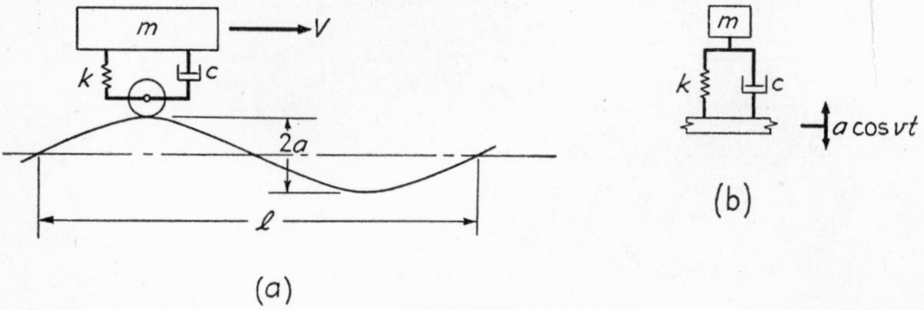

(a)

(b)

Fig. 3–22.

Example. The sketch 3–22a may be considered as a first approximation of an automobile being driven on a rough road. The approximations made are: (1) that only a single degree of freedom exists, (2) that the tires do not have any elastic effects, (3) that the road surface may be considered to be simple harmonic in nature, (4) that the car is being driven at a velocity of V ft. per sec., and (5) the distance from peak to peak of the road surface is l ft. Required: To find the amplitude of motion of the automobile.

SOLUTION. Fig. 3–22b is the equivalent of the system shown in Fig. 3–22a. Therefore the equation of motion is Eq. (3–93). To find ν:

$$\tau = \frac{l}{V} \quad \text{sec.}$$

But

$$\tau = \frac{2\pi}{\nu} \quad \text{sec.}$$

then

$$\nu = \frac{2\pi V}{l} \quad \text{radians/sec.}$$

$$\text{Ampl.} = \frac{F}{k}\mu = \frac{a}{k}\sqrt{k^2 + \left(\frac{2\pi V c}{l}\right)^2}\,\mu$$

3–11. Accelerometer and Vibrometer. The need for a solution to the problem of the mass on a moving support has led to the design of an instrument which can be used to measure the acceleration and the amplitude

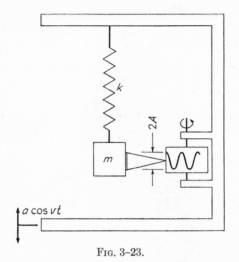

Fig. 3–23.

of a vibrating machine. This instrument consists of a frame which can be clamped to a vibrating machine. Attached to the frame is a spring and a mass. The mass has attached to it a stylus which records on a rotating drum which itself is attached to the frame of the instrument. Fig. 3–23 is a schematic diagram of this instrument. Since the frame is clamped to the vibrating machine, the frame motion is $a \cos vt$, which is the motion of the machine. The motion of the mass of the instrument, since there is no damping, is of the form

$$x = \frac{a}{1 - \beta^2} \cos vt \qquad (3\text{--}94)$$

The record on the rotating drum will be the difference between the motion of the mass and the frame, since the drum is rigidly attached to the frame. Let A be the amplitude of the drum recording. Then

$$A = \frac{a}{1 - \beta^2} - a = \frac{a\beta^2}{1 - \beta^2} = \frac{av^2}{\omega_n^2 - v^2} \qquad (3\text{--}95)$$

Since we have assumed that the vibrating machine has simple harmonic motion, the acceleration of the machine therefore is $-av^2$.

The natural frequency, ω_n, is a characteristic of the measuring instrument. The selection of the values for ω_n is at the freedom of the user of the instrument. Let us consider two choices of ω_n.

a. When $\omega_n \gg \nu$. This selection can be accomplished by using a very stiff spring and a small mass. Then $\omega_n{}^2 - \nu^2$ is nearly equal to $\omega_n{}^2$ and

$$A \doteqdot \frac{a\nu^2}{\omega_n{}^2} \qquad (3\text{-}96)$$

The recorded amplitude A times $\omega_n{}^2$, which is now a known machine factor, is a recording of the acceleration of the machine. When the measuring instrument is used with a stiff spring and small mass, the instrument is called an accelerometer.

b. When $\omega_n \ll \nu$. This selection can be accomplished by using a soft spring and a relatively large mass. Under these circumstances $\omega_n{}^2 - \nu^2$ is very nearly equal to $-\nu^2$ and

$$A \doteqdot - \frac{a\nu^2}{\nu^2} = -a \qquad (3\text{-}97)$$

When a soft spring and large mass are used, the instrument records the amplitude of the vibrating machine and the instrument is then called a vibrometer.

In practice, the vibrometer-accelerometer comes with several sets of springs and masses. In order to get rid of the transient vibrations, a small amount of damping is built into the instrument. This insures that the transient vibrations will vanish in a short time.

3–12. Coulomb Damping. Heretofore all discussions concerning damping have taken for granted that the force of damping is proportional to the velocity. This type of damping, namely, viscous damping, lends itself very nicely to mathematical treatment. However, there are many instances of damping which are caused by dry friction. Such damping is called constant or Coulomb damping. The Coulomb friction force is directly proportional to the load normal to the sliding surfaces and in most cases can be considered to be constant. The sign of the force is opposite to the displacement, the result of which is to create a sign change every half cycle.

Let us consider the case of a free, Coulomb-damped spring-and-mass system. Fig. 3–24 depicts the conditions of a mass sliding over a friction plane. In Fig. 3–24a the motion is away from the equilibrium position and the friction force f ($f = \mu W$, where μ is the coefficient of friction between the mass and the plane) is toward the equilibrium position. Fig. 3–24b shows the motion toward the equilibrium position and the force f is in the opposite direction. Let us derive the equation of motion for cases (*a*) and (*b*).

$$
\begin{array}{cc}
(a) & (b) \\
-kx - f = m\ddot{x} & -kx + f = m\ddot{x} \\
m\ddot{x} + kx = -f & m\ddot{x} + kx = +f
\end{array}
\qquad (3\text{-}96)
$$

Each of the differential equations is valid for a half cycle. A solution, therefore, for either of Eqs. (3–96) is valid only for a half cycle. The solutions of Eqs. (3–96) will not be effected here. It will suffice to say that they are second-order linear differential equations with constant R.H.S. The solutions will be harmonic plus a constant term and they do not possess a damping term in the sense that we are using it. It is interesting to note that the natural frequency is $\sqrt{k/m}$ for either case and is independent of the friction force, f.

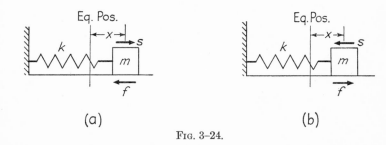

(a)   (b)

FIG. 3–24.

The amplitude decay for each half cycle can be found by solving Eqs. (3–96). As an example of the energy method, let us find the amplitude decay for each half cycle by accounting for the energy change. The half cycle will start when the mass is at the extreme position to the right. Let this position be denoted by x_0. At x_0 the velocity will be zero. The extreme position to the left will be $x_0 - \Delta x$, where Δx is the amplitude decay during the half cycle. The velocity at the extreme left position is again zero. Then the change of kinetic energy for the half cycle is zero. As a result, the energy balance requires only that the change in potential energy be equal to the work done by the force of friction, or

$$\tfrac{1}{2}k[x_0{}^2 - (x_0 - \Delta x)^2] = f(2x_0 - \Delta x) \qquad (3\text{–}97)$$

Expanding, we get

$$\tfrac{1}{2}k(2x_0\Delta x - \Delta x^2) = f(2x_0 - \Delta x)$$

$$\Delta x = 2f/k \qquad (3\text{–}98)$$

The amplitude decay for the first half cycle is $2f/k$. If we repeat this process for the subsequent half cycles we find that the decay is constant for each half cycle. The decay then is linear, and for each cycle there is an amplitude decay of $4f/k$. The amplitudes versus time are shown in Fig. 3–25. The amplitude will decay until the spring force equals the friction force, and motion will stop a short distance away from the equilibrium position. The fact that the mass will not return to the equilibrium position is usually apparent in many measuring instruments. Tapping an instrument to zero it out does help to return the indicator of the instrument toward the equilibrium position.

The case of the forced, Coulomb-damped system is, mathematically speaking, fairly complicated and is, therefore, beyond the scope of this

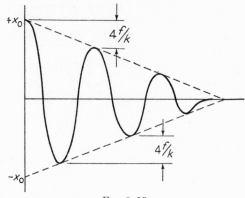

FIG. 3–25.

text. The solution of the forced Coulomb-damped system has been published by Den Hartog[3] in a paper which discusses mixed Coulomb- and viscous-damped systems.

Example. The system depicted by Fig. 3–24 has the following known physical constants: $k = 800$ lbs./in., $mg = 200$ lbs. After an initial displacement of 0.55 in. was given to the system, the following amplitudes of displacement were observed at the end of each period: 0.45, 0.35, 0.25, 0.15. On the basis of the above data, determine the coefficient of friction between the mass and the plane.

SOLUTION. It is apparent that the decay for each cycle is 0.1 in. Then

$$4f/k = 0.1$$

$$f = \frac{0.1 \times 800}{4} = 20.0 \text{ lbs.}$$

But

$$\mu = \frac{f}{W} = \frac{20}{200}$$

$$\mu = 0.1$$

3–13. Energy Dissipated by Damping. An energy balance of a vibrating system requires that the work done by the exciting force be equal to the

[3] J. P. Den Hartog "Forced Vibrations with Combined Coulomb and Viscous Friction," *Trans.*, ASME, APM 53–9–107, 1931.

energy dissipated in the damper. Since the energy dissipated by the transient motion is dissipated over a short period of time, this discussion will be limited to the energy loss during the steady-state vibration.

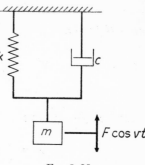

The force acting on the system (Fig. 3–26) at any time t is $F \cos \nu t$. The work done by this force over a cycle will be

$$W = \int_0^\tau F \cos \nu t \, dx \qquad (3\text{–}99)$$

The displacement of the mass has the form of

$$x = A \cos (\nu t - \psi) \qquad (3\text{–}100)$$

then

$$dx = -A\nu \sin (\nu t - \psi) \, dt \qquad (3\text{–}101)$$

Fig. 3–26.

Substituting Eq. (3–101) into Eq. (3–99) results in

$$W = \int_0^\tau FA\nu \cos \nu t \cdot \sin (\psi - \nu t) \, dt \qquad (3\text{–}102)$$

Note that $-\sin (\nu t - \psi) = \sin (\psi - \nu t)$. Expanding the $\sin (\psi - \nu t)$ as the sine of the difference of two angles, we get

$$W = FA\nu \int_0^\tau [\sin \psi \cos^2 \nu t - \cos \psi \sin \nu t \cos \nu t] \, dt \qquad (3\text{–}103)$$

Since

$$\int_0^\tau \cos^2 \nu t \, dt = \frac{\tau}{2}$$

and

$$\int_0^\tau \sin \nu t \cos \nu t \, dt = \sin^2 \frac{\nu \tau}{2} = \sin^2 \pi = 0$$

then

$$W = \frac{FA\nu\tau \sin \psi}{2} = FA\pi \sin \psi \text{ in.-lbs./cycle} \qquad (3\text{–}104)$$

The work done by the exciting force per cycle must be equal to the energy dissipated by the damper during each cycle. The value of the damping force is $c\dot{x}$. Since

$$\dot{x} = -A\nu \sin (\nu t - \psi) \qquad (3\text{–}105)$$

then

$$W_c = \int_0^\tau - cA\nu \sin (\nu t - \psi) \, dx \qquad (3\text{–}106)$$

Substituting dx, Eq. (3–101), into Eq. (3–106) yields:

$$W_c = cA^2\nu^2 \int_0^\tau \sin^2 (\nu t - \psi)\, dt = \pi cA^2\nu \qquad (3\text{–}107)$$

Since $W = W_c$,

$$FA\pi \sin \psi = \pi cA^2\nu \qquad (3\text{–}108)$$

then

$$\sin \psi = \frac{Ac\nu}{F} \qquad (3\text{–}109)$$

From Eq. (3–60), we see that

$$A = \frac{F}{k} \frac{1}{\sqrt{(1 - \beta^2)^2 + (2\zeta\beta)^2}} = \frac{F}{k}\,\mu \qquad (3\text{–}110)$$

Then

$$\sin \psi = \frac{c\nu}{k}\,\mu \qquad (3\text{–}111)$$

and

$$W = W_c = \frac{\pi c\nu F^2}{k^2}\,(\mu)^2 \quad \text{in.-lbs./cycle} \qquad (3\text{–}112)$$

Eq. (3–112) represents the energy dissipated during one cycle of steady-state conditions for a system with viscous damping.

Since not all damping actions are of the viscous type, the concept of energy dissipation during a cycle leads us to the idea of finding an equivalent viscous-damping constant for damped systems which are not viscous. If we select a viscous-damping value which will give an energy loss during a cycle equal to that dissipated by a non-viscous-damped system during a cycle, it may be said that we have an equivalence of damping, c_e. The use of an equivalent damping constant does not truly represent the original system. However, in many cases it allows us to get an approximate solution to a problem which cannot be solved exactly by conventional methods. If we are principally interested in the magnitude of the vibration, then the use of an equivalent damping constant gives us the maximum amplitude with sufficient accuracy for many engineering problems.

Let us consider the replacement of Coulomb damping by equivalent viscous damping. The equivalent system may be represented by the differential equation

$$m\ddot{x} + c_e\dot{x} + kx = F \cos \nu t \qquad (3\text{–}113)$$

Let us assume that the form of the steady-state solution of Eq. (3–113) is

$$x = D \cos (\nu t - \psi) \qquad (3\text{–}114)$$

During half a cycle the mass travels the distance $2D$. Therefore the friction force f does work of $4Df$ over a complete cycle. Then from Eq. (3–112), we get

$$\frac{\pi c_e \nu F^2}{k^2} (\mu)^2 = 4Df \tag{3–115}$$

and

$$c_e = \frac{4Dfk^2}{\pi \nu F^2 (\mu)^2} \tag{3–116}$$

Since

$$D = \frac{F}{k} (\mu) \tag{3–117}$$

then

$$c_e = \frac{4fk}{\pi \nu F (\mu)} \tag{3–118}$$

and

$$\mu = \frac{1}{\sqrt{(1 - \beta^2)^2 + (2\zeta_e \beta)^2}} \tag{3–119}$$

where

$$\zeta_e = \frac{c_e}{c_c}$$

Substituting Eq. (3–119) into Eq. (3–118) and solving for c_e yields:

$$c_e = \frac{4f}{k\nu} \cdot \frac{(1 - \beta^2)}{\sqrt{\pi^2 F^2 - 4^2 f^2}} \tag{3–120}$$

Eq. (3–120) is valid as long as $f < (\pi/4)F$. In practical cases, the force of dry friction is small. When $f > (\pi/4)F$, c_e becomes imaginary and Eq. (3–120) is not valid. It can be seen that when $f = (\pi/4)F$, c_e becomes infinite and the system cannot move. We should also note that when $\beta = 1$, $c_e = 0$ and there is no damping effect at resonance. We can look at this resonance phenomenon from another point of view. For Coulomb damping to be effective, f must be less than $(\pi/4)F$. When at resonance, the power input is greater than the friction force, the result of which is a building up of the amplitude.

The solution for Eq. (3–113) then is

$$x = \frac{F}{k} \cdot \frac{\cos (\nu t - \alpha)}{(1 - \beta^2) \sqrt{1 + \dfrac{16f^2}{k^4 (\pi^2 F^2 - 16f^2)}}} \tag{3–121}$$

where

$$\alpha = \tan^{-1} \frac{4f}{k^2 \sqrt{\pi^2 F^2 - 16f^2}} \tag{3–122}$$

Example. A mass weighing 20 lbs. is attached to a spring having a spring constant of 40 lbs./in. The mass rests on a plane and is oscillated by a force $10 \cos \nu t$. The coefficient of sliding friction is 0.15. What is the value of the equivalent damping constant, and what is the maximum amplitude under steady-state conditions if the frequency ratio is $\frac{3}{4}$?

SOLUTION:

$$\omega_n = \sqrt{\frac{k}{m}} = \sqrt{\frac{40 \times 386}{20}} = 27.8 \text{ radians/sec.}$$

$$\nu = \tfrac{3}{4}\omega_n = 20.8 \text{ radians/sec.}$$

$$f = \mu W = 0.15 \times 20 = 3.0 \text{ lbs.}$$

$$F = 10 \text{ lbs.}$$

Then

$$c_e = \frac{4f}{k\nu} \cdot \frac{(1 - \beta^2)}{\sqrt{\pi^2 F^2 - 16f^2}} = \frac{4 \times 3[1 - (\tfrac{3}{4})^2]}{40 \times 20.8\sqrt{\pi^2 \times 100 - 16 \times 9}}$$

$$c_e = 2.18 \times 10^{-4} \text{ lbs.-sec./in.}$$

$$x_{\max} = \frac{F}{k} \cdot \frac{1}{(1 - \beta^2)\sqrt{1 + \dfrac{16f^2}{k^4(\pi^2 F^2 - 16f^2)}}}$$

$$x_{\max} = \frac{10}{40} \cdot \frac{1}{[1 - (\tfrac{3}{4})^2]\sqrt{1 + \dfrac{16 \times 9}{40^4[\pi^2 \times 100 - (16 \times 9)]}}}$$

$$x_{\max} = 0.571 \text{ in.}$$

We should note that the dry friction has no calculable effect on the displacement. A lighter spring and an increase of the coefficient of friction would help decrease the amplitude. We may draw the conclusion that the introduction of Coulomb damping as a means of diminishing the amplitude of vibration is not so effective as the introduction of viscous damping.

BIBLIOGRAPHY

CREDE, CHARLES E. *Vibration and Shock Isolation.* New York: John Wiley & Sons, Inc., 1951.

DEN HARTOG, J. P. *Mechanical Vibrations.* 4th ed. New York: McGraw-Hill Book Co., Inc., 1956.

MYKLESTAD, N. O. *Fundamentals of Vibration Analysis.* New York: McGraw-Hill Book Co., Inc., 1956.

THOMSON, WILLIAM TYRRELL. *Mechanical Vibrations.* 2d ed. Englewood Cliffs, N. J.: Prentice-Hall, Inc., 1953.

TIMOSHENKO, S. *Vibration Problems in Engineering.* 3d ed. Princeton, N. J.: D. Van Nostrand Co., Inc., 1955.

PROBLEMS

3-1. A cylinder of radius r and weight W is connected to two springs so that it is free to oscillate on the plane which supports it without slipping (Fig. P3-1). A small initial angle of rotation θ_0 is given to the cylinder and the cylinder is then allowed to oscillate. Determine the equation for the oscillation.

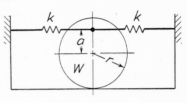

FIG. P3-1.

3-2. If the arm in Fig. P3-2 has a weight W_1 and the cylinder has a weight of W_2, determine the equation of motion for an initial displacement of θ_0. Assume no slippage takes place between the cylinder and the concave surface.

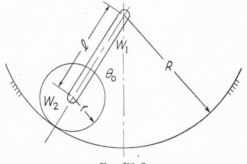

FIG. P3-2.

3-3. A machine which has been mounted on four equal springs placed at each corner of the machine base has been observed to cause a vertical static deflection to the springs of 2 in. What is the natural frequency of the machine and spring mount in the vertical direction?

3-4. A spring, whose constant is k, is cut in half. A mass, which slides over a frictionless plane, is mounted between the halves as shown in Fig. P3-4. The system is allowed to oscillate and the period is observed to be 1 sec. A simi-

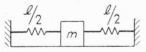
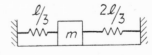

FIG. P3-4.

lar spring is cut so that one part is $\frac{1}{3}$ and the other $\frac{2}{3}$ of the original spring length. Determine the period of oscillation when the same mass is mounted between the spring parts.

3–5. A mass is supported by a helical spring which in turn is attached to a leaf spring, as shown in Fig. P3–5. If the mass weighs 15 lbs., determine the natural frequency of the system if the physical characteristics of the springs are:

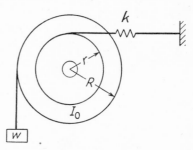

Leaf Spring	Helical Spring
thickness $= \frac{3}{8}$ in.	$d = \frac{3}{16}$ in.
width $= 2$ in.	$D = 1$ in.
length $= 10$ in.	$n = 10$ turns
$E = 30 \times 10^6$ psi.	$G = 12 \times 10^6$ psi.

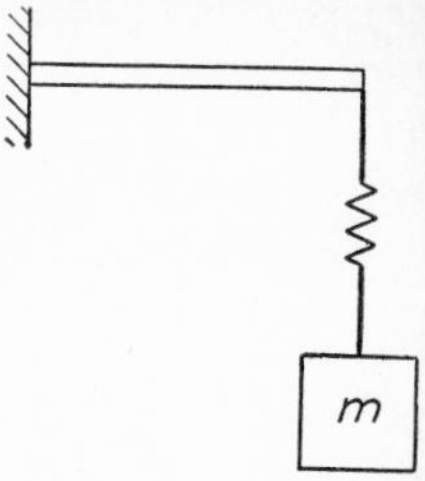

FIG. P3–5.

3–6. Rework Problem 3–5, substituting $\frac{1}{16}$-in. diameter wire in place of the $\frac{3}{16}$-in. diameter wire for the helical spring. Explain the lack of effect of the leaf spring.

3–7. A connecting rod is supported at the wrist-pin end by a knife-edge (Fig. P3–7). It is then displaced and allowed to oscillate as a pendulum. The weight of the rod is 8 lbs., and the center of gravity is 9 in. from the knife-edge pivot. If the frequency of oscillation is found to be 42 cycles/min., what is the moment of inertia of the rod about its center of gravity?

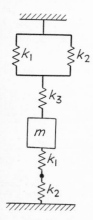

FIG. P3–7.

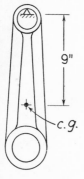

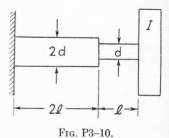

FIG. P3–8.

3–8. Determine the frequency of oscillation of the system sketched in Fig. P3–8. The combined moment of inertia of the two pulleys, which are keyed together, is I_0.

3–9. Determine the natural frequency of the system sketched in Fig. P3–9.

3–10. An inertia disc is attached to a stepped shaft, as shown in Fig. P3–10. If the narrower portion of the shaft has a torsional spring constant of k_t, what is the natural frequency of the system?

FIG. P3–9.

3–11. Derive Eq. (3–47).

FIG. P3–10.

3-12. A mass weighing 50 lbs. is supported at the center of an 8-ft.-long steel beam which is simply supported. If the beam has an area moment of inertia of 0.42 in.^{4} and a weight of 7.6 lbs./ft., what is the natural frequency of the system? What is the natural frequency of the system if the weight of the beam is neglected?

3-13. Fig. P3–13 is a schematic diagram of a viscous-damped phonograph arm. What is the value of c if the arm is to be critically damped?

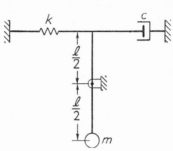

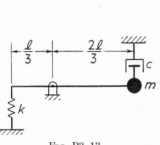

FIG. P3–13.

FIG. P3–14.

3-14. A mass is attached to one end of a rod which is pivoted at the center. At the other end are attached a spring and a dashpot, as shown in Fig. P3–14. If the mass is displaced by a small angle θ_0, write the equation for the damped oscillation. At what value of c will the system no longer vibrate?

3-15. A steel cantilever spring, $k = 3EI/l^3$, supports a mass m (Fig. P3–15). A dashpot is attached to the mid-point of the spring. Determine the natural damped frequency of the system.

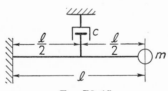

FIG. P3–15.

3-16. If two successive amplitudes for the system in Fig. P3–15 are 0.152 in. and 0.083 in., determine the value of the damping ratio ζ. If the mass weighs 1 lb. and the spring constant is 10 lbs./in., determine the damping value of the dashpot.

3-17. A mass-spring-damper system is found to have a logarithmic decrement of 1.3. If the mass weighs 50 lbs. and the spring constant is 100 lbs./in., (a) determine the damping constant; (b) if the system is initially displaced 1 in., determine the amplitude of vibration at the end of 0.1 sec.

3-18. A mass-spring-damper system when oscillated is found to have a logarithmic decrement of 2.0. If the spring constant is 16 lbs./in. and the critical damping constant is 0.3, determine the maximum absolute displacement the system will achieve if the system is given an initial velocity of 25 in./sec.

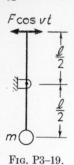

$F \cos vt$

$\dfrac{\ell}{2}$

$\dfrac{\ell}{2}$

m

Fig. P3–19.

3–19. A pendulum bob is attached to a rigid weightless rod which is pivoted at its center. If a forcing function acts on the other end of the rod, determine the complete solution for the oscillation if the system starts from rest. Comment as to why a test of the above system would not check out the complete solution.

3–20. A spring-mass system is attached to an oscillating force, as shown in Fig. P3–20. Determine the equation for the oscillation for the mass if the system starts from rest.

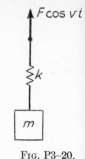

$F \cos vt$

k

m

Fig. P3–20.

3–21. Determine the steady-state solution for the torsional pendulum (Fig. P3–21) which is being activated by a varying torque.

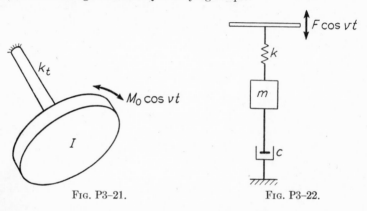

k_t

$M_0 \cos vt$

I

Fig. P3–21.

$F \cos vt$

k

m

c

Fig. P3–22.

3–22. A spring-mass-dashpot system is arranged as shown in Fig. P3–22. Determine the equation for steady-state conditions.

3–23. A spring-mass-dashpot system is arranged as shown in Fig. P3–23. Determine the equation for the steady-state conditions.

3–24. A spring-mass-dashpot system is arranged as shown in Fig. P3–24. Determine the steady-state solution.

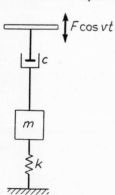

$F \cos vt$

c

m

k

Fig. P2–23.

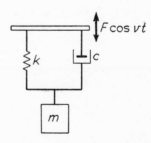

$F \cos vt$

k c

m

Fig. P3–24.

3-25. A spring-mass system is acted upon by a resonant force $F \cos \sqrt{k/m}\, t$. If the system starts from an initial displacement x_0, determine the equation of motion.

3-26. A spring-mass system is acted upon by a resonant force $F \cos \sqrt{k/m}\, t$. If the system starts from the equilibrium position with an initial velocity v_0, determine the equation of motion.

3-27. Reconsider the case of a spring-mass system acted upon by a resonant force. Let the forcing function be $F \sin \omega_n t$. Determine the equation of motion when the initial conditions are $x = \dot{x} = 0$. Compare your answer to Eq. (3–81). Can you reconcile the two answers?

3-28. A spring-mass system which starts from rest is activated by a resonant disturbing force of $2.0 \cos \omega_n t$. If the spring constant is 50 lbs./in. and the mass weighs 10 lbs., determine the amplitude at the end of 1 sec.

3-29. A spring-mass system which starts from rest is activated by a resonant disturbing force of $2.0 \sin \omega_n t$. If the spring constant is 50 lbs./in. and the mass weighs 10 lbs., determine the amplitude at the end of 1 sec.

3-30. A motor weighing 750 lbs. is mounted on four springs each having a spring constant of 600 lbs./in. The motor is known to have an unbalance of 4 oz.-in. at its operating speed of 875 rpm. Find the maximum amplitude of vibration.

3-31. A motor weighing 750 lbs. is mounted on four springs each having a spring constant of 600 lbs./in. A dashpot-type damper is mounted between the base of the motor and the foundation. The system as installed has a damping ratio of $\zeta = 0.20$. The motor is known to have a 4 oz.-in. unbalance at its operating speed of 875 rpm. Find the maximum amplitude of vibration.

3-32. A shaker screen is operated by a spring-mounted motor which has a large unbalance. The resonant amplitude is found to be 0.75 in. When the motor speed is increased well beyond the resonance point, the amplitude of vibration is found to have a limiting value of 0.10 in. Determine the damping ratio.

3-33. A machine is mounted on springs whose equivalent spring constant is k. The machine is so mounted that vibration in one direction only is allowed. Part of the machine is a piston of mass m_p which is assumed to move with simple harmonic motion with a maximum amplitude of r. If the frequency of the piston motion is ν radians/sec., determine the steady-state solution of the system. *Note:* The mass m_p is included in the total mass of the machine M.

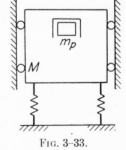

Fig. 3–33.

3-34. If the total mass of the machine in Problem 3-33 weighs 800 lbs. and the mass of the piston assembly weighs 6.0 lbs., determine the spring constants for two sets of springs which will give a limiting amplitude of 0.15 in. The piston has a stroke of 4.0 in. and operates at 200 strokes/min.

3-35. If the machine described in Problem 3-33 is mounted on springs having a constant of 995 lbs./in., what must the damping value of a dashpot be, when inserted between the base of the machine and the foundation, for an amplitude limitation 0.07 in.?

3–36. A diesel engine weighing 2200 lbs. is operated at 1100 rpm. The engine is mounted on four springs, each having a constant of 450 lbs./in. Four dashpots are used in conjunction with the springs, and each dashpot has a damping value of 50 lbs.-sec./in. What is the transmissibility of the system? What is the transmissibility if the dashpots are removed?

3–37. If we wish to limit the transmissibility of the diesel engine force in Problem 3–36 to 1.5 percent, what will the value of the new springs have to be when no damping is being used? What will be the consequence if the dampers of Problem 3–36 are used with the new springs?

3–38. Determine the transmissibility of a refrigeration unit which weighs 65 lbs. and has a total spring constant of 60 lbs./in. if the compressor unit operates at 520 rpm.

3–39. An air compressor is mounted on four equal springs. Determine the spring constant for each spring if the transmissibility is to be 10 percent of the driving force. The compressor weighs 85 lbs. and is operated at 600 rpm.

3–40. A single-cylinder diesel engine operating at 600 rpm is supported by springs. The static deflection of the springs is 1.5 in. The weight of the engine is 800 lbs. and the piston assembly is 28 lbs. The stroke is 4.0 in. A record of free vibration shows an amplitude decay of 60 percent for consecutive amplitudes. Determine (a) the amplitude at steady-state conditions, (b) the transmissibility, (c) the force transmitted to the foundation.

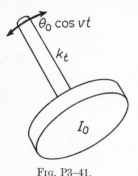

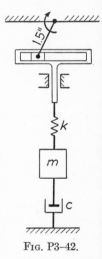

3–41. The free end of a weightless shaft in Fig. P3–41 is given an oscillatory motion of $\Theta_0 \cos vt$. Write the D.E. for this system and solve.

FIG. P3–41.

FIG. P3–42.

3–42. A scotch yoke drives a spring-mass-damper system as shown in Fig. P3–42. Determine the amplitude of motion of the mass if

$$\text{Crank rpm} = 600$$

$$\text{Crank} = 1.5 \text{ in.}$$

$$mg = 90 \text{ lbs.}$$

$$k = 80 \text{ lbs./in.}$$

$$c = 5 \text{ lbs.-sec./in.}$$

3-43. A scotch yoke drives a spring-mass-damper system as shown in Fig. P3-43. Determine the amplitude of motion if

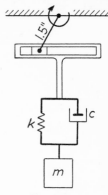

$$\text{Crank rpm} = 600$$

$$\text{Crank} = 1.5 \text{ in.}$$

$$mg = 90 \text{ lbs.}$$

$$k = 80 \text{ lbs./in.}$$

$$c = 5 \text{ lbs.-sec./in.}$$

FIG. P3-43.

3-44. Determine the equations of motion for the three systems sketched in Fig. P3-44 if the motion at the support is $a \cos vt$.

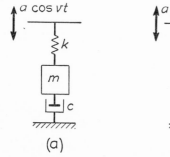
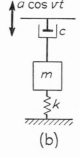
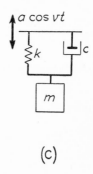

(a) (b) (c)

FIG. P3-44.

3-45. Determine the steady-state amplitude of the mass in Fig. P3-45 if the mass weighs 60 lbs., $k = 20$ lbs./in., and $c = 1.0$ lbs.-sec./in. The motion of the support is governed by $2 \cos 20t$ in.

3-46. If the natural frequency of a vibrometer is ω_{nv}, determine the limiting frequency of the amplitude if the instrument is to record within an accuracy of α percent.

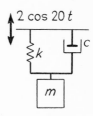

3-47. A mass is supported by springs, the k value of which is 160 lbs./in. The system is restrained by rollers on all sides so that the vibration occurs in one direction only. The static deflection of the system is 1.5 in. A free vibration test shows that the natural frequency is 153.2 cycles/min. and that there is an amplitude decay of 0.16 in. during a complete cycle. Determine the nature of the damping and its value.

FIG. P3-45.

3-48. Show that the resonant amplitude for a Coulomb-damped system is infinite.

3-49. Determine the amount of energy dissipated during a cycle when the damping force is proportional to the square of the velocity.

3-50. From the solution of Problem 3–49, find the equivalent damping constant for a forced system when the damping force is proportional to the square of the velocity.

3-51. A mass attached to a spring is supported by a plane surface (Fig. P3–51). The coefficient of friction between the mass and the plane is 0.10. Determine from the physical constants listed below, an equivalent viscous-damping constant.

$$mg = 200 \text{ lbs.}$$

$$k = 100 \text{ lbs./in.}$$

$$F = 26 \text{ lbs.}$$

$$\nu = 10 \text{ radians/sec.}$$

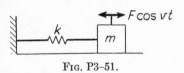

Fig. P3–51.

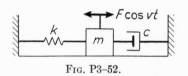

Fig. P3–52.

3-52. A mass attached to a spring and damper is supported by a plane surface (Fig. P3–52). The coefficient of friction between the mass and the plane is 0.10. Determine from the physical constants listed below a single equivalent viscous-damping constant.

$$mg = 200 \text{ lbs.}$$

$$k = 100 \text{ lbs.}$$

$$F = 26 \text{ lbs.}$$

$$\nu = 10 \text{ radians/sec.}$$

$$c = 0.5 \text{ lb.-sec./in.}$$

CHAPTER 4

SYSTEMS WITH SEVERAL DEGREES OF FREEDOM

4–1. Single Mass. In the previous chapters the discussion was limited to systems of a single mass with a single degree of freedom. It is possible for a single mass to have more than one degree of freedom. Consider a mass in the shape of a cube. Let the mass be supported by a set of eight

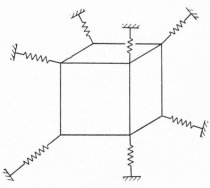

Fig. 4–1.

springs, each attached to one of the eight corners of the cube, as seen in Fig. 4–1. Let us now examine the possible number of degrees of freedom possessed by the cube. Even though the springs constrain motion, the cube acts like a particle in free space and has six degrees of freedom. Three such degrees of freedom are translations along the x, y, and z axes. The other three are rotations about the three axes.

When a body has six degrees of freedom, there are six natural or principal modes of vibrations. Three principal modes are parallel to three mutually perpendicular axes. The other three are rotations about these axes. Under certain circumstances, each mode of vibration may take place without exciting the other modes. The body is then said to be vibrating in a principal mode. In general, the vibration of a body may be resolved into components in the principal modes. When a body is vibrating in one of the principal modes, it is said to be uncoupled in the direction of the normal mode. By terming it uncoupled, we mean that a disturbance along an axis will produce only vibrations of the principal mode along the same axis. The foregoing statement includes the intent of rotation as well as translation. Restating the definition of uncoupled action, we can say that if a force acting parallel to one of the axes only produces a vibration in translation parallel to the axis, the vibration is uncoupled in that direction. Along the same line of reasoning, if a torque producing a rotation about an axis causes a vibration rotationally about that axis only, then the vibration is uncoupled in the direction of the rotation. It is possible at times to alter a vibrating system so that the mode of vibration becomes a principal mode. When this uncoupling is accomplished, the mode of vibrations is said to be decoupled. Decoupling can be achieved at times by altering some of the physical parameters of the system.

The equations of motion describing Fig. 4–1 are six in number, one equation for each degree of freedom. Since the handling of six simultaneous equations is too cumbersome for use as a demonstration problem, it will serve our purpose to use a case of two degrees of freedom. This mathematically simpler type of problem will be used to demonstrate the coupling action.

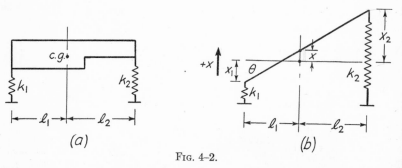

Fig. 4–2.

Consider the system sketched in Fig. 4–2a. It is essentially a mass supported on two springs k_1 and k_2. We will limit the motion to the plane of the paper and further restrict the motion in the lateral direction. These limitations allow the body to have only two degrees of freedom, the motion in the x direction and the rotation about the center of gravity. Let us now displace the body upward. If we assume a lack of symmetry, the body will possess a translation x and a rotation θ. The distances x_1 and x_2 are the amounts the springs k_1 and k_2 are respectively displaced. We now satisfy the two basic equations of motion.

$$F = ma \qquad (1\text{--}24)$$

$$T = I\alpha \qquad (1\text{--}25)$$

Substituting the forces into Eq. (1–24), we get

$$-k_1x_1 - k_2x_2 = m\ddot{x} \qquad (4\text{--}1)$$

Satisfying Eq. (1–25) yields

$$k_1 x_1 l_1 - k_2 x_2 l_2 = I\ddot{\theta} \tag{4-2}$$

From Fig. 4–2b, which is a schematic representation of the system, we can see that

$$x_1 = x - l_1\theta \qquad \text{and} \qquad x_2 = x + l_2\theta \tag{4-3}$$

The values of Eqs. (4–3) are substituted into Eqs. (4–1) and (4–2), yielding:

$$-k_1(x - l_1\theta) - k_2(x + l_2\theta) = m\ddot{x}$$
$$k_1 l_1(x - l_1\theta) - k_2 l_2(x + l_2\theta) = I\ddot{\theta} \tag{4-4}$$

Rearranging Eq. (4–4), we get the equations of motion in a form which will aid our analysis.

$$m\ddot{x} + (k_1 + k_2)x - (k_1 l_1 - k_2 l_2)\theta = 0$$
$$I\ddot{\theta} + (k_1 l_1^2 + k_2 l_2^2)\theta - (k_1 l_1 - k_2 l_2)x = 0 \tag{4-5}$$

An examination of Eqs. (4–5) shows that each of the two equations of motion is expressed in terms of both x and θ, thereby demonstrating that the motion of the mass is a coupled one, since each of the equations is interdependent on the other. In this problem the factor which causes the coupling action is $(k_1 l_1 - k_2 l_2)$. If this term were set equal to zero, then the coupling action would cease and we would have a decoupled set of equations of motion. To decouple the motion requires only a suitable selection of springs: that is,

$$\frac{k_1}{k_2} = \frac{l_2}{l_1} \tag{4-6}$$

When the physical parameters are governed by Eq. (4–6) then we can readily see that the equations governed by Eqs. (4–5) become independent of each other and the system has become decoupled.

It will be of interest to set up a test to determine whether a system is uncoupled, without determining the equations of motion. This test can be achieved by applying a force through the center of gravity in the direction of the motion desired. Applying this to our demonstration problem, we see from methods of elementary statics that a moment results. We therefore get a rotation as well as a translation as the result of the applied force. The system then is coupled. Only when $k_1 l_1 = k_2 l_2$ does the couple vanish. The body then is in pure translation. Let us now formalize this test for determining whether the system is coupled or not.

Rule: If the sole effect of a force applied at the center of gravity of a body is to cause the body to move in pure translation, the mode of vibration in the direction of translation is uncoupled from the other modes.

If a torque applied at the center of gravity causes a pure rotation to take place, then the mode of vibration about the axis about which the torque is applied is uncoupled.

Let us now decouple the system, as depicted in Fig. 4–2. We accomplish this by setting $k_1 l_1 = k_2 l_2$ and as a result

$$m\ddot{x} + (k_1 + k_2)x = 0$$

and   (4–7)

$$I\ddot{\theta} + (k_1 l_1^2 + k_2 l_2^2)\theta = 0$$

From these decoupled equations we see that there are two natural frequencies:

$$\omega_{nx} = \sqrt{\frac{k_1 + k_2}{m}}$$

(4–8)

$$\omega_{n\theta} = \sqrt{\frac{k_1 l_1^2 + k_2 l_2^2}{I}}$$

The two natural frequencies indicate that when a forcing function which has a frequency equal to either of the natural frequencies acts on the body, the system will be at resonance, and the mode of vibration will be the principal mode corresponding to that resonance. That is, when $\nu = \omega_{nx}$, the mode of vibration will be in translation, and when $\nu = \omega_{n\theta}$, the mode will be in rotation. When the forcing function is not at either of the resonant frequencies, the mode of vibration will consist of modal components from the two resonant modes.

Let us now determine the natural frequencies of the coupled system governed by Eq. (4–5). We assume a solution in the form of

$$x = X_0 \cos \omega_n t$$

$$\theta = \Theta_0 \cos \omega_n t$$

(4–9)

The above solution is selected since we can expect harmonic motion. The selection of ω_n as the circular frequency is based on the fact that we have a free system. Substituting the values of Eqs. (4–9) and their derivatives into Eq. (4–5), and since $\cos \omega_n t$ cannot be zero for all t, we get

$$(k_1 + k_2 - m\omega_n^2)X_0 - (k_1 l_1 - k_2 l_2)\Theta_0 = 0$$

$$-(k_1 l_1 - k_2 l_2)X_0 + (k_1 l_1^2 + k_2 l_2^2 - I\omega_n^2)\Theta_0 = 0 \qquad (4\text{–}10)$$

It is necessary that we satisfy Eqs. (4–10) by setting the determinant, $|D| \equiv 0$, since X_0 and Θ_0 are arbitrary and can only be determined in terms of each other.

$$|D| \equiv \begin{vmatrix} k_1 + k_2 - m\omega_n^2 & -(k_1 l_1 - k_2 l_2) \\ -(k_1 l_1 - k_2 l_2) & k_1 l_1^2 + k_2 l_2^2 - I\omega_n^2 \end{vmatrix} \equiv 0 \qquad (4\text{–}11)$$

Setting the $|D| = 0$ results in an equation known as the characteristic equation, where $\omega_n{}^2$ are the roots of the characteristic equation. The characteristic equation is

$$\omega_n{}^4 - \left[\frac{k_1 + k_2}{m} + \frac{k_1 l_1{}^2 + k_2 l_2{}^2}{I} \right] \omega_n{}^2$$

$$+ \left[\frac{(k_1 + k_2)(k_1 l_1{}^2 + k_2 l_2{}^2)}{mI} - \frac{(k_1 l_1{}^2 - k_2 l_2{}^2)^2}{mI} \right] = 0 \quad (4\text{--}12)$$

Eq. (4–12) is a quadratic equation in $\omega_n{}^2$. The roots of the equation are found in the usual manner.

$$\omega_{n1,2}{}^2 = \frac{1}{2} \left(\frac{k_1 + k_2}{m} + \frac{k_1 l_1{}^2 + k_2 l_2{}^2}{I} \right)$$

$$\pm \sqrt{ \frac{1}{4} \left(\frac{k_1 + k_2}{m} - \frac{k_1 l_1{}^2 + k_2 l_2{}^2}{I} \right)^2 + \frac{(k_1 l_1 - k_2 l_2)^2}{mI} } \quad (4\text{--}13)$$

Eq. (4–13) represents the two natural frequencies of the mass when coupling exists. Let us examine the natural frequencies when the coupling factor $(k_1 l_1 - k_2 l_2)$ is small. We expand the radical in a binomial expansion, using only the first two terms of the expansion, since the coupling factor is small.

The binomial expansion takes the form of

$$a^{1/2} \left(1 - \frac{x}{a} \right)^{1/2} = a^{1/2} \left(1 - \frac{1}{2} \frac{x}{a} - \cdots \right) \doteqdot a^{1/2} - \frac{1}{2} \frac{x}{a^{1/2}} \quad (4\text{--}14)$$

where

$$a = \frac{1}{4} \left(\frac{k_1 + k_2}{m} - \frac{k_1 l_1{}^2 + k_2 l_2{}^2}{I} \right)^2$$

and

$$x = \frac{(k_1 l_1 - k_2 l_2)^2}{mI}$$

Then Eq. (4–13) becomes, for a small coupling factor,

$$\omega_{n1,2}{}^2 = \frac{1}{2} \left[\frac{k_1 + k_2}{m} + \frac{k_1 l_1{}^2 + k_2 l_2{}^2}{I} \right]$$

$$\pm \left[\frac{1}{2} \left(\frac{k_1 + k_2}{m} - \frac{k_1 l_1{}^2 + k_2 l_2{}^2}{I} \right) - \frac{2(k_1 l_1 - k_2 l_2)^2}{mI \left(\dfrac{k_1 + k_2}{m} - \dfrac{k_1 l_1{}^2 + k_2 l_2{}^2}{I} \right)} \right]$$

$$(4\text{--}15)$$

Eq. (4–15) may be written in shorthand notation as

$$\omega_{n1}{}^2 = \frac{k_1 + k_2}{m} - b = \omega_{nx}{}^2 - b$$

and

$$\omega_{n2}{}^2 = \frac{k_1 l_1{}^2 + k_2 l_2{}^2}{I} + b = \omega_{n\theta}{}^2 + b \tag{4-16}$$

where

$$b = \frac{2(k_1 l_1 - k_2 l_2)^2}{mI\left(\dfrac{k_1 + k_2}{m} - \dfrac{k_1 l_1{}^2 + k_2 l_2{}^2}{I}\right)}$$

a small quantity.

Eqs. (4–16) demonstrate that the decoupled frequencies are bracketed by the coupled frequencies; that is, the coupled frequencies will always lie below and above the decoupled natural frequencies.

Example. A refrigeration unit, weighing 120 lbs., consists of a motor and a compressor. The unit, mounted on a bed plate, can be considered to be equal to two cylinders, each having a diameter of 10 in. and a length of

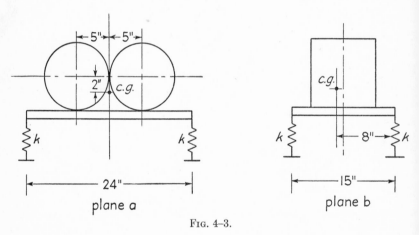

Fig. 4–3.

10 in. The cylinders are positioned as shown in Fig. 4–3. The cylinders are so placed that the center of gravity in the front elevation is equidistant from the spring mounts, and in the right elevation the center of gravity is $\frac{1}{2}$ in. off center, as shown. If the motor and compressor each operate at 860 rpm, select four springs, each having the same spring constant, so that none of the resonant modes is excited at operational speed. The unit is so mounted that there is no side sway in either direction.

SOLUTION. Let us call the plane depicted by the front elevation plane a and the right elevation plane b. There are three degrees of freedom: rotation in plane a and b and oscillation in the vertical direction. Because of symmetry, the mode which rotates in plane a is uncoupled from the other two. The uncoupled frequency is

$$\omega_{n\theta a} = \sqrt{\frac{4l_a{}^2 k}{I_a}}$$

where

$$I_a = 2\left[\frac{1}{2} \times \frac{60}{386}(5^2) + \frac{60}{386}(5^2 + 2^2)\right]$$

$$I_a = 12.90 \text{ lb.-in.-sec.}^2$$

Then

$$\omega_{n\theta a} = \sqrt{\frac{4 \times 12^2 k}{12.90}} = 6.68\sqrt{k}$$

The other two modes cannot be uncoupled because of the requirement that all springs be equal. These modes can be determined by considering the equipment as depicted in plane b. The coupled frequencies may be found by application of Eq. (4–13), substituting the proper constants. Then

$$\omega_{nb}{}^2 = \frac{1}{2}\left[\frac{4k}{m} + \frac{2k(l_{1b}{}^2 + l_{2b}{}^2)}{I_b}\right]$$

$$\pm \sqrt{\frac{1}{4}\left[\frac{4k}{m} - \frac{2k(l_{1b}{}^2 + l_{2b}{}^2)}{I_b}\right]^2 + \frac{2k^2(l_{1b} - l_{2b})^2}{mI_b}}$$

$$I_b = 2\left[\frac{60}{386} \times \frac{1}{12}\left\{3 \times 5^2 + 10^2\right\} + \frac{60}{386}\left\{2^2 + \left(\frac{1}{2}\right)^2\right\}\right]$$

$$I_b = 5.85 \text{ lb.-in.-sec.}^2$$

$$\omega_{nb}{}^2 = \frac{k}{2}\left[\frac{4 \times 386}{120} + \frac{2(8^2 + 7^2)}{5.85}\right]$$

$$\pm k\sqrt{\frac{1}{4}\left[\frac{4 \times 386}{120} - \frac{2 \times 113}{5.85}\right]^2 + \frac{2 \times 1^2 \times 386}{120 \times 5.85}}$$

$$\omega_{nb}{}^2 = (25.75 \pm 12.92)k$$

$$\omega_{nb_1} = 3.58\sqrt{k}$$

$$\omega_{nb_2} = 6.22\sqrt{k}$$

The forcing frequency is

$$\nu = \frac{2\pi \times 860}{60} = 90.1 \text{ rad./sec.}$$

In making our selection of springs, it would be best if the forcing frequency operates well above the highest natural frequency, $\omega_{n\theta a}$. Therefore let $\beta = 2$. Then

$$\nu = 2\omega_{n\theta a}$$

and

$$k = \left(\frac{90.1}{2 \times 6.68}\right)^2$$

$$k = 45.4, \text{ say } 45 \text{ lb./in.}$$

By selecting a spring of 45 lb./in., we insure that no mode will be excited in either plane a or b.

4-2. Discs and Torsional Springs. A common type of problem concerning discs and shafts stems from the vibration analysis of the internal combustion engine. This type of problem, however, does not limit itself to the field of internal combustion engines but applies also to many other devices in which power is developed or transmitted.

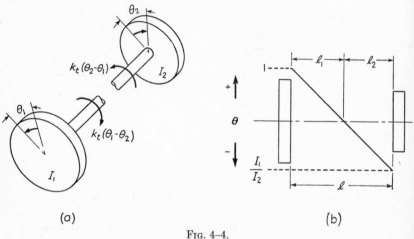

$$(a) \qquad\qquad\qquad (b)$$

Fig. 4–4.

a. Two Discs and One Shaft. Let two discs and a single shaft be arranged as in Fig. 4–4a. θ_1 and θ_2 are the respective absolute angular displacements of I_1 and I_2. The restoring torque on I_1 will be $k_t(\theta_1 - \theta_2)$, and the restoring torque on I_2 will be $k_t(\theta_2 - \theta_1)$. Then

$$I_1\ddot{\theta}_1 = -k_t(\theta_1 - \theta_2)$$
$$I_2\ddot{\theta}_2 = -k_t(\theta_2 - \theta_1)$$

$$(4\text{--}17)$$

Rearranging, we get

$$I_1\ddot{\theta}_1 + k_t\theta_1 - k_t\theta_2 = 0$$
$$I_2\ddot{\theta}_2 + k_t\theta_2 - k_t\theta_1 = 0$$

$$(4\text{--}18)$$

Eqs. (4–18) are a set of coupled equations of motion which cannot be decoupled. The coupling is due to the shaft which cannot be removed without destroying the original intent of the problem. These equations are solved in the manner used in Section 4–1. Let

$$\theta_1 = \Theta_1 \cos \omega_n t$$

and   (4–19)

$$\theta_2 = \Theta_2 \cos \omega_n t$$

then

$$(k_t - \omega_n^2 I)\Theta_1 - k_t \Theta_2 = 0$$
$$-k_t \Theta_1 + (k_t - \omega_n^2 I_2)\Theta_2 = 0$$

(4–20)

Setting the $|D| \equiv 0$, we find the characteristic equation to be

$$\omega_n^2[I_1 I_2 \omega_n^2 - k_t(I_1 + I_2)] = 0 \qquad (4\text{–}21)$$

Whence

$$\omega_n^2 = 0; \quad \frac{k_t(I_1 + I_2)}{I_1 I_2} \qquad (4\text{–}22)$$

The system has two natural frequencies, as is to be expected, for there are two masses. The frequency $\omega_n = 0$ occurs when the two discs and the shaft rotate as a single body, with no twist in the shaft; that is, the potential energy in the shaft is continuously zero and the solution is trivial. When there is a twist in the shaft, the natural frequency is governed by the second root of Eq. (4–22).

Returning to Eqs. (4–20), if we substitute the nonzero value of ω_n^2 into either of the equations, we get the relationship

$$\frac{\Theta_1}{\Theta_2} = -\frac{I_2}{I_1} \qquad (4\text{–}23)$$

This quantity is the ratio of the angular displacement of the discs. One of these angular displacements must be arbitrarily chosen. Let

$$\Theta_1 = 1$$

then

$$\Theta_2 = -\frac{I_1}{I_2} \qquad (4\text{–}24)$$

It can be seen that for a positive angular displacement of Θ_1 there will result a negative displacement of Θ_2, and, as a result, the two discs oscillate in opposition to each other.

Let us plot Eq. (4–24) as shown in Fig. 4–4b, using the ordinate to represent the angular displacement and the abscissa to represent the shaft position. Since the shaft material follows Hooke's law, the line connecting the angular displacement of the discs represents the angular displacement of the shaft. It can be seen that the line representing the angular displacement of the shaft intersects the center line of the shaft. The point of intersection is called a node. A node of a system is a point of zero amplitude of vibration.

We can take advantage of the node to determine the natural frequency of the two-discs-and-shaft system. Since there is no vibration at the node, the system may be broken up into two torsional pendulums of I_1 and I_2 with l_1 and l_2 the length of the shafts, respectively. There must be an added restriction to this separation; namely, that the two pendulums must have the same natural frequency. Then

$$\omega_n{}^2 = \frac{k_{t1}}{I_1} = \frac{k_{t2}}{I_2} \qquad (4\text{--}25)$$

From Eq. (3–21) we can see that

$$\frac{k_{t1}}{k_{t2}} = \frac{l_2}{l_1} \qquad (4\text{--}26)$$

As a consequence of Eq. (4–26),

$$\frac{I_1}{I_2} = \frac{l_2}{l_1} \qquad (4\text{--}27)$$

Whence

$$l_1 = \frac{I_2 l}{I_1 + I_2}$$

and $\qquad (4\text{--}28)$

$$l_2 = \frac{I_1 l}{I_1 + I_2}$$

Now

$$k_{t1} = \frac{\pi d^4 G}{32 l_1} = \frac{\pi d^4 G}{32 l} \left(\frac{I_1 + I_2}{I_2} \right) = k_t \left(\frac{I_1 + I_2}{I_2} \right)$$

and

$$k_{t2} = \frac{\pi d^4 G}{32 l_2} = \frac{\pi d^4 G}{32 l} \left(\frac{I_1 + I_2}{I_1} \right) = k_t \left(\frac{I_1 + I_2}{I_1} \right) \qquad (4\text{--}29)$$

Then by substituting either of Eqs. (4–29) into Eq. (4–25), we get

$$\omega_n{}^2 = \frac{k_t(I_1 + I_2)}{I_1 I_2}$$

We must note that the nodal point method finds only one natural frequency. It will be the natural frequency which causes the node. Even when there are several nodes, if the nodes are known, we can sometimes determine the natural frequency causing that particular mode of vibration by the nodal point method.

b. Two Discs and Two Shafts.   Fig. 4–5a shows a two-disc–two-shaft arrangement.   The equations of motion are found in the usual manner. They are

$$-k_{t1}\theta_1 - k_{t2}(\theta_1 - \theta_2) = I_1\ddot{\theta}_1$$

$$-k_{t2}(\theta_2 - \theta_1) = I_2\ddot{\theta}_2$$

(4–30)

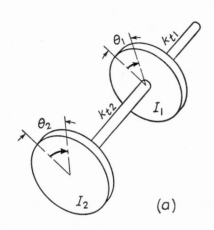

(a)

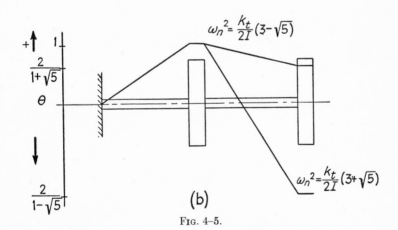

(b)

Fig. 4–5.

Rearranging yields

$$I_1\ddot{\theta}_1 + (k_{t1} + k_{t2})\theta_1 - k_{t2}\theta_2 = 0$$

$$I_2\ddot{\theta}_2 + k_{t2}\theta_2 - k_{t2}\theta_1 = 0$$

(4–31)

Assuming solutions in the form of

$$\theta_1 = \Theta_1 \cos \omega_n t$$

$$\theta_2 = \Theta_2 \cos \omega_n t$$

(4–32)

we find that the characteristic equation is

$$\omega_n{}^4 - \left[\frac{k_{t1} + k_{t2}}{I_1} + \frac{k_{t2}}{I_2}\right]\omega_n{}^2 + \frac{k_{t1}k_{t2}}{I_1I_2} = 0 \qquad (4\text{-}33)$$

The roots of Eq. (4-33) are the natural frequencies of the system. They are

$$\omega_{n1,2}{}^2 = \frac{1}{2}\left[\frac{k_{t1} + k_{t2}}{I_1} + \frac{k_{t2}}{I_2}\right]$$

$$\pm \frac{1}{2}\sqrt{\left(\frac{k_{t1} + k_{t2}}{I_1}\right)^2 + \left(\frac{k_{t2}}{I_2}\right)^2 + 2\left(\frac{k_{t2}{}^2 - k_{t1}k_{t2}}{I_1I_2}\right)} \quad (4\text{-}34)$$

If we let

$$\omega_{ij}{}^2 = \frac{k_{ti}}{I_j} \qquad i = 1, 2, \qquad j = 1, 2,$$

then Eq. (4-34) can be written in the following form

$$\omega_{n1,2}{}^2 = \tfrac{1}{2}[\omega_{11}{}^2 + \omega_{21}{}^2 + \omega_{22}{}^2]$$

$$\pm \tfrac{1}{2}\sqrt{(\omega_{11}{}^2 + \omega_{21}{}^2)^2 + \omega_{22}{}^4 + 2(\omega_{21}{}^2\omega_{22}{}^2 - \omega_{11}{}^2\omega_{22}{}^2)} \quad (4\text{-}35)$$

Determining the nodal points for this problem is very laborious because of the unwieldiness of Eq. (4-35). In order that this process may be simplified, let $k_{t1} = k_{t2} = k_t$ and $I_1 = I_2 = I$. Then Eq. (4-33) becomes

$$\omega_n{}^4 - \frac{3k_t}{I}\omega_n{}^2 + \frac{k_t{}^2}{I^2} = 0 \qquad (4\text{-}36)$$

and

$$\omega_{n1,2}{}^2 = \frac{1}{2}\frac{k_t}{I}(3 \mp \sqrt{5}) \qquad (4\text{-}37)$$

It can be readily shown that

$$\frac{\Theta_1}{\Theta_2} = \frac{2}{1 \pm \sqrt{5}} \qquad (4\text{-}38)$$

Eq. (4-38) is plotted in Fig. 4-5b. It is interesting to note that we have two modes of vibration. The first has one nodal point, which occurs at the fixed end, and both discs oscillate in the same direction; that is, the relative angle between the two discs is always positive. The second has two nodal points, one at the fixed end, the other somewhere on the shaft connecting the two discs. The discs, for the second mode, oscillate opposed to each other, that is, the relative angle between the two discs is always negative. In general, there will be as many nodal points as the degree of the natural frequency.

c. *Several Discs and Several Shafts.* Starting with the first disc I_1 of the torsional system depicted by Fig. 4-6, the equations of motion may be written as a set of simultaneous equations:

$$-k_{t1}(\theta_1 - \theta_2) = I_1\ddot{\theta}_1$$

$$-k_{t1}(\theta_2 - \theta_1) - k_{t2}(\theta_2 - \theta_3) = I_2\ddot{\theta}_2$$

$$-k_{t2}(\theta_3 - \theta_2) - k_{t3}(\theta_3 - \theta_4) = I_3\ddot{\theta}_3 \qquad (4\text{--}39)$$

$$\cdot \quad \cdot \quad \cdot \quad \cdot \quad \cdot \quad \cdot \quad \cdot \quad \cdot \quad \cdot \quad \cdot \quad \cdot \quad \cdot$$

$$-k_{t(n-1)}(\theta_n - \theta_{n-1}) = I_n\ddot{\theta}_n$$

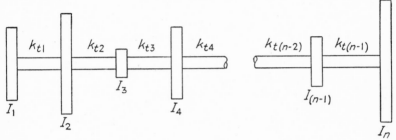

FIG. 4–6.

We assume a solution in the form of

$$\theta_i = \Theta_i \cos \omega_n t \qquad (4\text{--}40)$$

Substituting Eq. (4–40) and its time derivatives into Eq. (4–39) yields

$$I_1\omega_n{}^2\Theta_1 = k_{t1}(\Theta_1 - \Theta_2)$$

$$I_2\omega_n{}^2\Theta_2 = k_{t1}(\Theta_2 - \Theta_1) + k_{t2}(\Theta_2 - \Theta_3)$$

$$I_3\omega_n{}^2\Theta_3 = k_{t2}(\Theta_3 - \Theta_2) + k_{t3}(\Theta_3 - \Theta_4)$$

$$\cdot \quad \cdot \quad \cdot \quad \cdot \quad \cdot \quad \cdot \quad \cdot \quad \cdot \quad \cdot \quad \cdot \quad \cdot \quad \cdot \quad \cdot$$

$$I_n\omega_n{}^2\Theta_n = k_{t(n-1)}(\Theta_n - \Theta_{n-1}) \qquad (4\text{--}41)$$

Addition of Eqs. (4–41) results in

$$[I_1\Theta_1 + I_2\Theta_2 + I_3\Theta_3 + \cdots + I_n\Theta_n]\omega_n{}^2 = 0 \qquad (4\text{--}42)$$

Since the right-hand side of each equation of Eqs. (4–41) represents the torque, then the interpretation of Eq. (4–42) is that the sum of the external torques equals zero. This result, of course, is to be expected, since the system outlined by Fig. 4–6 is a free one. Then Eq. (4–42) can be satisfied only when there is no external torque.

From the first of Eqs. (4–41) we can see that

$$\Theta_2 = \left(1 - \frac{I_1\omega_n{}^2}{k_{t1}}\right)\Theta_1$$

From the second equation of the same set we find that

$$\Theta_3 = \Theta_2 - \frac{(I_1\Theta_1 + I_2\Theta_2)\omega_n^2}{k_{t2}}$$

In like manner it can be shown that

$$\Theta_4 = \Theta_3 - \frac{(I_1\Theta_1 + I_2\Theta_2 + I_3\Theta_3)\omega_n^2}{k_{t3}}$$

Generalizing the above equations, we may say that

$$\Theta_n = \Theta_{n-1} - \frac{\omega_n^2 \sum_{i=1}^{n-1} I_i\Theta_i}{k_{t(n-1)}} \tag{4-43}$$

Substituting the values of Eq. (4–43) into Eq. (4–42) will yield the characteristic equation for determining the natural frequencies of the

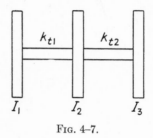

Fig. 4–7.

system. Let us try to find the natural frequencies for a three-disc-and-two-shaft system as seen in Fig. 4–7. For the system in Fig. 4–7, Eq. (4–42) becomes

$$(I_1\Theta_1 + I_2\Theta_2 + I_3\Theta_3)\omega_n^2 = 0$$

By repeated substitution of the relationship governed by Eq. (4–43) into the above equation, we get

$$\left\{ I_1\Theta_1 + I_2\left(1 - \frac{I_1\omega_n^2}{k_{t1}}\right)\Theta_1 \right.$$
$$\left. + I_3\left[\left(1 - \frac{I_1\omega_n^2}{k_{t1}}\right)\left(1 - \frac{I_2\omega_n^2}{k_{t2}}\right) - \omega_n^2 I_1\right]\Theta_1 \right\} \omega_n^2 = 0$$

Since Θ_1 is arbitrary, it cannot be equal to zero except for a trivial case. Then the characteristic equation is

$$\omega_n^2\{I_1 I_2 I_3 \omega_n^4 - [(I_1 I_2 + I_1 I_3)k_{t2} + (I_2 I_3 + I_1 I_3)k_{t1}]\omega_n^2 + k_{t1}k_{t2}(I_1 + I_2 + I_3)\} = 0 \tag{4-44}$$

One of the roots of Eq. (4–44) is

$$\omega_n{}^2 = 0 \tag{4–45}$$

This condition occurs when the three discs rotate as a solid mass and there is no twist in the shafts. The two other roots are

$$\omega_{n1,2}{}^2 = \frac{(I_1 I_2 + I_1 I_3) k_{t2} + (I_2 I_3 + I_1 I_3) k_{t1}}{2 I_1 I_2 I_3}$$

$$\pm \frac{1}{2} \sqrt{\frac{[(I_1 I_2 + I_1 I_3) k_{t2} + (I_2 I_3 + I_1 I_3) k_{t1}]^2}{(I_1 I_2 I_3)^2} - \frac{(I_1 + I_2 + I_3) k_{t1} k_{t2}}{I_1 I_2 I_3}}$$

or

$$\tag{4–46}$$

$$\omega_{n1,2}{}^2 = \tfrac{1}{2}[\omega_{11}{}^2 + \omega_{12}{}^2 + \omega_{22}{}^2 + \omega_{23}{}^2]$$

$$\pm \tfrac{1}{2} \sqrt{[\omega_{11}{}^2 + \omega_{12}{}^2 + \omega_{22}{}^2 + \omega_{23}{}^2]^2 - [\omega_{13}{}^2 \omega_{22}{}^2 + \omega_{11}{}^2 \omega_{23}{}^2 + \omega_{11}{}^2 \omega_{22}{}^2]}$$

For the case when $I_1 = I_2 = I_3 = I$ and $k_{t1} = k_{t2} = k_t$, we get

$$\omega_{n1,2}{}^2 = \frac{2k_t}{I} \mp \frac{1}{2} \sqrt{\left(\frac{4k_t}{I}\right)^2 - \frac{12k_t{}^2}{I^2}}$$

$$\omega_{n1,2}{}^2 = \frac{k_t}{I}, \frac{3k_t}{I} \tag{4–47}$$

By substituting Eq. (4–47) into Eq. (4–43), the angular displacements may be found. These displacements are plotted in Fig. 4–8. When

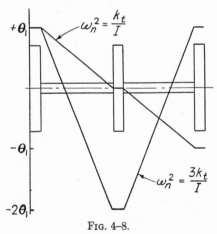

FIG. 4–8.

$\omega_{n1}{}^2 = k_t/I$, there is one node; and when $\omega_{n2}{}^2 = 3k_t/I$, there are two nodes. For the third node which is required when there are three natural frequencies, we have an infinity of points when $\omega_n{}^2 = 0$, for there is no twist in the shaft.

4–3. Holzer Tabulation Method. When more than three discs and two shafts are used to represent a vibrational system, the direct method of solution becomes so unwieldy that it is best to resort to another method of solution. There are several methods by which the natural frequencies of shaft-and-disc systems (these methods also apply to mass-and-spring systems) may be found. Only one such method will be put forward here, the method first demonstrated by H. Holzer.[1,2] The author's preference for the Holzer method results from his familiarity with the method because of several years of using it. Other methods, such as Graeffe's, are equally effective, but since each method leads to the same end result, only the Holzer method will be presented here.

The Holzer tabulation method is based upon two equations previously derived. They are repeated below:

$$\omega_n{}^2 \sum_{i=1}^{n} I_i \Theta_i = 0 \qquad (4\text{–}42)$$

and

$$\Theta_n = \Theta_{n-1} - \frac{\omega_n{}^2}{k_{t(n-1)}} \sum_{i=1}^{n-1} I_i \Theta_i \qquad (4\text{–}43)$$

If we select a value of $\omega_n{}^2$ which when applied to Eq. (4–42) satisfies the equation, then we have selected an exact $\omega_n{}^2$ of the system. In order to satisfy Eq. (4–42) it is necessary to evaluate the angular displacement of each disc. This can be done by means of Eq. (4–43). The procedure is one of trial and error until Eq. (4–42) is satisfied. The method is a tabular one. Θ_1, which is arbitrary, is selected equal to 1. Table 4–1 is the tabular layout in symbolic form for a three-disc–two-shaft system, when $k_{t1} = k_1$ and $k_{t2} = k_2$.

Holzer tabulation procedure:

1. Assume a value of $\omega_n{}^2$.
2. Fill in the known values into the proper blocks, such as I_1, I_2, I_3, k_1, k_2, k_3, etc.
3. Row 1: col. 3 is $\Theta_1 = 1$; col. 4 equals col. 2 times col. 3; col. 5 has the same value as col. 4; col. 7 is col. 5 divided by col. 6.
4. Row 2: from Eq. (4–43) we see that subtracting col. 7, row 1, from col. 3, row 1, yields Θ_2, col. 3, row 2; col. 4 is col. 2 times col. 3; col. 5 is $\omega_n{}^2\sum (I_1\Theta_1 + I_2\Theta_2)$, which is found by adding col. 4, row 2, to col. 5, row 1; col. 7 is obtained by dividing col. 5 by col. 6.

[1] H. Holzer, *Die Berechnung der Drehschwingungen* (Berlin: Springer-Verlag OHG, 1921).
[2] F. M. Lewis, "Torsional Vibrations in the Diesel Engine," *Trans. Soc. of Naval Arch. and Marine Eng.*, vol. 33 (1925).

TABLE 4-1.

	(1) I	(2) $\omega_n^2 I$	(3) Θ	(4) $\omega_n^2 I\Theta$	(5) $\omega_n^2\sum I\Theta$	(6) k_t	(7) $\dfrac{\omega_n^2}{k_t}\sum I\Theta$
1	I_1	$\omega_n^2 I_1$	1	$\omega_n^2 I_1$	$\omega_n^2 I_1$	k_1	$\dfrac{\omega_n^2}{k_1} I_1$
2	I_2	$\omega_n^2 I_2$	$1 - \dfrac{\omega_n^2}{k_1} I_1$	$\omega_n^2 I_2\left(1 - \dfrac{\omega_n^2}{k_1} I_1\right)$	$\omega_n^2\left[I_1 + I_2\left(1 - \dfrac{\omega_n^2}{k_1} I_1\right)\right]$	k_2	$\dfrac{\omega_n^2}{k_2}\left[I_1 + I_2 \left(1 - \dfrac{\omega_n^2}{k_1} I_1\right)\right]$
3	I_3	$\omega_n^2 I_3$	$1 - \dfrac{\omega_n^2}{k_1} I_1 - \dfrac{\omega_n^2}{k_2}\left[I_1 + I_2\left(1 - \dfrac{\omega_n^2 I_1}{k_1}\right)\right]$	$\omega_n^2 I_3\left\{1 - \dfrac{\omega_n^2}{k_1} I_1 - \dfrac{\omega_n^2}{k_2}\left[I_1 + I_2\left(1 - \dfrac{\omega_n^2}{k_1} I_1\right)\right]\right\}$	$\omega_n^2\left[I_1 + I_2\left(1 - \dfrac{\omega_n^2}{k_1} I_1\right) + I_3\left\{1 - \dfrac{\omega_n^2}{k_1} I_1 - \dfrac{\omega_n^2}{k_2}\left(1 - \dfrac{\omega_n^2}{k_1} I_1\right) + I_2\left(1 - \dfrac{\omega_n^2}{k_1} I_1\right)\right\}\right]$		

5. Row 3: Col. 3 is determined by subtracting col. 7, row 2, from col. 3, row 2; this is Θ_3; col. 4 is col. 3 times col. 2; col. 5 is the sum of col. 5, row 2, and col. 4, row 3.

6. If col. 5, row 3, equals zero, then the guess for $\omega_n{}^2$ is a correct one. If the value of col. 5, row 3, does not equal zero, the value of $\omega_n{}^2$ is changed and the process is repeated.

Note that when col. 5, row 3, is set equal to zero, we have the characteristic equation from which $\omega_n{}^2$ can be found. The characteristic equation is

$$\omega_n{}^2 \Sigma I\Theta = \omega_n{}^2 \left\{ \frac{I_1 I_2 I_3}{k_1 k_2} \omega_n{}^4 - \left[\frac{I_1}{k_1} (I_2 + I_3) + \frac{I_3}{k_2} (I_1 + I_2) \right] \omega_n{}^2 \right.$$
$$\left. + (I_1 + I_2 + I_3) \right\} = 0 \qquad (4\text{–}44)$$

Numerical Example. A four-cylinder diesel motor-generator is represented by discs and shafts as sketched in Fig. 4–9. The discs I_1 through I_4 each represent a piston assembly. I_5 is the flywheel and I_6 the generator.

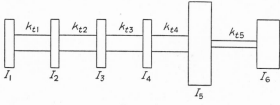

FIG. 4–9.

The shafts k_{t1}, k_{t2}, k_{t3} represent the elastic members between the cylinders. k_{t4} and k_{t5} are the shafts between the engine and flywheel and flywheel and generator, respectively. Determine the first two natural frequencies if the physical parameters are:

$$I_1 = I_2 = I_3 = I_4 = 4{,}000 \text{ lbs.-in.-sec}^2.$$

$$I_5 = 90{,}000 \text{ lbs.-in.-sec}^2.$$

$$I_6 = 40{,}000 \text{ lbs.-in.-sec}^2.$$

$$k_{t1} = k_{t3} = 800 \times 10^6 \text{ lbs.-in./radian}$$

$$k_{t2} = 500 \times 10^6 \text{ lbs.-in./radian}$$

$$k_{t4} = 600 \times 10^6 \text{ lbs.-in./radian}$$

$$k_{t5} = 20 \times 10^6 \text{ lbs.-in./radian}$$

SOLUTION. As a first approximation to the first natural frequency, let us lump the system into two discs. Since k_{t5} is a relatively soft spring, we can expect the diesel engine and flywheel to act as one disc and the generator as another. This grouping is shown in Fig. 4–10. We find the natural frequency of this assumed system by applying Eq. (4–22). Then

$$\omega_n{}^2 = \frac{k_{t5}(I_1{}' + I_2{}')}{I_1{}' I_2{}'}$$

$$\omega_n{}^2 = \frac{20 \times 10^6 (10.6 \times 10^4 + 4.0 \times 10^4)}{10.6 \times 10^4 \times 4.0 \times 10^4} = 690 \ (\text{radians/sec.})^2$$

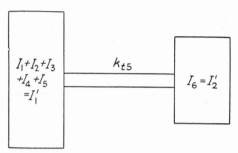

FIG. 4–10.

We now set up the framework for the Holzer tabulation solution, using as the first trial, Table 4–2a. The sum of the external torque does not quite equal zero. The question that now arises is whether $\omega_n{}^2$ shall be raised or

TABLE 4–2a.

FIRST TRIAL FOR FIRST NATURAL FREQUENCY: $\omega_n{}^2 = 690$							
	(1)	(2)	(3)	(4)	(5)	(6)	(7)
	I	$\omega_n{}^2 I \times 10^{-6}$	θ	$\omega_n{}^2 I \theta \times 10^{-6}$	$\omega_n{}^2 \sum I \theta \times 10^{-6}$	$k_t \times 10^{-6}$	$\dfrac{\omega_n{}^2}{k_t} \sum I \theta$
1	4,000	2.76	1.000	2.76	2.76	800	0.00345
2	4,000	2.76	0.997	2.75	5.51	500	0.0110
3	4,000	2.76	0.986	2.72	8.23	800	0.0103
4	4,000	2.76	0.976	2.69	10.92	600	0.0182
5	90,000	62.1	0.958	59.49	70.41	20	3.520
6	40,000	27.6	−2.562	−70.71	−0.30		

lowered for the next trial. Fig. 4–11 shows a plot of the external torque vs. $\omega_n{}^2$ for a generalized system. It can be seen that the external torque has a plus value as it approaches the first natural frequency, a negative value as it approaches the second natural frequency, and a plus value as it approaches the third natural frequency. As a rule we can say that the odd natural frequencies are approached from a plus residual and the even natural frequencies are approached from a negative residual. Another conclusion that can be drawn is that for each sign change in column 5, we have passed

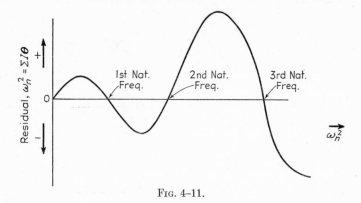

Fig. 4–11.

through a natural frequency. This conclusion allows us to determine which natural frequency we are at merely by counting the sign changes. Table 4–2a, then, shows that we have gone slightly beyond the first natural frequency. For the next trial, we can lower the ω_n^2 to, say, $\omega_n^2 = 688$. The results of the second trial are shown in Table 4–2b. The residual is

TABLE 4–2b.

	SECOND TRIAL FOR FIRST NATURAL FREQUENCY: $\omega_n^2 = 688$						
	(1) I	(2) $\omega_n^2 I \times 10^{-6}$	(3) θ	(4) $\omega_n^2 I \theta \times 10^{-6}$	(5) $\omega_n^2 \sum I \theta \times 10^{-6}$	(6) $k_t \times 10^{-6}$	(7) $\dfrac{\omega_n^2}{k_t} \sum I \theta$
1	4,000	2.75	1.000	2.75	2.75	800	0.00344
2	4,000	2.75	0.997	2.74	5.49	500	0.0110
3	4,000	2.75	0.986	2.71	8.20	800	0.0103
4	4,000	2.75	0.976	2.68	10.88	600	0.0181
5	90,000	61.92	0.958	59.31	70.19	20	3.510
6	40,000	27.5	−2.552	70.18	−0.01		

now very nearly zero, and the first natural frequency may be taken as $\omega_n^2 = 688$ with reasonable accuracy. The error between $\omega_n^2 = 690$ and $\omega_n^2 = 688$ is actually smaller than the errors we will find in converting an actual diesel motor-generator into discs and straight shafts. In many cases, the first natural frequency can be found with sufficient accuracy by combining the system into two discs with the softest spring between them, as is done in the example.

Estimating the second natural frequency is not quite so easy as estimating the first. There are two possible places where the second node might occur: in the shaft k_{t2} or in the shaft k_{t4}. To assume that one or the other of the shafts will contain the nodal point will be a good starting point. We will assume that a node will occur in k_{t2}. We then combine I_1 and I_2. The remaining I's are lumped into a single disc. The problem now is to connect the two hypothetical discs with a shaft that will represent the elasticity of the system. Since the shafts connecting the masses are all nearly equal (we can neglect k_{t5}), the effective shaft must be softer than any of the individual shafts. We therefore propose to connect the hypothetical discs with a shaft having a spring constant equal to the shafts k_{t1}, k_{t2}, and k_{t3} when they are connected in series. Then

$$k_{te} = \cfrac{1}{\cfrac{1}{k_{t1}} + \cfrac{1}{k_{t2}} + \cfrac{1}{k_{t3}}} = 222 \times 10^6 \text{ lb.-in./radian}$$

Fig. 4–12 is the schematic representation of the system which we will use

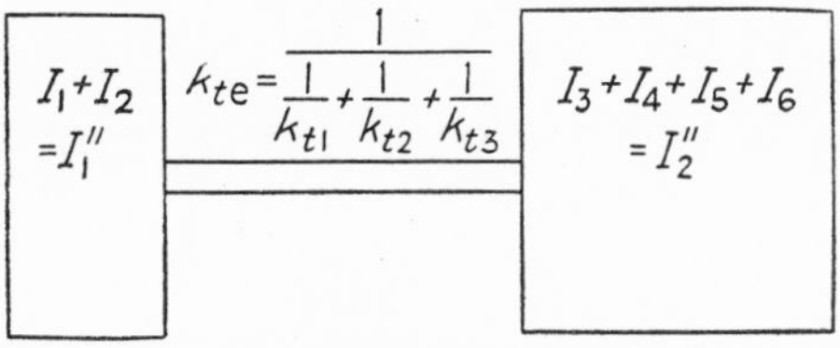

FIG. 4–12.

to get a starting point for our first tabulation trial. The natural frequency of the hypothetical system is

$$\omega_n{}^2 = \frac{k_{te}(I_1'' + I_2'')}{I_1'' I_2''} = \frac{222 \times 10^6 (0.8 + 13.8)10^4}{0.8 \times 10^4 \times 13.8 \times 10^4}$$

$$= 29,400 \ (\text{radians/sec.})^2$$

For our first trial for the second natural frequency let us use $\omega_n{}^2 = 29,000$. The results of this trial appear in Table 4–3a. It is now apparent that the guess that the second node would occur in the shaft k_{t2} was not a good one. The sign change takes place for Θ_5. The node, therefore, occurs in shaft k_{t4}. It is not necessary, however, to make a new arrangement of the discs. It can be seen from the first trial that the third natural frequency has not yet been reached, therefore we reduce the value of $\omega_n{}^2$. Then, for the next trial, let us use $\omega_n{}^2 = 20,000$.

TABLE 4–3*a*.

FIRST TRIAL FOR SECOND NATURAL FREQUENCY: $\omega_n{}^2 = 29{,}000$							
	(1)	(2)	(3)	(4)	(5)	(6)	(7)
	I	$\omega_n{}^2 I \times 10^{-6}$	θ	$\omega_n{}^2 I \theta \times 10^{-6}$	$\omega_n{}^2 \sum I\theta \times 10^{-6}$	$k_t \times 10^{-6}$	$\dfrac{\omega_n{}^2}{k_t} \sum I\theta$
1	4,000	116	1.000	116	116	800	0.145
2	4,000	116	0.855	99	215	500	0.430
3	4,000	116	0.425	49	264	800	0.330
4	4,000	116	0.095	11	275	600	0.458
5	90,000	2,610	−0.364	−955	−680	20	−34.0
6	40,000	1,160	33.6	38,970	38,290		

Table 4–3*b* is the second trial, when $\omega_n{}^2 = 20{,}000$. Now the second natural frequency has not been reached, since the residual is negative. The residual, though negative, is smaller than that of the first trial. We may assume that the second natural frequency is closer to $\omega_n{}^2 = 20{,}000$ than to $\omega_n{}^2 = 29{,}000$.

TABLE 4–3*b*.

SECOND TRIAL FOR SECOND NATURAL FREQUENCY $\omega_n{}^2 = 20{,}000$							
	(1)	(2)	(3)	(4)	(5)	(6)	(7)
	I	$\omega_n{}^2 I \times 10^{-6}$	θ	$\omega_n{}^2 I \theta \times 10^{-6}$	$\omega_n{}^2 \sum I\theta \times 10^{-6}$	$k_t \times 10^{-6}$	$\dfrac{\omega_n{}^2}{k_t} \sum I\theta$
1	4,000	80	1.000	80	80	800	0.100
2	4,000	80	0.900	72	152	500	0.304
3	4,000	80	0.596	48	200	800	0.250
4	4,000	80	0.346	28	228	600	0.380
5	90,000	1,800	−0.034	−61	167	20	8.35
6	40,000	800	−8.384	−6,707	−6,540		

For the third trial, we use $\omega_n{}^2 = 25{,}000$. This selection should bracket the natural frequency between $\omega_n{}^2 = 20{,}000$ and $\omega_n{}^2 = 25{,}000$. Table 4–3*c* represents the third trial. The second natural frequency again has been passed. We now know that the natural frequency lies somewhere between the values of the second and the third trial.

For our next trial we take $\omega_n{}^2 = 22{,}500$. This selection is contained in Table 4–3*d*. We find the residual to be quite small and we can let this

TABLE 4–3c.

		(1) I	(2) $\omega_n^2 I \times 10^{-6}$	(3) θ	(4) $\omega_n^2 I \theta \times 10^{-6}$	(5) $\omega_n^2 \sum I\theta \times 10^{-6}$	(6) $k_t \times 10^{-6}$	(7) $\dfrac{\omega_n^2}{k_t} \sum I\theta$
THIRD TRIAL FOR SECOND NATURAL FREQUENCY: $\omega_n^2 = 25{,}000$								
1		4,000	100	1.000	100	100	800	0.125
2		4,000	100	0.875	88	188	500	0.376
3		4,000	100	0.499	50	238	800	0.298
4		4,000	100	0.201	20	258	600	0.430
5		90,000	2,250	−0.229	−515	−257	20	−12.850
6		40,000	1,000	12.621	12,621	12,364		

trial be our final one. If greater accuracy is desired, an extra trial can be made at, say, $\omega_n^2 = 22{,}200$.

TABLE 4–3d.

		(1) I	(2) $\omega_n^2 I \times 10^{-6}$	(3) θ	(4) $\omega_n^2 I \theta \times 10^{-6}$	(5) $\omega_n^2 \sum I\theta \times 10^{-6}$	(6) $k_t \times 10^{-6}$	(7) $\dfrac{\omega_n^2}{k_t} \sum I\theta$
FOURTH TRIAL FOR SECOND NATURAL FREQUENCY $\omega_n^2 = 22{,}500$								
1		4,000	90	1.000	90	90	800	0.113
2		4,000	90	0.887	80	170	500	0.340
3		4,000	90	0.547	49	219	800	0.274
4		4,000	90	0.273	25	244	600	0.407
5		90,000	2,025	−0.134	−271	−27	20	−1.350
6		40,000	900	1.220	1,098	1,071		

Column 3 gives the angle of twist for each disc. Then from the solutions of the first and second natural frequencies, we can plot the elastic curve from the angle of twist of each disc. This is shown in Fig. 4–13. Nothing will be gained by determining the third natural frequency. The procedure would be the same. We would again assume that the new node would occur in shaft k_{t2}. This time we would have to stiffen the spring somewhat to get a proper hypothetical system. We can use the same system as depicted in Fig. 4–13, but we now change the shaft to k_{t2}. This change gives us an $\omega_n^2 = 66{,}200$. If one carries through the tabulation for this value, he will find that it is below the third natural frequency.

The curious student may carry out the computation for the third natural frequency for his own satisfaction.

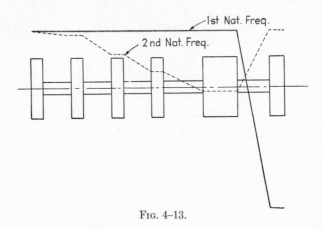

FIG. 4–13.

4–4. Masses and Springs. In our discussion of several degrees of freedom, we have in the main limited ourselves to the analysis of discs and shafts. This discussion, however, may easily be extended to systems consisting of masses and springs. The analysis and the form of the resulting

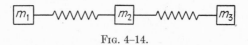

FIG. 4–14.

equations are identical with those of the previous discussion. To bear this statement out, let us consider the problem of three masses and two springs, Fig. 4–14. This problem is analogous to the problem of three discs and two shafts. The equations of motion are

$$m_1\ddot{x}_1 + k_1(x_1 - x_2) = 0$$

$$m_2\ddot{x}_2 + k_1(x_2 - x_1) + k_2(x_2 - x_3) = 0$$

$$m_3\ddot{x}_3 + k_2(x_3 - x_2) = 0 \tag{4–48}$$

where x_1, x_2, and x_3 are the respective absolute displacements of m_1, m_2, and m_3. We assume a solution of the form

$$x_1 = X_1 \cos \omega_n t$$

$$x_2 = X_2 \cos \omega_n t$$

$$x_3 = X_3 \cos \omega_n t \tag{4–49}$$

The characteristic equation is found to be

$$\omega_n^2[m_1 m_2 m_3 \omega_n^4 - \{(m_1 m_2 + m_1 m_3)k_2 + (m_2 m_3 + m_1 m_3)k_1\}\omega_n^2 \\ + k_1 k_2 (m_1 + m_2 + m_3)] = 0 \qquad (4\text{--}50)$$

Eq. (4–50) is identical in form to Eq. (4–44), which is the characteristic equation of three discs and two shafts. The roots of the equation are identical to the second of Eqs. (4–46), where now $\omega_{ij}^2 = k_i/m_j$.

Mass-and-spring systems of greater number of degrees of freedom may be readily solved by the Holzer method. We merely substitute m for I, k for k_t and X for Θ in the basic equations, Eqs. (4–42) and (4–43), which the Holzer tabulation has to satisfy. For a system of linear vibrations these basic equations become

$$\omega_n^2 \sum_{i=1}^{n} m_i X_i = 0$$

$$X_n = X_{n-1} - \frac{\omega_n^2}{k_{n-1}} \sum_{i=1}^{n-1} m_i X_i \qquad (4\text{--}51)$$

4–5. Geared Torsional Systems. Torsional systems are often interconnected by a set of gears. The geared system raises a problem, since the inertia discs are not being operated at the same angular speed throughout the system. Let us consider a torsional system consisting of two discs mounted on shafts which are connected by a pair of gears, whose speed

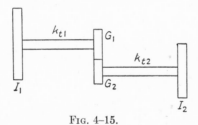

Fig. 4–15.

ratio is n, Fig. 4–15. If we apply a torque to disc I_1, it will be displaced by an angle θ_1. By virtue of the fact that a movement through gear G_1 will be amplified (or reduced) in gear G_2 by the speed ratio n, then for a displacement of θ_1 for I_1, there will be a corresponding displacement of $n\theta_1$ for I_2. Stated mathematically,

$$\theta_2 = n\theta_1 \qquad (4\text{--}52)$$

We will now attempt to formulate a new hypothetical system without gears which will be equivalent to the original system. A necessary requirement for a new system is that the energies, both kinetic and potential, of the old be maintained in the new. We first select one branch of the geared system to remain unaltered. Let I_1 and k_{t1} remain unchanged. We can relate I_2 and k_{t2} of the old system to the new by writing

$$T_2 = \tfrac{1}{2} I_2 \dot\theta_2{}^2 = \tfrac{1}{2} I_2 n^2 \dot\theta_1{}^2$$

$$V_2 = \tfrac{1}{2} k_{t2} \theta_2{}^2 = \tfrac{1}{2} k_{t2} n^2 \theta_1{}^2 \tag{4-53}$$

We can see from Eqs. (4–53) that we need only alter the old system by multiplying I_2 and k_{t2} by n^2 to convert to the new layout. That is, the new disc is now $n^2 I_2$ and the new spring is $n^2 k_{t2}$. The entire new system will now operate at the angular speed of I_1.

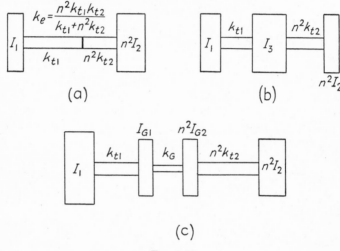

Fig. 4–16.

In creating the new layout, the problem of the inertias of G_1 and G_2 arises. In most problems the inertias of the discs are very large compared with the inertias of the gears. If such be the case, we can neglect the inertias of the gears and represent the new system as drawn in Fig. 4–16a. The shafts k_{t1} and $n^2 k_{t2}$ are connected in series and the equivalent spring constant becomes

$$k_e = \frac{n^2 k_{t1} k_{t2}}{k_{t1} + n^2 k_{t2}} \tag{4-54}$$

If, however, the inertias of the gears cannot be neglected, then a third disc must be inserted. The third disc will have a total inertia of

$$I_3 = I_{G1} + n^2 I_{G2} \tag{4-55}$$

and it is placed into the system as shown in Fig. 4–16b.

In the two hypothetical, but equivalent, layouts, we have neglected the elasticity of the two gears. The stiffness of gears in mesh is usually considerable, and the elasticity may usually be neglected with impunity. We can, however, account for the elasticity of the gears if we wish. With greater use of plastic gears, an occasion might arise where the elasticity of the gears is appreciable. For such a case, the arrangement is shown in Fig. 4–16c, where k_G is the stiffness of the gears and may be determined by test.

The above analysis may be used for systems that are interconnected by pulleys and belts. We can account for the inertias of the pulleys and the elasticity of the belts, which may be considerable. Fig. 4–16c will apply to such a system when the pulley inertias and belt elasticity are taken into account.

Example. Determine the natural frequency of a geared system as shown in Fig. 4–15 if $2I_1 = I_2$, $k_{t1} = k_{t2} = k_t$, and $n = 2$. Assume that the inertias and the elasticity of the gears are negligible.

SOLUTION. The new system will be the same as depicted in Fig. 4–16a. By applying Eq. (4–22), we get

$$\omega_n^{\;2} = \frac{(n^2 k_t^{\;2})(I_1 + 2n^2 I_1)}{(k_t + n^2 k_t)(2I_1^{\;2})}$$

Simplifying yields

$$\omega_n = \sqrt{\frac{18 k_t}{5 I_1}}$$

If the original system were not geared, the natural frequency would be

$$\omega_n = \sqrt{\frac{3 k_t}{4 I_1}}$$

4–6. Branched Systems. Branched systems occur whenever we have more than one power input or take-off. An automobile engine transmits power to both of the rear wheels through a differential: a single marine engine may drive two propellers by way of a gear box. These are only two examples of branched systems. Let us consider a branched system such as is shown in Fig. 4–17. The determination of the natural frequencies of such a system can be effected by using the Holzer method.

We start the solution by first assuming a unit angle of twist at one end of one of the branches, say I_1. The Holzer method is applied until the disc from which the branches are joined is reached. In our case, it is I_5. The solution is temporarily broken off at this point. We proceed to make a similar analysis for the other branch until we again reach the junction.

From each of the two analyses we can compute a θ_5. Since θ_5 can have only one value, we modify the amplitude of one of the branches by multiplying it by a factor α which is the amplitude ratio of the two θ_5's. Only when the two branches are identical will α be equal to one. Since the

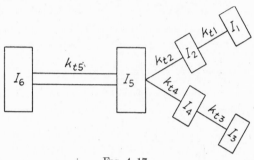

FIG. 4–17.

torque is proportional to the angle of twist, we multiply the torque of the modified branch by α and add this quantity to the torque of the other branch. The sum of these torques will be the total torque acting on I_5. We now proceed with the Holzer method for the rest of the main branch.

Example. Determine the first natural frequency of the system of Fig. 4–17 if

$I_1 = 5$ lbs.-in.-sec^2. $k_{t1} = 120$ lbs.-in./radian

$I_2 = 8$ lbs.-in.-sec^2. $k_{t2} = 200$ lbs.-in./radian

$I_3 = 10$ lbs.-in.-sec^2. $k_{t3} = 150$ lbs.-in./radian

$I_4 = 5$ lbs.-in.-sec^2. $k_{t4} = 120$ lbs.-in./radian

$I_5 = 10$ lbs.-in.-sec^2. $k_{t5} = 50$ lbs.-in./radian

$I_6 = 15$ lbs.-in.-sec^2.

SOLUTION. Table 4–4 is the first trial using $\omega_n{}^2 = 4.0$. The starting point was determined by assuming that the first node would occur in k_{t5}. Discs I_1, I_2, I_3, I_4, and I_5 are lumped together and are connected to I_6 by shaft k_{t5}. This combination calls for an $\omega_n{}^2 = 4.64$. However, since the lumped system will be somewhat stiffer than the actual system, we select $\omega_n{}^2 = 4.0$ as a starting point.

The residual of minus 7 is close enough for our purpose. The negative residual indicates that we have passed through the first natural frequency. For greater accuracy, the next trial would be $\omega_n{}^2 = 3.9$. This trial will give a residual of plus 1. The first natural frequency will occur, then, at an $\omega_n{}^2$ slightly greater than 3.9.

TABLE 4–4.

			First Trial $\omega_n^2 = 4.0$				
Disc No.	I	$\omega_n^2 I$	θ	$\omega_n^2 I\theta$	$\omega_n^2 \sum I\theta$	k_t	$\dfrac{\omega_n^2}{k_t}\sum I\theta$
1	5	20	1.000	20.0	20.0	120	0.167
2	8	32	0.833	26.7	46.7	200	0.234
5	10	40	0.599	24.0	70.7		
3	10	40	1.000	40.0	40.0	150	0.267
4	5	20	0.733	14.7	54.7	120	0.456
5	10	40	0.277	11.1	65.8		
$\alpha = \dfrac{0.599}{0.277} = 2.16$				$\omega_n^2 \sum I\theta = 142$			
5			0.599		213	50	4.260
6	15	60	−3.660	−220	−7		

4–7. Vibration Absorber. The study of a two-mass–two-spring system with a forcing function applied to one of the masses has led to a very practical application of this problem.   A single mass on a spring which is being forced at, or very nearly at, resonance may have the vibration eliminated by attaching a small mass and spring of specified physical parameters to the first mass.   This arrangement is in effect a two-mass–two-spring system with one of the masses being forced.   When a system is designed as described above, the small mass and spring is called a vibration or dynamic absorber.   Let us analyze the motion of a single mass-and-spring system with a vibration-absorber attached, as seen in Fig. 4–18.   The differential equations of motion are

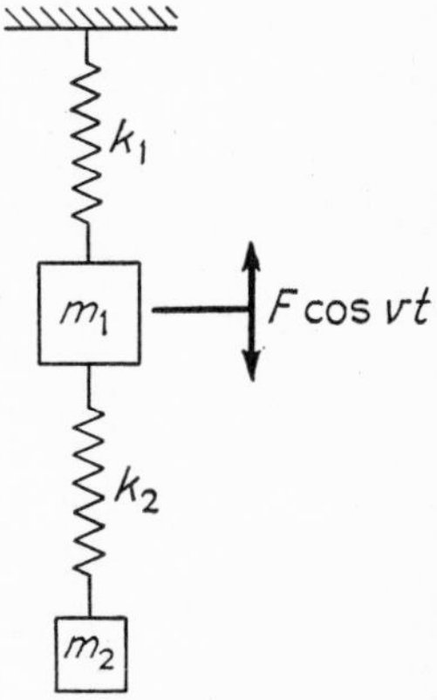

$$m_1\ddot{x}_1 + k_1 x_1 + k_2(x_1 - x_2) = F\cos \nu t$$
$$m_2\ddot{x}_2 + k_2(x_2 - x_1) = 0 \qquad (4\text{--}56)$$

FIG. 4–18.

We assume a steady-state solution of the form

$$x_1 = X_1 \cos \nu t$$
$$x_2 = X_2 \cos \nu t \qquad (4\text{--}57)$$

then

$$(k_1 + k_2 - m_1\nu^2)X_1 - k_2X_2 = F$$
$$-k_2X_1 + (k_2 - m_2\nu^2)X_2 = 0 \qquad (4\text{--}58)$$

Solving for X_1 and X_2, we get

$$X_1 = \frac{F(k_2 - m_2\nu^2)}{(k_1 + k_2 - m_1\nu^2)(k_2 - m_2\nu^2) - k_2{}^2}$$

$$X_2 = \frac{Fk_2}{(k_1 + k_2 - m_1\nu^2)(k_2 - m_2\nu^2) - k_2{}^2} \qquad (4\text{--}59)$$

If we let $\omega_{ij}{}^2 = k_i/m_j$ and $\beta_{ij} = \nu/\omega_{ij}$, Eqs. (4–59) may be written as

$$X_1 = \frac{F}{k_1} \frac{1 - \beta_{22}{}^2}{\left[1 + \dfrac{k_2}{k_1} - \beta_{11}{}^2\right][1 - \beta_{22}{}^2] - \dfrac{k_2}{k_1}}$$

$$X_2 = \frac{F}{k_1} \frac{1}{\left[1 + \dfrac{k_2}{k_1} - \beta_{11}{}^2\right][1 - \beta_{22}{}^2] - \dfrac{k_2}{k_1}} \qquad (4\text{--}60)$$

When $\nu^2 = \omega_{22}{}^2$, then Eqs. (4–60) reduce to

$$X_1 = 0$$

$$X_2 = -\frac{F}{k_2}$$

Eqs. (4–61) show that the vibration of the forced mass m_1 has been eliminated. The force on m_1 is completely absorbed by the vibration-absorber. In the design of a vibration-absorber, one must be careful that the strength of the spring of the absorber is sufficient to sustain the force F.

X_1 will be zero whenever $\nu^2 = \omega_{22}{}^2$. This statement means that the forced mass will be stationary whatever its natural frequency may be. The real advantage, however, of the vibration-absorber occurs when ω_{11} is in the neighborhood of ν.

The denominator of Eqs. (4–60) when set equal to zero is the characteristic equation. The characteristic equation, when $\beta_{11} = \beta_{22}$ is

$$\beta^4 - \beta^2\left(2 + \frac{k_2}{k_1}\right) + 1 = 0 \qquad (4\text{--}61)$$

Whence

$$\beta^2 = 1 + \frac{k_2}{2k_1} \pm \sqrt{\frac{k_2}{k_1}\left(1 + \frac{k_2}{4k_1}\right)} \qquad (4\text{--}62)$$

When β^2 has the values described by Eq. (4–62), both the masses, m_1 and

m_2, will have infinitely larger amplitudes. The resonance frequencies which are now two in number will depend upon the k_2/k_1 ratio. Fig. 4–19 is a plot of the absolute amplitude of $|X_1|$ and $|X_2|$, when $k_2/k_1 = \frac{1}{10}$. This graph clearly shows the limitations of the vibration-absorber. It is very satisfactory for a constant-speed system but cannot operate satisfactorily when the forcing function has a variable frequency. The frequency range over which the absorber is effective is extremely narrow. The constant-speed requirement is a severe limitation on the usefulness of the vibration-absorber.

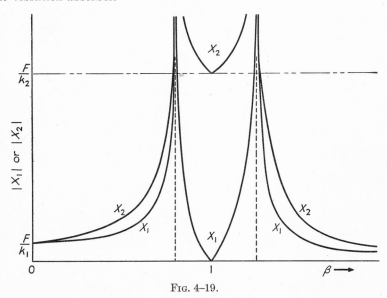

FIG. 4–19.

Example. A variable-speed centrifugal water pump, used for laboratory testing, vibrates so violently at 764 rpm that it is impossible to read the pressure gage at the pump discharge. It is proposed that a $\frac{1}{4}$-in. steel rod be attached to the pump by drilling and tapping the case. A weight can then be attached to the end of the rod so that the weight and rod act as a dynamic absorber. What should the weight and the free length of the rod be?

Since the pump will now have two resonant frequencies, it will be necessary to remove the absorber when tests are run in the neighborhood of these frequencies. What will the resonant frequencies be if the pump weighs 277 lbs. when filled with water?

SOLUTION:

$$\nu = \frac{764}{60} \times 2\pi = 80.0 \text{ radians/sec.}$$

If m_2 and k_2 represent the mass and the spring constant of the absorber, then

$$k_2/m_2 = (80.0)^2 = 6400 \text{ (radians/sec.)}^2$$

and

$$k_2 = \frac{3EI}{l^3} = \frac{3 \times 30 \times 10^6}{l^3} \times \frac{\pi}{4}\left(\frac{1}{8}\right)^4 = \frac{17{,}260}{l^3} \text{ lbs./in.}$$

Substituting, we get

$$\frac{17{,}260 \times 386}{l^3 W_2} = 6400$$

$$l^3 W_2 = 1040 \text{ lbs.-in.}^3 \tag{a}$$

If we arbitrarily let $l = 10$ in., then

$$W_2 = 1.040 \text{ lbs.}$$

Since a $\frac{1}{4}$-in. steel rod weighs 0.167 lb./linear foot, we subtract the effective weight of the rod from W_2.

$$W_{\text{absorber}} = W_2 - \tfrac{1}{3} W_{\text{rod}}$$

$$W_{\text{absorber}} = 1.040 - \tfrac{1}{3} \times \tfrac{10}{12} \times 0.167 = 0.994 \text{ lb.}$$

A weight of 0.994 lb. attached to a $\frac{1}{4}$-in. steel rod 10 in. long will be a satisfactory dynamic absorber. Any other combination of weight and rod length which satisfies equation (a) will also satisfy our requirement. To determine the new resonant frequencies we need only solve Eq. (4–62). However, we do not know the spring constant of the pump mounting. We do know that 764 rpm is the resonant speed of the pump before the absorber is mounted. Then

$$\frac{k_1}{m_1} = 6400 \text{ (radians/sec.)}^2$$

and

$$k_1 = 6400 \times \frac{277}{386} = 4590 \text{ lbs./in.}$$

Now

$$\beta^2 = 1 + \frac{k_2}{2k_1} \pm \sqrt{\frac{k_2}{k_1}\left(1 + \frac{k_2}{4k_1}\right)} \tag{4–62}$$

and since $k_2 = 17.26$ lbs./in., we get, by substituting the proper values into Eq. (4–62),

$$\frac{6400}{\omega_n{}^2} = 1 + \frac{17.26}{2 \times 4590} \pm \sqrt{\frac{17.26}{4590}\left(1 + \frac{17.26}{4 \times 4590}\right)}$$

$$\frac{6400}{\omega_n{}^2} = 1 + \tfrac{1}{2}(0.00376) \pm \sqrt{0.00376(1 + \tfrac{1}{4} \times 0.00376)}$$

$$\omega_{n1,2}{}^2 = \frac{6400}{1.063} \; ; \frac{6400}{0.940}$$

$$\omega_{n1,2}{}^2 = 6020 \; ; 6800$$

$$\omega_{n1,2} = 77.6 \; , 82.5 \text{ radians/sec.}$$

The new resonant speeds are 741 rpm and 788 rpm. These speeds are so close to the pump speed that when the absorber is removed, large amplitudes of vibration will be experienced at the above-mentioned speeds. We can redesign the absorber so that there is a wider spread between the resonant frequencies. Let

$$l = 5$$

then

$$k_2 = 138 \text{ lbs./in.}$$

and

$$W_2 = 8.32 \text{ lbs.}$$

The weight of the free length of the rod to be subtracted from W_2 is now 0.023 lb. Then W_{absorber} is 8.30 lbs. The resonant speeds will occur at 701 rpm and 833 rpm. This is a better spread of the resonant frequencies than in the first design.

BIBLIOGRAPHY

DEN HARTOG, J. P. *Mechanical Vibrations.* 4th ed. New York: McGraw-Hill Book Co., Inc., 1956.

HANSEN, H. M., and CHENEA, PAUL F. *Mechanics of Vibration.* New York: John Wiley & Sons, Inc., 1952.

THOMSON, WILLIAM TYRELL. *Mechanical Vibrations.* 2d ed. Englewood Cliffs, N. J.: Prentice-Hall, Inc., 1953.

PROBLEMS

4-1. A disc of mass m and radius r is attached to a soft helical spring as shown in Fig. P4-1. The spring has two spring constants: one, the linear constant

$$k = \frac{Gd^4}{8nD^3}$$

the other, a rotational spring constant

$$k_t = \frac{Ed^4}{64nD}$$

Determine the uncoupled natural frequencies of the disc for a free vibration.

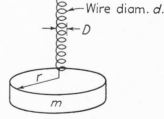

FIG. P4-1.

4-2. What must the diameter of the helix of the spring in Problem 4-1 be if both modes of vibration are to be excited simultaneously?

4-3. If an external torque of $M_0 \cos \nu t$, where

$$\nu = \sqrt{\frac{Gd^4}{8nD^4m}} \ .$$

is applied to the disc in Problem 4–1, which mode of vibration will be excited?

4-4. A mass m, whose moment of inertia is I, is attached, as shown in Fig. P4–4, to a weightless rod. The ends of the rod are supported by identical springs. Determine the natural frequencies of the system, if the system is restricted to plane motion and no side sway is permitted.

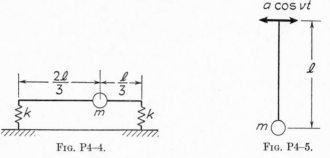

Fig. P4–4.   Fig. P4–5.

4-5. A simple pendulum is activated by a harmonic displacement at its pivot point (Fig. P4–5). Show that there are two modes of vibration, one when $\nu < \omega_n$, the other when $\nu > \omega_n$.

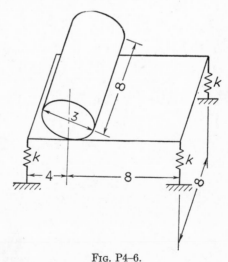

Fig. P4–6.

4-6. A cylinder, 3 in. $\times$ 8 in., weighs 16 lbs. and is supported by a weightless platform. Four springs, each having a spring constant of $k = 10$ lbs./in., support the four corners of the platform, as shown in Fig. P4–6. Determine the natural frequencies of the system.

4–7. Determine the natural frequencies and the modes of vibration for the system shown in Fig. P4–7. Assume motion occurs in one plane only and that there is no side sway.

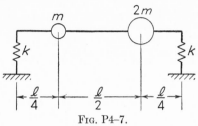

FIG. P4–7.

4–8. An automobile traveling over a rough road may be represented schematically as in Fig. P4–8 for a first approximation. Determine the amplitude of vibration of the body of the car and the natural frequencies of the system, if we assume that motion takes place only in the vertical direction. The mass and stiffness of the tires are to be taken into account.

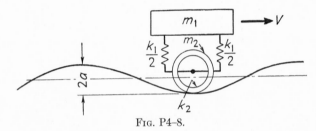

FIG. P4–8.

4–9. Two pendulums are interconnected by a spring attached to the masses, as shown in Fig. P4–9. Determine the natural frequencies of the system.

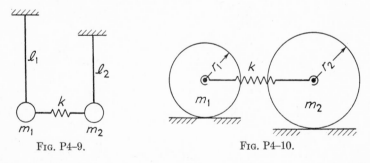

FIG. P4–9.   FIG. P4–10.

4–10. Two cylinders are connected by a spring as shown in Fig. P4–10. Determine the natural frequencies of the system. Assume that the cylinders roll without slipping.

4–11. Two diesel-electric locomotives are coupled together. Each locomotive weighs 80,000 lbs. The coupling which connects the diesels has a stiffness of 20,000 lbs./in. What are the natural frequencies of the system?

4-12. Determine the steady-state equations of motion for I_1 and I_2 (Fig. P4-12), if I_2 is activated by an external torque $M_0 \cos \nu t$.

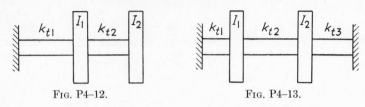

FIG. P4-12. FIG. P4-13.

4-13. Determine the angular displacement of I_2 in terms of Θ_1 for the two modes of vibration for the system in Fig. P4-13, when Θ_1 is the initial displacement of I_1.

4-14. Determine the equations of motion and the natural frequencies of the system shown in Fig. P4-14.

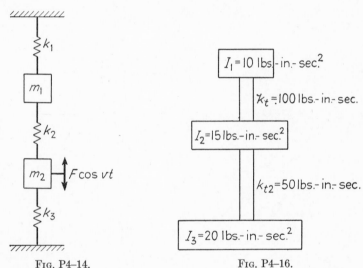

FIG. P4-14. FIG. P4-16.

4-15. If the springs in Fig. P4-14 each have a spring value of 10 lbs./in. and each mass weighs 2 lbs., determine the equations of motion and the natural frequencies when $F = 2$ lbs. and $\nu = 30$ radians/sec.

4-16. For the system shown in Fig. P4-16, determine the first two non-trivial natural frequencies and the amplitude ratios for those frequencies by means of the Holzer method.

4-17. What is the third natural frequency of the system shown in Fig. P4-17?

4-18. For the system shown in Fig. P4-18, determine the first two non-trivial natural frequencies and the amplitude ratios for those frequencies by means of the Holzer method.

4-19. If the moment of inertia of the 10-T. gear is 1.0 and the 30-T. inertia is 9.0, determine the first two natural frequencies of the geared system shown in Fig. P4-19.

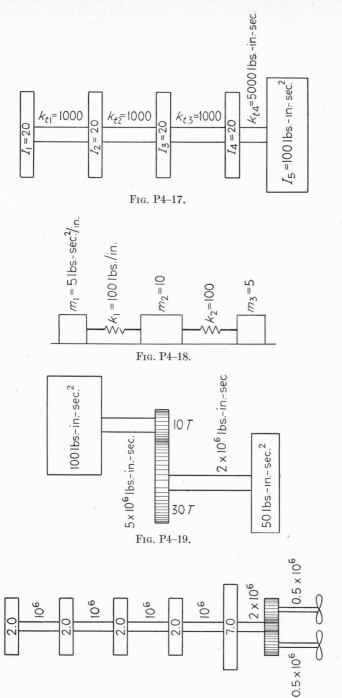

Fig. P4–17.

Fig. P4–18.

Fig. P4–19.

Fig. P4–20.

4-20. A marine drive has a 10 : 1 reduction system which drives the twin propellers (Fig. P4–20). If each propeller with the entrained water has an equivalent moment of inertia of 0.8 lb.-in.-sec.^{2}, determine the second natural frequency of the system. Neglect the inertia of the gears.

4-21. Determine the first and third natural frequencies of the branched system shown in Fig. P4–21.

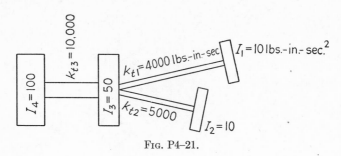

FIG. P4–21.

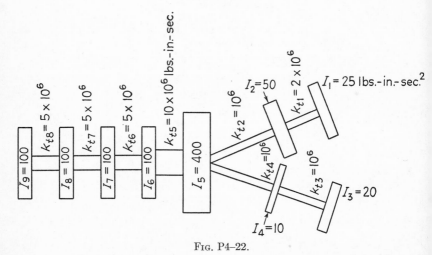

FIG. P4–22.

4-22. Determine the fundamental frequency of the system shown in Fig. P4–22.

4-23. A spring-and-mass system is found to be in resonance when the forcing frequency is 30 radians/sec. The mass weighs 772 lbs. A 50-lb. absorber is attached to the system. Determine the new resonant frequencies.

4-24. A machine which is mounted on springs is found to have a resonant frequency at 600 rpm. A tuned vibration-absorber weighing 4 lbs. is attached to the system, and new resonant frequencies of 480 and 750 rpm are found. Design an absorber so that the resonant frequencies will be 420 and 852 rpm.

CHAPTER 5

BEAMS AND SHAFTS

5–1. Introduction. Beams and shafts are distinctly different machine elements. A beam can be defined as a stationary structural member; a shaft is a rotating structural member. The difference between two members notwithstanding, we can group beams and shafts under a single heading. This grouping is possible because the differential equation of motion of a laterally vibrating beam is identical with the differential equation of whirling of a rotating shaft. By lateral vibration of a beam, we mean that the deflection resulting from the vibration of the beam is in the y direction, as depicted in Fig. 5–1a. The whirling of a shaft is a somewhat different phenomenon. When a shaft is rotated, the shaft will

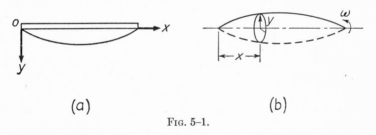

(a)   (b)

Fig. 5–1.

assume an elastic deflection. The deflected configuration will be rotated around the axis of rotation, Fig. 5–1b. This rotation is known as whirling. A more complete discussion of whirling will follow in Section 5–2.

No attempt will be made in this chapter to derive the equations of motion for beams and shafts in an exact manner. We will discuss, instead, methods of approximate solutions—solutions which have fairly wide acceptance in engineering practice. The exact solutions will be reserved for Chapter 7, which will be devoted to discussions of vibration in continuous mediums.

5–2. Critical Speeds. The introduction of approximate methods for determining the natural frequencies of beams and shafts should be preceded by a discussion of the concept of the critical speed. This concept for a simple system will lay a proper background for the future analysis of shafts and rotors.

A critical speed is said to exist when the frequency of the rotation of a shaft equals one of the natural frequencies of the shaft. Since shafts have an infinite number of natural frequencies, there will exist an infinite number of critical speeds. In actual practice we never encounter more than the first few critical speeds. This condition is the result of the limited speed range in which most machinery is operated. In shaft and rotor design, determination of the critical speed is important only so that it can be avoided. The reason for avoiding the critical speed lies in the large amplitudes of vibration that are developed at or near the critical speed resonance. Theoretically, when critical speed resonance is achieved, the amplitude of vibration becomes infinite. In actuality, there is always some damping present, and the amplitudes have large but finite values.

The critical speed phenomenon can be classed as a case of dynamic instability. This dynamic instability may be best understood by analyzing a weightless shaft to which a disc of mass m has been fastened. In order that the weightless shaft be simulated, let the shaft be placed in a vertical position as in Fig. 5–2a. It is assumed that the disc as mounted on the shaft is in static balance, but that a small amount of dynamic unbalance

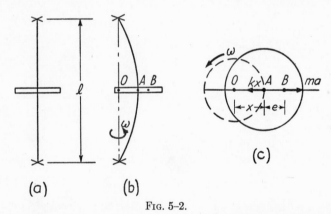

(a)   (b)

(c)

FIG. 5–2.

exists when the shaft is rotated. This unbalance will occur when the center of mass and the geometric center do not exactly coincide. Fig. 5–2b is a sketch of the shaft and disc being rotated at an angular speed of ω radians/sec. As a result of the dynamic unbalance, there will exist a centrifugal force which will cause the shaft to deflect. The shaft will rotate in this deflected configuration, and is then said to be whirling. Let B be the center of mass and A the geometric center of the disc. Fig. 5–2c is a plan view of the disc in the deflected configuration showing these relationships. The deflection of the shaft is x, the center of rotation O, and e is the eccentricity or distance between the center of mass and the geometric center.

The centrifugal force, ma, is equal to $m(x + e)\omega^2$ and is acting radially. The reactive force will be equal to the spring constant of the shaft times the deflection, kx, where

$$k = \frac{48EI}{l^3}$$

since the disc is fastened at the center of the shaft. Then

$$m(x + e)\omega^2 = kx$$

or   (5–1)

$$x = \frac{e}{\dfrac{k}{m\omega^2} - 1}$$

Since $\sqrt{k/m}$ is the natural frequency of the shaft and disc, and since we have defined the natural frequency as being equal to the critical speed, ω_{cr}, Eq. (5–1) may be written as

$$x = \frac{e}{\dfrac{\omega_{cr}{}^2}{\omega^2} - 1} \tag{5–2}$$

Let us consider the implications of Eq. (5–2) as the frequency ratio ω_{cr}/ω takes successively increasing values. At a frequency ratio less than one, x has a positive value and the whirling takes place as depicted in Fig. 5–2. As the ratio approaches the value of unity, the amplitudes become very large, and at the value of unity the amplitudes are infinite. At the value of $\omega_{cr}/\omega = 1$ the system becomes dynamically unstable and will destroy itself in a short period of time. When $\omega_{cr}/\omega > 1$, x is negative; that is, e is to the left of the geometric center. When this happens there is

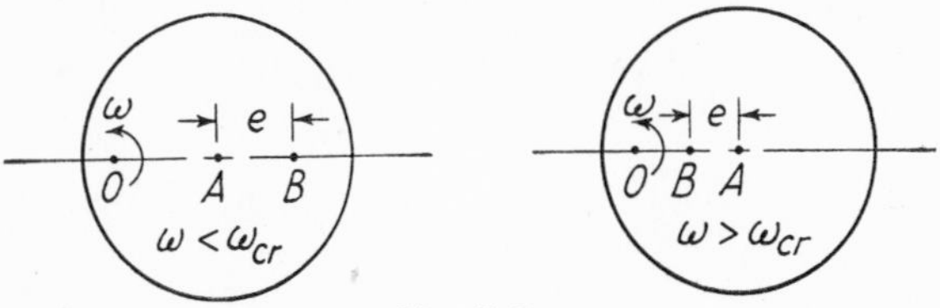

Fig. 5–3.

a phase-angle shift of 180°. As ω_{cr}/ω becomes very large, the amplitude diminishes and approaches zero in the limit. Fig. 5–3 shows the relative position of e for $\omega_{cr}/\omega < 1$ and for $\omega_{cr}/\omega > 1$. The sketch indicates that for speeds less than the critical speed, the unbalance rotates on the outside of the geometric center, and that for speeds greater than the critical speed, the unbalance rotates on the inside of the geometric center.

The single-disc system described above has by its nature only one critical speed. It does give us, however, some insight into the action of a rotating shaft. When a shaft is rotated beyond a critical speed, a phase-angle shift is noted. Since there is inherent damping in every shaft system, the phase angle will not be 180° but some lesser value.

5–3. Rayleigh Method. Lord Rayleigh,[1] in his classic text on sound, has suggested an approximate method by which the fundamental natural frequency of a beam may be found with reasonable accuracy. The essential part of the Rayleigh method is the assumption of a reasonable dynamic deflection curve and the application of the energy method to determine the fundamental frequency.

For a conservative system, the maximum potential energy is equal to the maximum kinetic energy. Let us apply this relationship to a beam of uniform cross-section.

The potential energy of a beam in bending is

$$V = \tfrac{1}{2} \int_0^l M \, d\theta \tag{5–3}$$

where M is the bending moment and $d\theta$ is the change of slope of the beam resulting from the applied bending moment. From the beam theory relations, we know that

$$\frac{d\theta}{dx} = -\frac{M}{EI} \qquad \text{or} \qquad d\theta = -\frac{M}{EI} \, dx \tag{5–4}$$

and

$$M = -EI \frac{d^2y}{dx^2}$$

Substituting the first of the relations of Eqs. (5–4) into Eq. (5–3), we get

$$V = \frac{1}{2EI} \int_0^l M^2 \, dx \tag{5–5}$$

When the second of the relations of Eqs. (5–4) is substituted into Eq. (5–5), we see that

$$V = \frac{EI}{2} \int_0^l \left(\frac{d^2y}{dx^2} \right)^2 dx \tag{5–6}$$

The kinetic energy of the beam is

$$T = \tfrac{1}{2} \int_0^l m(y\omega)^2 \, dx \tag{5–7}$$

[1] John William Strutt, Lord Rayleigh, *Theory of Sound* (New York: Dover Publications, 1945).

where m is the mass per unit length and ω is the circular frequency of the vibration.

Eqs. (5–6) and (5–7) are the maximum potential and kinetic energy respectively of the beam.

Equating Eqs. (5–6) and (5–7) yields the following relationship:

$$EI \int_0^l \left(\frac{d^2y}{dx^2}\right)^2 dx = m\omega^2 \int_0^l y^2 \, dx \tag{5–8}$$

and

$$\omega^2 = \frac{EI}{m} \frac{\displaystyle\int_0^l \left(\frac{d^2y}{dx^2}\right)^2 dx}{\displaystyle\int_0^l y^2 \, dx} \tag{5–9}$$

Eq. (5–9) yields the fundamental frequency of the vibration if the exact deflection y is known. Rayleigh proposed that a reasonable deflection curve be assumed. For an error of 10 percent in the assumed deflection curve, the error in the fundamental frequency will be $\sqrt{10}$ percent. If, of course, the exact deflection curve is assumed, then the results from Eq. (5–9) will be exact.

Example. Determine the fundamental frequency of a cantilever beam loaded only by its own weight by assuming a reasonable deflection curve.

SOLUTION. First we sketch the cantilever beam in its deflected position, Fig. 5–4. This sketch suggests that a cosine curve may fit this deflection. We take, then, as the equation of the deflection

$$y = y_0 \left(1 - \cos\frac{\pi x}{2l}\right) \tag{a}$$

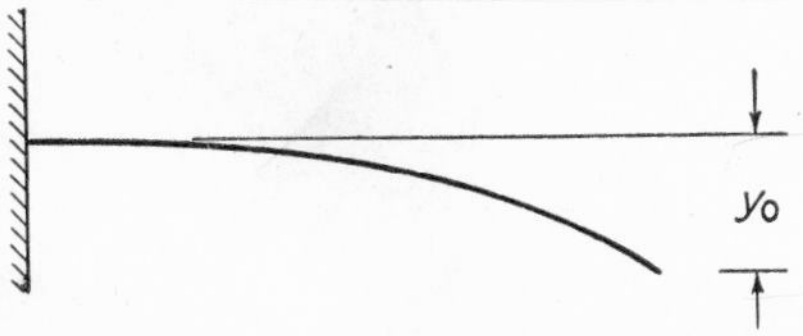

FIG. 5–4.

We check the end condition of the beam and find that at $x = 0$, $y = 0$, and at $x = l$, $y = y_0$, which agrees with the end conditions as depicted in Fig. 5–4. Then

$$\frac{d^2y}{dx^2} = y_0 \frac{\pi^2}{4l^2} \cos\frac{\pi x}{2l} \tag{b}$$

We can now check our boundary conditions for the moments. From equation (b), we see that the moment at $x = 0$ equals a constant and at $x = l$ equals zero. The moment for the right-hand end of the beam is correct. We do not know, however, the exact value of the moment at $x = 0$, but we are probably not too far off, since three of the four boundary conditions are satisfied. Substituting equations (a) and (b) into Eq. (5-9), we get

$$\omega^2 = \frac{EI}{m} \frac{\int_0^l \left(y_0 \frac{\pi^2}{4l^2} \cos \frac{\pi x}{2l} \right)^2 dx}{\int_0^l \left(y_0 \left\{ 1 - \cos \frac{\pi x}{2l} \right\} \right)^2 dx}$$

Now

$$\int_0^l \cos^2 \frac{\pi x}{2l} = \left| \frac{x}{2} + \frac{2l}{\pi} \sin \frac{\pi x}{l} \right|_0^l = \frac{l}{2}$$

and

$$\int_0^l \left(1 - \cos \frac{\pi x}{2l} \right)^2 = \left| x - \frac{4l}{\pi} \sin \frac{\pi x}{2l} + \frac{x}{2} + \frac{2l}{\pi} \sin \frac{\pi x}{l} \right|_0^l = \left(\frac{6}{4} - \frac{4}{\pi} \right) l$$

Then

$$\omega^2 = \frac{EI}{m} \frac{y_0{}^2 \frac{\pi^4}{16l^4} \cdot \frac{l}{2}}{y_0{}^2 \left(\frac{6}{4} - \frac{4}{\pi} \right) l} = \frac{EI}{ml^4} \cdot \frac{\pi^4}{16 \left(3 - \frac{8}{\pi} \right)}$$

$$\omega = \frac{\pi^2}{4 \sqrt{3 - \frac{8}{\pi}}} \sqrt{\frac{EI}{ml^4}} = 3.66 \sqrt{\frac{EI}{ml^4}}$$

The exact solution for the fundamental of a cantilever beam is 3.52 times the quantity under the radical. The error is slightly less than 4.0 percent of the correct solution. We should note that the frequency obtained by the assumed deflection is higher than the exact solution. This condition will always be true. The exact solution will represent a minimum of constraint. The above statement can be proved, but it is beyond the scope of this text to establish proof that the exact frequency will be the lowest obtainable.

Another approach to selecting a deflection curve to be applied to the Rayleigh method is to assume that the dynamic deflection curve is proportional to the static deflection curve. That is:

$$y = A y_{\text{static}} \tag{5-10}$$

Then, upon substituting Eq. (5–10) and its derivatives into Eq. (5–9), we get

$$\omega^2 = \frac{EI}{m} \frac{\int_0^l A^2 \left(\frac{d^2 y_{static}}{dx^2}\right)^2 dx}{\int_0^l A^2 y^2_{static}\, dx} \tag{5–11}$$

Since the proportionality constant A vanishes from Eq. (5–11), we get

$$\omega^2 = \frac{EI}{m} \frac{\int_0^l \left(\frac{d^2 y_{static}}{dx^2}\right)^2 dx}{\int_0^l y^2_{static}\, dx} \tag{5–12}$$

Eq. (5–12) may be used in place of Eq. (5–9) when the static deflection curve is used instead of an assumed dynamic deflection curve.

Example. Determine the fundamental frequency of a cantilever beam with constant cross-section by assuming that the dynamic deflection curve is proportional to the static deflection curve.

SOLUTION. The static deflection curve of a cantilever beam loaded by its own weight is

$$y = \frac{qx^2}{24EI} (x^2 + 6l^2 - 4lx)$$

where q is the weight per unit length of the beam. Hence,

$$\frac{d^2 y}{dx^2} = \frac{q}{EI} \left(\frac{x^2}{2} + \frac{l^2}{2} - lx\right)$$

then

$$\omega^2 = \frac{EI}{m} \frac{\int_0^l \left(\frac{q}{EI}\right)^2 \left(\frac{x^2}{2} + \frac{l^2}{2} - lx\right)^2 dx}{\int_0^l \left(\frac{qx^2}{24EI}\right)^2 (x^2 + 6l^2 - 4lx)^2\, dx}$$

$$\omega^2 = \frac{EI}{m} \cdot \frac{\dfrac{l^5}{20}}{\dfrac{1}{576} \times \dfrac{104 l^9}{45}} = 12.46 \frac{EI}{ml^4}$$

$$\omega = 3.53 \sqrt{\frac{EI}{ml^4}}$$

In the above example, we find that the static deflection curve is nearly proportional to the actual dynamic deflection curve, since the above solution is nearly equal to the exact solution.

The Rayleigh method is quite a powerful tool for determining an approximate answer for the fundamental natural frequency. Theoretically, there is nothing to prevent the use of the Rayleigh method in determining the higher frequencies. There is, however, a severe limitation placed upon this method for the higher frequencies. We have to assume a fairly reasonable deflection curve, and in order to do so, the nodal points of the higher modes of vibration have to be known with good accuracy. The exact positions of the nodal points are quite difficult to predict. We will therefore apply the Rayleigh method to the fundamental frequency only.

5–4. Beam with Concentrated Loads. Upon occasion it is necessary to determine the natural frequency of a uniform cross-section beam or shaft which is loaded with several concentrated loads. This type of loading may represent several gears or pulleys upon a shaft. In actuality, the load due to a gear or pulley is not concentrated. However, if the shaft be relatively long compared to the length of the gear or pulley hub, the representation of the load by a concentrated one is a good approximation.

If the loads are relatively large when compared to the weight of the shaft, we can afford to neglect the weight of the shaft. Rephrasing, we can say that if the deflections of the shaft caused by the concentrated loads are large compared to the deflections caused by the weight of the shaft itself, then the weight of the shaft may be neglected. However, if the above is not the case, then the weight of the shaft may be represented by several concentrated loads so distributed that the deflection caused by these concentrated loads is very nearly equal to the deflections caused by the weight of the shaft.

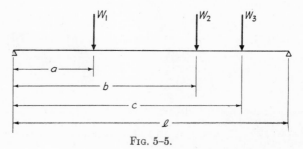

FIG. 5–5.

Let us now consider a simply supported shaft or beam of uniform cross-section upon which have been placed three concentrated loads as depicted in Fig. 5–5. The shaft, being an elastic member, will serve as a spring with respect to the loads. As a result of the elasticity, the deflections due to the load will be reflected in strain or potential energy. The maximum potential energy will be one-half the sum of the individual loads times their respective deflections. That is:

$$V_{\max} = \tfrac{1}{2}(W_1 y_1 + W_2 y_2 + W_3 y_3) \qquad (5\text{–}13)$$

where y_1, y_2, and y_3 are the deflections under the loads W_1, W_2, and W_3, respectively.

Inasmuch as the loads cause dynamic deflections, the system will also possess kinetic energy. The total maximum kinetic energy will be

$$T_{\max} = \frac{\omega^2}{2g}(W_1 y_1{}^2 + W_2 y_2{}^2 + W_3 y_3{}^2) \qquad (5\text{–}14)$$

Since we are dealing with a conservative system, we can equate the maximum potential energy to the maximum kinetic energy. In so doing we will get an equation involving the frequency of the shaft, ω. Then

$$\omega^2 = \frac{g(W_1 y_1 + W_2 y_2 + W_3 y_3)}{(W_1 y_1{}^2 + W_2 y_2{}^2 + W_3 y_3{}^2)} \qquad (5\text{–}15)$$

If the deflections are known we can proceed to determine the first approximate natural frequency of the above system from Eq. (5–15). It is a small step to generalize the above equation to cover the case of any number of concentrated loads. To generalize Eq. (5–15), we need only write:

$$\omega^2 = \frac{g \sum\limits_{i=1}^{n} W_i y_i}{\sum\limits_{i=1}^{n} W_i y_i{}^2} \qquad (5\text{–}16)$$

where

$$i = 1, 2, 3, \cdots n$$

Example. A solid steel shaft of uniform diameter of 2 in. is simply supported. The shaft, in turn, supports two concentrated loads as shown in the sketch of Fig. 5–6. Determine the approximate first natural frequency of the system.

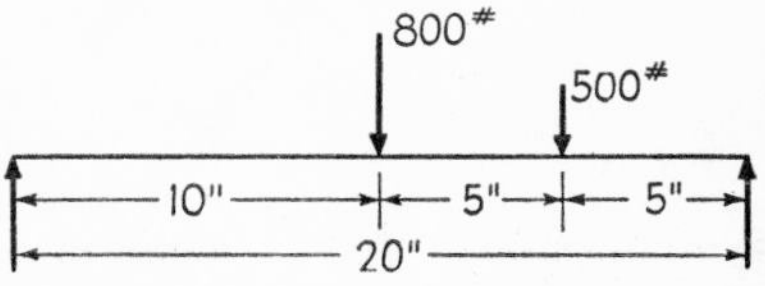

FIG. 5–6.

SOLUTION. Let us denote the position of the 800-lb. applied load by 1, and the position of the 500-lb. by 2. Then the deflection at position 1 will consist of two parts:

(1) y_{11}; the deflection at point 1 due to load 1 (800 lbs.); (2) y_{12}; the deflection at point 1 due to load 2 (500 lbs.).

Then

$$y_1 = y_{11} + y_{12}$$

In like manner

$$y_2 = y_{21} + y_{22}$$

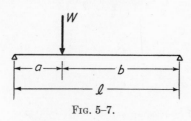

Fig. 5–7.

The static deflection equation of a simply supported beam with a single concentrated load, as sketched in Fig. 5–7, is:

$$y = \frac{Wbx}{6EIl}(l^2 - x^2 - b^2) \qquad 0 \le x \le a$$

Then

$$y_{11} = \frac{800 \times 10 \times 10}{6EI \times 20}(\overline{20}^2 - \overline{10}^2 - \overline{10}^2) = \frac{400 \times 10^3}{3EI}$$

$$y_{12} = \frac{500 \times 5 \times 10}{6EI \times 20}(\overline{20}^2 - \overline{10}^2 - \overline{5}^2) = \frac{137 \times 10^3}{6EI}$$

$$y_1 = y_{11} + y_{12} = \frac{156.2 \times 10^3}{EI}$$

By interchanging a and b we find

$$y_{21} = \frac{800 \times 10 \times 5}{6EI \times 20}(\overline{20}^2 - \overline{5}^2 - \overline{10}^2) = \frac{275 \times 10^3}{3EI}$$

$$y_{22} = \frac{500 \times 5 \times 15}{6EI \times 20}(\overline{20}^2 - \overline{15}^2 - \overline{5}^2) = \frac{46.9 \times 10^3}{EI}$$

$$y_2 = y_{21} + y_{22} = \frac{138.5 \times 10^3}{EI}$$

We now substitute the values of y_1 and y_2 into Eq. (5–16). We get

$$\omega^2 = \frac{386\left(800\,\frac{156.2 \times 10^3}{EI} + 500\,\frac{138.5 \times 10^3}{EI}\right)}{800\left(\frac{156.2 \times 10^3}{EI}\right)^2 + 500\left(\frac{138.5 \times 10^3}{EI}\right)^2}$$

$$\omega^2 = 2.576EI \times 10^{-3}$$

Now

$$EI = 30 \times 10^6 \times \frac{\pi}{4} \times 1^4 = 23.56 \times 10^6$$

then

$$\omega^2 = 2.576 \times 23.56 \times 10^3 = 6.910 \times 10^4$$

and

$$\omega = 263 \text{ radians/sec.},$$

$$f = 2520 \text{ cycles/min.}$$

5–5. Graphical Solution of Nonuniform Cross-Section Beams. In Section 5–4, the restriction placed on the beam was that it had to be of uniform cross-section. This restriction, however, does not apply to the validity of Eq. (5–16). Only the method for determining the deflection under loads is subject to the above restriction. For beams or shafts of nonuniform cross-section, we usually determine the deflections by means of a graphical method.

Let us review the fundamental relationships which are a consequence of the beam theory. For the case of a constant cross-section beam, when we define $y = f(x)$, we get

$$\frac{dy}{dx} = \theta \qquad \text{slope relationship}$$

$$-\frac{d^2y}{dx^2} = \frac{M}{EI} \qquad \text{moment relationship}$$

$$-\frac{d^3y}{dx^3} = \frac{V}{EI} \qquad \text{shear relationship} \tag{5–17}$$

$$\frac{d^4y}{dx^4} = \frac{q}{EI} \qquad \text{load relationship}$$

Note: When the cross-section of the beam is not uniform, then

$$-\frac{d}{dx}\left(EI(x)\frac{d^2y}{dx^2}\right) = V$$

and

$$\frac{d^2}{dx^2}\left(EI(x)\frac{d^2y}{dx^2}\right) = q \tag{5–18}$$

We can see from the beam theory equations that the relationship between the load and the deflection is a quadruple integral. When we graphically integrate the load diagram four times, the result will be the deflection curve, if we have judiciously selected the proper constants.

We can eliminate two of the integrations by merely drawing the moment diagram, for the relationship between the load and the moment diagram is that of a double integral. The moment diagram can be determined by finding the reactions at the beam supports and then calculating the moments at various critical positions on the beam. Another method, used in some text books, is to determine the moment diagram with the aid of a funicular polygon.[2] The former of these two methods will be used in this text because of its straightforward simplicity.

The next step after the moment diagram has been determined is to modify the diagram by dividing the ordinate by I or EI. This modified moment diagram will represent the M/I or M/EI for a beam of variable cross-section if I is a known function of x. As a matter of fact, if I is a constant, the graphical solution method is still valid. Now all that remains is to integrate the modified diagram twice. The result of the second integration will be the deflection curve or E times the deflection curve, depending upon whether the modified moment diagram was obtained by dividing by EI or I.

Once the deflection curve has been obtained, we measure the deflections under the loads and insert their value in Eq. (5–16), thereby determining the approximate fundamental natural frequency of the beam or shaft. The accuracy obtained will be dependent upon the number of segments into which the beam has been divided. The greater the number of the divisions, the greater will be the accuracy, for the resultant deflection curve consists of straight lines which only approximate the smooth deflection curve.

The graphical method allows for the weight of the beam itself to be taken into account in determining the deflection. However, if the loads are very large compared with the weight of the beam, we can neglect the weight of the beam without incurring too great an error.

Fig. 5–8 is a graphical solution of a stepped shaft loaded as shown. The following is a step-by-step account of the procedure.

1. Lay out the beam to scale. In our case the scale is 3 in. = 12 in., giving us a scale factor of $S_1 = 4$. The diameters of the shaft do not necessarily have to be to scale, since they take no part in the graphical construction.

2. Determine the reactions:

$$R_1 = \frac{500 \times 10 + 300 \times 6}{18} = 378 \text{ lbs.}$$

$$R_2 = \frac{500 \times 8 + 300 \times 12}{18} = 422 \text{ lbs.}$$

[2] Fred B. Seely and Newton E. Ensign, *Analytic Mechanics for Engineers* (3d ed.; New York: John Wiley & Sons, Inc., 1941).

Having found the reactions, we can determine the moments. The moments at the ends of the shaft are zero, since the shaft is simply supported. There will be two points where the slope of the diagram changes; these occur at the points of load application. The moments at these points are

$$M_{500} = 3024 \text{ in.-lbs.}$$

$$M_{300} = 2432 \text{ in.-lbs.}$$

For convenience, we let 1 in. of the moment ordinate equal 2000 in.-lbs. or $S_2 = 2000$. The moment diagram is then laid out to scale.

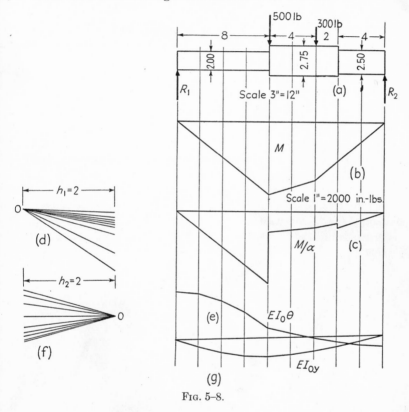

Fig. 5–8.

3. Our task is now to modify the moment diagram. Since E is a constant, we neglect it for the time being. Instead of dividing the moment diagram by I, which may be a large number, let us divide the moment diagram by a number α_i, defined below. Let the moment of inertia of the smallest diameter section of the shaft be denoted by I_0. Then the ratio of I of any other section to I_0 will be α_i, that is,

$$\frac{I_i}{I_0} = \alpha_i \tag{5-19}$$

Then $I_1/I_0 = \alpha_1$ and $I_2/I_0 = \alpha_2$, where I_1 is the I of the 2.75-in. diameter section and I_2 is the I of the 2.50-in. diameter section. Since the moments of inertia are proportional to the fourth power of the diameters, then

$$\alpha_1 = \frac{d_1{}^4}{d_0{}^4} \qquad \text{and} \qquad \alpha_2 = \frac{d_2{}^4}{d_0{}^4}$$

Wherever there is a change of section or an applied load, the ordinate at this change of section or applied load is divided by the proper α_i. This division results in the diagram shown in Fig. 5–8c. The scale of the ordinates is still 2000 in.-lbs./in.

4. The shaft is now divided into sections sufficiently numerous so that the integrations will be reasonably accurate. In our example, intervals of 2 in. have been selected. Had the shaft been a longer one, then larger intervals would have been taken. We now project the mid-point of each section horizontally onto a vertical line. These projections are then connected to the pole O, which is placed on the horizontal extension of the base line of the M/α diagram. The distance h, from the vertical line to the pole, is arbitrarily selected; in our case, $h_1 = 2$ in. We now connect point 1 with the pole O and then draw a line parallel to O–1 across the first section of the shaft. We repeat this process for point 2, but draw the line parallel to O–2, intersecting the second section but contiguous to the point on O–1 which is on the boundary line to both sections. We repeat this process until the $EI_0\theta$ curve, Fig. 5–8e, is completed. The scale factor of $EI_0\theta$ is now

$$S_\theta = S_1 S_2 h_1$$

$$S_\theta = 4 \times 2000 \times 2 = 16 \times 10^3$$

This scale factor is of little importance at this point. However, should we desire to determine the slope at any point, it will be the vertical distance from a line (not drawn) connecting the two extremities of the slope diagram to the point in question. After measuring this distance we multiply its value by S_θ and divide by EI_0 to determine the angle. The S_θ factor, however, should be calculated, since it will be used to determine the scale factor for the deflections.

5. The integration process is again repeated. This time, however, we may select the pole O in any arbitrary position. This selection of the pole is shown in Fig. 5–8f. The resulting deflection curve is shown in Fig. 5–8g. The deflections at loads 500 and 300 respectively measure along the vertical between the point and the base line 0.41 in. and 0.32 in. The scale factor is now

$$S_y = S_1 S_\theta h_2 = 4 \times 16 \times 10^3 \times 2 = 128 \times 10^3$$

Then

$$EI_0 y_{500} = 0.41 \times 128 \times 10^3 = 52.5 \times 10^3$$

$$EI_0 y_{300} = 0.32 \times 128 \times 10^3 = 41.0 \times 10^3$$

Now

$$EI_0 = 30 \times 10^6 \times \frac{\pi (1)^4}{4} = 23.6 \times 10^6$$

Then

$$y_{500} = \frac{52.5 \times 10^3}{23.6 \times 10^6} = 2.22 \times 10^{-3}$$

and

$$y_{300} = \frac{41.0 \times 10^3}{23.6 \times 10^6} = 1.74 \times 10^{-3}$$

The deflections are now inserted into Eq. (5–16) and as a result

$$\omega^2 = \frac{386(500 \times 2.22 + 300 \times 1.74)10^{-3}}{(500 \times \overline{2.22}^2 + 300 \times \overline{1.74}^2)10^{-6}}$$

$$\omega^2 = 18.7 \times 10^4$$

$$\omega = 432 \text{ radians/sec.}$$

$$f = 4130 \text{ cycles/min.}$$

The approximate first natural frequency of the loaded shaft is 4130 cycles/min.

The graphical method is equally applicable to rotors. A rotor may be reduced to its equivalence in stepped shaft parameters. Several shafts or rotors which are coupled together, such as turbine and generator rotors, may be analyzed by the graphical method. The difficulty that arises for the coupled-rotor system is that we are usually dealing with a statically indeterminate system, and methods other than elementary ones have to be used to determine the reactions. If the coupling used is the type that does not transmit a bending moment, each of the rotors is dealt with separately and no difficulty should be experienced.

5–6. Crankshafts. The crankshaft is a troublesome member of the shaft family. The crankshaft is not a separate entity; there are appendages such as pistons and connecting rods which have inertia effects upon the shaft. An exact straightforward analysis of the crankshaft problem has not as yet been found to be feasible. Our approach to this problem, therefore, shall be through an attempt to create an equivalent system of discs and shafts which will give us a reasonable approximation to the correct answer.

The crankshaft problem is inherent in prime movers such as diesel and gasoline engines. Though other pieces of machinery such as the pump and the compressor may also have crankshafts, we shall devote our analysis to the internal combustion engine. Our discussions, however, will not be limited to the internal combustion engine; they will apply to any other piece of machinery which has a crankshaft. The problem at hand is mainly to reduce the rotating and reciprocating parts of an engine to a system simple enough to respond to analysis within the framework of the tools we have at hand: namely, discs and straight shafts. In reducing an engine to an equivalent system, we have to resort to approximations. These approximations, whether based upon theory or empirical data, can give fair results if we do not try to push them too far.

Let us center our attention upon an internal combustion engine. The main rotating element is the crankshaft. Here we meet with no great difficulty, for we can with fair accuracy determine its mass moment of inertia about the axis of rotation. The connecting rod, however, is not quite so simple, for one end of the connecting rod which is attached to the shaft is moving in pure rotation while the other end, connected to the piston, is enjoying a reciprocating motion. The piston, of course, also has a reciprocating motion. Basically, our problem is to determine the moment of inertia of a single disc which will be equivalent or nearly so to the three elements mentioned above: the crankshaft, the connecting rod, and the piston.

Let us start with the crankshaft. Fig. 5–9 shows that part of a crankshaft which is apportioned to a cylinder of an engine. To determine the moment of inertia, we break the crankshaft into parts.

1. Journals:

$$I = \frac{mr^2}{2} = \frac{A\gamma\pi D_1{}^4}{32g} \quad \text{lb.-in.-sec.}^2 \tag{5–20}$$

where γ = specific weight; lbs./in.^{3}

2. Crankpin:

$$I_{CR} = I + mR^2 = \frac{B\pi D_2{}^2\gamma}{4g}\left[\frac{D_2{}^2}{8} + R^2\right] \tag{5–21}$$

3. Crank Webs:

$$I_{CR} = I + m\left(\frac{R}{2}\right)^2 = \frac{THW\gamma}{g}\left[\frac{H^2 + W^2}{12} + \left(\frac{R}{2}\right)^2\right]$$

$$I_{CR} = \frac{THW\gamma}{4g}\left[\frac{H^2 + W^2}{3} + R^2\right] \tag{5–22}$$

The total moment of inertia of the crankshaft section is

$$I_{\text{shaft}} = \frac{A\gamma\pi D_1^{4}}{32g} + \frac{\pi BD_2^{2}\gamma}{4g}\left[\frac{D_2^{2}}{8} + R^2\right] + \frac{THW\gamma}{4g}\left[\frac{H^2 + W^2}{3} + R^2\right]$$

$$I_{\text{shaft}} = \frac{\pi\gamma}{4g}\left[\frac{AD_1^{4}}{8} + BD_2^{2}\left(\frac{D_2^{2}}{8} + R^2\right) + \frac{THW}{\pi}\left(\frac{H^2 + W^2}{3} + R^2\right)\right]$$

$$(5\text{–}23)$$

Fig. 5–9 is a simplification of an actual crankshaft. Actually, there would be counterbalances attached to the crank, the moment of inertia of which would have to be added to I_{shaft}. The crank webs, in actuality, are not simple blocks, as depicted, but are usually of a shape that does not allow its moment of inertia to be readily calculated. In such circumstances, we resort to a graphical method of determining the moment of inertia. Such a method is described by W. Ker Wilson.[3]

We now consider the problem of the connecting rod. The procedure is to apportion part of the weight to the rotating mass—that is, to the crank —and part of the weight to the reciprocating mass—that is, to the piston assembly. According to Wilson[4] we may assign three-fifths to two-thirds of the weight to the rotating mass and the balance to the reciprocating mass. The apportionment may be determined with a bit more accuracy by determining the weight reaction at each end. If the center of gravity of the connecting rod is known, we may determine the weight reaction at each end by means of statical considerations. Fig. 5–10 represents a connecting rod whose total weight and center of gravity are known. By elementary static we know that

$$W_1 + W_2 = W$$

$$W_1 = \frac{Wb}{L}$$

$$W_2 = \frac{Wa}{L} \qquad (5\text{–}24)$$

The portion of the weight we assign to the crank is W_1 and that to the piston assembly is W_2.

The above analysis is only an approximate one. We have attempted to determine a problem in dynamics by means of a statical approach. Only when one of the reactive weights acts at the center of percussion is the static solution correct. The method described above, however, does yield fairly good results. At this point we will not try to evaluate the inertia

[3] W. Ker Wilson, *Practical Solution of Torsional Vibration Problems* (3d ed.; London: Chapman & Hall, 1956).
[4] *Ibid.*

effects of the connecting rod as a separate entity. It will be more convenient to combine the effects of the rod with the piston assembly. Since the piston assembly is solely in reciprocating motion and an equivalent

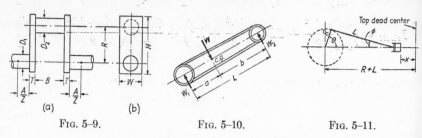

FIG. 5–9.   FIG. 5–10.   FIG. 5–11.

system will be in rotary motion, the common factor will have to be the kinetic energy. That is, the kinetic energy of the two systems will have to be equal. Consider the sketch of a piston, Fig. 5–11. We will first determine the equation for the displacement of the piston and subsequently determine the velocity.

Let x be the displacement of the piston with reference to the top dead center of the crank. At any time t,

$$x = L + R - L \cos \phi - R \cos \theta \tag{5-25}$$

From the geometric configuration, we see that

$$L \sin \phi = R \sin \theta$$

and

$$\cos \phi = \sqrt{1 - \left(\frac{R}{L}\right)^2 \sin^2 \theta} \tag{5-26}$$

Substituting, we get

$$x = L + R - L \sqrt{1 - \left(\frac{R}{L}\right)^2 \sin^2 \theta} - R \cos \theta$$

$$x = L \left(1 - \sqrt{1 - \left(\frac{R}{L}\right)^2 \sin^2 \theta}\right) + R(1 - \cos \theta) \tag{5-27}$$

Eq. (5–27) is an exact expression of the displacement with respect to θ, the crank angle. By substituting

$$\theta = \omega t \tag{5-28}$$

we get an exact expression of displacement with respect to time.

In order to simplify Eq. (5–27), let us expand $\sqrt{1 - (R/L)^2 \sin^2 \theta}$ by means of the binomial theorem, which results in

$$\sqrt{1 - \left(\frac{R}{L}\right)^2 \sin^2 \theta} = 1 - \frac{1}{2}\left(\frac{R}{L}\right)^2 \sin^2 \theta + \frac{\frac{1}{2}(-\frac{1}{2})}{2!}\left(\frac{R}{L}\right)^4 \sin^4 \theta + \cdots \tag{5-29}$$

Our first approximation will be to take only the first two terms of the expansion. We can see that the third is always small since R/L is less than one. Substituting the above, we now have for the displacement

$$x \doteq L\left[1 - 1 + \frac{1}{2}\left(\frac{R}{L}\right)^2 \sin^2\theta\right] + R(1 - \cos\theta)$$

or
(5-30)

$$x \doteq R\left[1 - \cos\theta + \frac{1}{2}\frac{R}{L}\sin^2\theta\right]$$

Substituting Eq. (5-28) into Eq. (5-30), we get the displacement with respect to time,

$$x \doteq R\left[1 - \cos\omega t + \frac{1}{2}\frac{R}{L}\sin^2\omega t\right] \tag{5-31}$$

The velocity is now determined by differentiating Eq. (5-31) with respect to time.

$$\dot{x} \doteq R\omega\left[\sin\omega t + \frac{1}{2}\frac{R}{L}\sin 2\omega t\right]$$

or

$$\dot{x} \doteq R\omega\left[\sin\theta + \frac{1}{2}\frac{R}{L}\sin 2\theta\right] \tag{5-32}$$

We are now in a position to write the kinetic energy of the piston.

$$T = \tfrac{1}{2}mv^2 \doteq \tfrac{1}{2}mR^2\omega^2\left[\sin\theta + \frac{1}{2}\frac{R}{L}\sin 2\theta\right]^2 \tag{5-33}$$

Since we are to replace the piston by an inertia disc, then

$$T \doteq \frac{I_e\omega^2}{2} \tag{5-34}$$

Equating Eq. (5-33) to Eq. (5-34), we find that

$$I_e \doteq mR^2\left[\sin\theta + \frac{R}{L}\sin 2\theta\right]^2 \tag{5-35}$$

We see that the equivalent moment of inertia is a function of the crank angle and therefore is a variable with the position of the crank. This variability does not suit our purpose. We therefore determine the average value for the inertia disc as the crank angle rotates from 0 to 2π radians. We need only integrate Eq. (5-35) and divide the result by the interval 2π to obtain the average.

$$I_{e\,\text{av}} \doteq \frac{mR^2}{2\pi}\left[\int_0^{2\pi}\sin^2\theta\,d\theta + \frac{R}{L}\int_0^{2\pi}\sin\theta\sin 2\theta\,d\theta + \frac{1}{4}\frac{R^2}{L^2}\int_0^{2\pi}\sin^2 2\theta\,d\theta\right]$$

(5-36)

$$I_{e\,\text{av}} \doteq mR^2 \left[\frac{1}{2} + \frac{1}{8}\left(\frac{R}{L}\right)^2 \right] \tag{5-37}$$

Since L must be greater than R, it is customary to neglect the second term of Eq. (5–37). With the above approximation in mind, we can say that the equivalent moment of inertia of a piston is approximately equal to one-half the mass of the piston times the square of the crank radius, or

$$I_e \doteq \frac{mR^2}{2} \tag{5-38}$$

It is convenient to combine the connecting rod with the piston assembly so that a single inertia disc will represent both elements. We may state this combination mathematically as

$$I_e \doteq [M_{\text{rot}} + \tfrac{1}{2}M_{\text{rec}}]R^2 \tag{5-39}$$

where M_{rot} is the rotating mass, that is, W_1/g, and M_{rec} is the reciprocating mass, that is, $W_2 + W_p$.
Then

$$I_e \doteq \left[\frac{W_1}{g} + \frac{W_2 + W_p}{2g} \right] R^2 \tag{5-40}$$

We may now combine Eqs. (5–23) and (5–40) to represent the inertia disc which will be equivalent to the crankshaft, connecting rod, and piston assembly for a single cylinder. This combination gives us

$$I_{\text{total}} \doteq \frac{\pi\gamma}{4g} \left[\frac{A D_1{}^4}{8} + B D_2{}^2 \left(\frac{D_2{}^2}{8} + R^2 \right) + \frac{THW}{\pi} \left(\frac{H^2 + W^2}{3} + R^2 \right) \right]$$
$$+ \left[W_1 + \frac{W_2 + W_p}{2} \right] \frac{R^2}{g} \tag{5-41}$$

Having converted the mass effects of the system into equivalent (approximate) inertia discs, our next task is to design an equivalent elastic system which will take the form of straight shafts. Analytical expressions for the elasticity of the crankshaft have been worked out by both W. Ker Wilson[5] and S. Timoshenko.[6] In both the analytical expressions, however, approximations have been made: use of these expressions may under certain circumstances lead to errors of a magnitude which we cannot tolerate. These errors are in part due to the fact that twist may accompany the bending in the webs. We can add to these errors the fillet effects at the webs, although they are not included in the analysis. With these and other complications, such as the clearance at the bearings, an exact mathematical solution of the elastic constants is not possible. B. C. Carter[7]

[5] *Ibid.*

[6] S. Timoshenko, *Vibration Problems in Engineering* (3d ed.; Princeton, N. J.: D. Van Nostrand Co., 1955).

[7] B. C. Carter, "An Empirical Formula for Crankshaft Stiffness," *Engineering*, July 13, 1928.

proposed a relatively simple empirical formula which seems satisfactorily to represent the elasticity of the crankshaft. Carter's formula for solid journals and crankpins is

$$L_e = D^4 \left[\frac{A + 0.8T}{D_1{}^4} + \frac{0.75B}{D_2{}^4} + \frac{1.5R}{TW^3} \right] \qquad (5\text{–}42)$$

where D is the diameter of an equivalent shaft and A, D_1, D_2, T, W, and R are defined by Fig. 5–9. If we substitute Eq. (5–42) into Eq. (3–21), the spring constant becomes

$$k_t = \frac{\pi G}{32} \left[\frac{1}{\dfrac{A + 0.8T}{D_1{}^4} + \dfrac{0.75B}{D_2{}^4} + \dfrac{1.5R}{TW^3}} \right] \qquad (5\text{–}43)$$

Carter's equation is fairly reliable for determining the over-all stiffness of the crankshaft. If we try breaking up Carter's formula into individual parts, such as the webs, crankpins, etc., each part will not be truly represented by the formula. This limitation does not affect us, since we will determine only the stiffness of the crankshaft as a whole (or at least that portion which is attributable to a single cylinder).

Example. Determine the equivalent system for a four-cylinder engine whose component parts are detailed below:

> Piston weight = 20 lbs.
> Connecting rod:
>   length = 11 in.
>   c.g. from crank end = 4 in.
>   weight = 2 lbs.
> Crankshaft dimensions as sketched in Fig. 5–12.
> Flywheel = 8 in. diam. × 2 in. width.

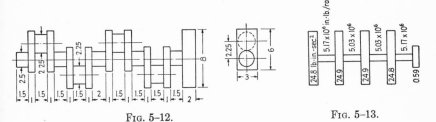

FIG. 5–12. FIG. 5–13.

SOLUTION. First we determine the weights to be assigned to the rotating and reciprocating masses. From Fig. 5–10 we see that

$$W_1 = \frac{2 \times 7}{11} = 1.27 \text{ lbs.}$$

and

$$W_2 = 0.73 \text{ lb.}$$

We repeat Eq. (5–41) for convenience in determining the equivalent inertia for each cylinder assembly.

$$I_e = \frac{\pi\gamma}{4g}\left[\frac{AD_1^4}{8} + BD_2^2\left(\frac{D_2^2}{8} + R^2\right) + \frac{THW}{\pi}\left(\frac{H^2 + W^2}{3} + R^2\right)\right]$$
$$+ \left[W_1 + \frac{W_2 + W_p}{2}\right]\frac{R^2}{g} \qquad (5\text{–}41)$$

Cylinder No. 1:

$$I_1 = \frac{\pi \times 0.283}{4 \times 386}\left[\frac{1.5(2.5)^4}{8} + 1.5(2.25)^2\left(\frac{\overline{2.25}^2}{8} + \overline{2.25}^2\right)\right.$$
$$\left. + \frac{(1)(6)(3)}{\pi}\left(\frac{3^2 + 6^2}{3} + \overline{2.25}^2\right)\right] + \left[1.27 + \frac{0.73 + 20.0}{2}\right]\frac{\overline{2.25}^2}{386}$$

$$I_1 = 24.8 \text{ lbs.-in.-sec.}^2$$

Cylinder No. 2:

$$I_2 = \frac{\pi \times 0.283}{4 \times 386}\left[\frac{\left(\frac{1.5}{2} + \frac{2}{2}\right)(2.5)^4}{8} + 1.5(2.25)^2\left(\frac{\overline{2.25}^2}{8} + \overline{2.25}^2\right)\right.$$
$$\left. + \frac{(1)(6)(3)}{\pi}\left(\frac{3^2 + 6^2}{3} + \overline{2.25}^2\right)\right] + \left[1.27 + \frac{0.73 + 20.0}{2}\right]\frac{\overline{2.25}^2}{386}$$

$$I_2 = 24.9 \text{ lbs.-in.-sec.}^2$$

Cylinder No. 3:

$$I_3 = I_2 = 24.9 \text{ lbs.-in.-sec.}^2$$

Cylinder No. 4:

$$I_4 = I_1 = 24.8 \text{ lbs.-in.-sec.}^2$$

Flywheel:

$$I_5 = \frac{Mr^2}{2} = \frac{\pi \times 4^2 \times 2 \times 0.283 \times 4^2}{2 \times 386}$$

$$I_5 = 59.0 \times 10^{-2} \text{ lbs.-in.-sec.}^2$$

The general equation for the equivalent springs is

$$k_t = \frac{\pi G}{32}\left[\frac{1}{\frac{A + 0.8T}{D_1^4} + \frac{0.75B}{D_2^4} + \frac{1.5R}{TW^3}}\right] \qquad (5\text{–}43)$$

Substituting into Eq. (5–43), we get

$$k_{t1} = \frac{\pi \times 12 \times 10^6}{32} \left[\frac{1}{\dfrac{1.5 + 0.8(1)}{(2.5)^4} + \dfrac{0.75 \times 1.5}{(2.25)^4} + \dfrac{1.5 \times 2.25}{1 \times 3^3}} \right]$$

$$k_{t1} = 5.17 \times 10^6, \text{ in.-lbs./radian}$$

$$k_{t2} = 5.03 \times 10^6, \text{ in.-lbs./radian}$$

$$k_{t3} = k_{t2} = 5.03 \times 10^6, \text{ in.-lbs./radian}$$

$$k_{t4} = k_{t1} = 5.17 \times 10^6, \text{ in.-lbs./radian}$$

This assumes that all of the crankshaft for cylinder No. 1 is effective. Fig. 5–13 is schematic of the equivalent system for the four-cylinder engine and flywheel.

5–7. Balancing. An outgrowth of the shaft problem is the consideration of shaft or rotor balance. It was seen in Section 5–2 that where an unbalance exists, the shaft and disc will whirl in a deflected configuration. The deflection is caused by the centrifugal force developed by the rotating of the unbalance of the disc. At the outset let us show that a static balancing does not necessarily put a system into dynamic balance. Consider the single disc in Fig. 5–14a. Here we have a static unbalance. We may

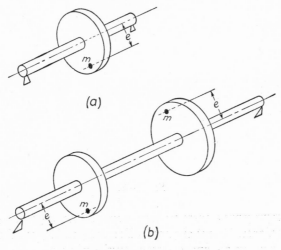

(a)

(b)

Fig. 5–14.

statically balance the single disc by an additional weight equal to the unbalance but opposite to the original eccentricity. By inspection we can see that the single disc will now not only be statically balanced but also be in dynamic balance. This dynamic balance is evident since the two centrifugal forces cancel each other. In fact, the balancing weight need not be equal to the unbalance: we merely need to place the balancing weight at a radial distance such that the centrifugal force developed will be equal to the centrifugal force of the unbalance.

When two discs are placed upon a shaft, Fig. 5–14b, the problem is not quite so simple. The arrangement of the unbalance in Fig. 5–14b is such that the system is statically balanced. Upon rotation, however, the system will be unbalanced since a bending moment is developed in the shaft. As a result of the bending moment, the shaft will rotate in a deflected configuration and whirling will result. The case of the two discs is therefore one of static balance and dynamic unbalance. We can easily balance the two-disc system by the same process employed in balancing the single disc. However, it is seldom convenient to balance a system in the planes in which the unbalances occur. In fact, in actual problems, the position and amounts of unbalance are not known, and therefore we shall try to show that any dynamically unbalanced system may be put into balance by correction in any two planes.

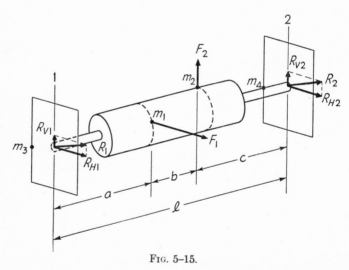

Fig. 5–15.

Fig. 5–15 represents a rotor with two unbalances, m_1 and m_2, which are conveniently placed 90° out of phase. Forces F_1 and F_2 are the centrifugal forces developed by m_1 and m_2 respectively when the rotor is operated at an angular speed ω. In general, we can write the equation for the centrifugal force as

$$\frac{W}{g}\omega^2 r = Wr\left(\frac{\omega^2}{g}\right) \qquad (5\text{–}44)$$

Since our analysis will be independent of the rotational speed we can consider the force F to be independent of ω^2/g. We may then say that

$$F = Wr \quad \text{oz.-in.} \tag{5-45}$$

It will be convenient to deal with F as defined by Eq. (5–45), for upon solution a known weight placed a certain number of inches from the center of rotation will effect our correction.

Let us now select any two convenient planes for balancing; in our case, we will select the planes at the bearing supports. From considerations of elementary statics, we find in the vertical direction that

$$\sum M_{V_2} = 0 = F_2 c - R_{V_1} l \tag{5-46}$$

Consequently

$$R_{V_1} = \frac{F_2 c}{l}$$

and $\qquad\qquad\qquad\qquad\qquad\qquad\qquad\qquad\qquad$ (5-47)

$$R_{V_2} = \frac{F_2(a + b)}{l}$$

R_{V_1} and R_{V_2} are equivalent unbalances, not reactions, due to the vertical unbalance. In a like manner, we find that the unbalances in the horizontal direction are

$$R_{H_1} = \frac{F_1(b + c)}{l}$$

and $\qquad\qquad\qquad\qquad\qquad\qquad\qquad\qquad\qquad$ (5-48)

$$R_{H_2} = \frac{F_1 a}{l}$$

The resultants of the vectors in planes 1 and 2 are the respective unbalances in planes 1 and 2. To correct the unbalances R_1 and R_2, we need only place weights diametrically opposite to the unbalances. The corrective weights must have oz.-in. values respectively equal to R_1 and R_2.

Example. Determine the necessary balancing corrections for the rotor in Fig. 5–15 if

$$F_1 = 8 \text{ oz.-in.}$$

$$F_2 = 10 \text{ oz.-in.}$$

$$a = 6 \text{ in.}$$

$$b = 8 \text{ in.}$$

$$c = 5 \text{ in.}$$

Solution.

$$R_{V_1} = \frac{F_2 c}{l} = \frac{10 \times 5}{19} = 2.63$$

$$R_{H_1} = \frac{F_1(b + c)}{l} = \frac{8 \times 13}{19} = 5.47$$

Then

$$R_1 = 6.07 \text{ oz.-in. acting } 25.6° \text{ clockwise from } R_{V_1}$$

$$R_{V_2} = \frac{F_2(a + b)}{l} = \frac{10 \times 14}{19} = 7.37$$

$$R_{H_2} = \frac{F_1 a}{l} = \frac{8 \times 6}{19} = 2.53$$

$$R_2 = 7.79 \text{ oz.-in. acting } 71.1° \text{ clockwise from } R_{V_2}$$

The proper oz.-in. values of R_1 and R_2 are placed in the correction planes in positions diametrically opposite to R_1 and R_2. The rotor is then in dynamic balance, and there will be no dynamic force acting on the bearings.

The unbalance in shafts or rotors, as they rotate about their principal axes of inertia, is due to lack of homogeneity of the metal and machining inaccuracies. The unbalance due to these random errors is not a predictable one. Therefore, the amount and position of the unbalance cannot be anticipated by the designer. Only by test can the amount of unbalance be determined. The prior discussion and calculations are purely academic. The discussion, however, does serve its purpose; the theory of balancing does give us an insight into the problem and lays a background for correcting unbalances by test.

There are two areas of balancing by test: (1) shop balancing for small shafts and rotors when the conditions of actual operation can be achieved in the shop; (2) field balancing for large rotors when the conditions of operation cannot be duplicated in the shop. The techniques of these two areas, though based upon the same theory, are distinctly different and require separate discussion.

Shop balancing, under modern methods of mass production, is usually performed upon some special type of machine designed for a particular type of product. Since there are a number of such machines in use, the reader will be best served by a discussion of a simple but basic type of balancing device. Such a balancing machine (Fig. 5–16), though crude, embodies the underlying principles of balancing common to all machines. The rotor is supported by bearings which in turn are attached to springs. The springs are so designed that each in turn may be rigidly locked so that spring action cannot take place. Balancing is done in any two convenient planes, (1) and (2). The procedure is first to lock spring a and then to rotate the rotor at resonant speed. A simple method for obtaining the necessary speed is to spin the rotor beyond its critical speed by means of compressed air blown over the rotor and then allow the rotor to slow down through its critical speed. Vibration measurements are made during the short period in which the rotor is trapped in the resonant zone. A high

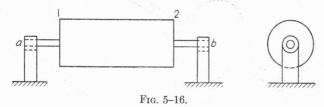

Fig. 5-16.

spot can be found in plane (2) by using chalk markings. By placing balancing wax or clay on the rotor at plane (2) opposite to the high spot, the vibrations can be eliminated. The process is repeated by freeing spring a and locking spring b, thereby balancing in plane (1). After balancing has been accomplished in both planes, the rotor may be checked with both springs unlocked. The wax or clay may be weighed and translated into weights to be added or removed for necessary balancing.

It is quite obvious that such a crude machine as described above would not be suitable for production balancing. A number of machines balance small rotors so nearly automatically that unskilled technicians may master the operation of a balancing machine in an extremely short period of time.

It is often inconvenient to balance a rotor in the shop. Such inconvenience may arise from the size, speed, thermal conditions of the rotor, etc. It is, therefore, necessary at times to balance a rotor in the field under operating conditions. E. L. Thearle[8] in 1934 presented a paper outlining in detail a procedure for field balancing of rotors. Thearle's method is still fundamental to the procedures used today. The following discussion is based upon Thearle's paper.

The problem is to balance a rotor while it is running at operating speed and conditions. We cannot improvise special mounts so that the vibrations in one plane are locked out while the vibrations in another plane are analyzed. We can, however, introduce known unbalances and then determine the effects of the original unbalance. Let us first consider a short rotor, Fig. 5-17, which is thin enough to be considered to be a disc rotating on a shaft. The disc is rotated at a given speed and the resulting amplitude of vibration is noted while the high spot on the disc is marked. Now a known weight W_1 is attached to the rotor in any convenient position, and while the rotor turns at the same speed as before, the amplitude and the high spot are again determined. Let the position of the high spot in the

[8] E. L. Thearle, "Dynamic Balancing of Rotating Machinery in the Field," *Trans.*, ASME, vol. 56, APM 56–19–745.

unweighted test be noted as a and in the weighted test as b. The displacement in the first test may be laid out to scale as Oa, Fig. 5–17b. Ob, the displacement of the weighted test, is drawn at an angle δ from Oa, where δ

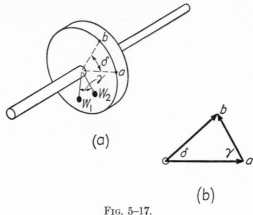

(a)

(b)

Fig. 5–17.

is the phase angle between the high spots a and b. The vector ab which closes the displacement polygon represents the change of vibration due to the known weight itself. If we now remove W_1 and replace it by a new weight

$$W_2 = \frac{Oa}{ab} W_1 \tag{5-49}$$

which has been displaced by the angle δ, we can see that it will be equal but opposite to the original vector displacement Oa, thereby annulling the original unbalance.

With the foregoing in mind we may now proceed to balance a long rotor by weight corrections in two planes. Fig. 5–18a is a sketch of a long rotor showing two known weights W_n' and W_f' attached. The subscripts n and f denote the near and far ends of the rotor. We first operate the rotor at a chosen speed without the addition of any trial weights, noting the amplitude of vibrations at the two correcting planes. The high spot positions at both ends are also noted. These amplitude vectors are plotted in Fig. 5–18b. A known weight W_n' is now attached at any position on the near correcting plane and a second test is made under the identical operating conditions of the first test. The amplitudes and phase angles at the near and far correcting planes are noted as N_2 and F_2, Fig. 5–18c. We note the W_n' has an effect upon F as well as N. The effect of W_n' is represented by the vectors A and αA at the near and far ends, respectively. The W_n' weight is now removed and W_f' is attached to the far end correcting plane. The test process is repeated and the results are shown in Fig. 5–18d. The test runs are now finished, but the task of determining the corrective

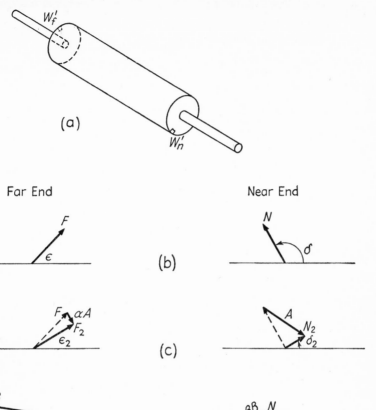

(a)

Far End   Near End

(b)

(c)

(d)

(e)

Fig. 5–18.

weights and their positions still remains. This determination can readily
be made from Fig. 5–18e. We are looking for a

$$W_n = \theta W_n'$$

and   (5–50)

$$W_f = \phi W_f'$$

where θ and ϕ are vectorial proportionality constants. θ and ϕ can be determined from the vectorial equations

$$\theta A + \phi \beta B = -N$$

and   (5–51)

$$\phi B + \theta \alpha A = -F$$

Whence

$$\theta = \frac{\beta F - N}{(1 - \alpha\beta)A}$$

and   (5–52)

$$\phi = \frac{\alpha N - F}{(1 - \alpha\beta)B}$$

We must remember that the values of θ and ϕ as given by Eqs. (5–52) are a result of vector algebra. The position for placing the balancing weights may be determined from the resultants of the vectors of Fig. 5–18c, the angular positions of which are measured from the vectors N and F.

It is beyond the purpose of this text to describe the equipment necessary to record the vibrations and phase angles. Thearle's paper discusses in detail the test equipment necessary. His paper also contains a sample calculation which will be of interest to those readers who wish to pursue the topic of rotor balancing beyond the coverage in this text.

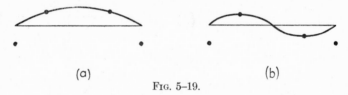

(a)   (b)

Fig. 5–19.

A word of caution is necessary concerning the speed at which a rotor is balanced. Whenever possible, the rotor should be balanced at the operating speed, or somewhere in the range of operating speeds if the rotor does not operate at a single speed. A rotor balanced while having a deflection configuration similar to one of the natural modes of vibration will not be in balance when another modal configuration is impressed on the rotor. Let us consider a rotor which has been balanced for the first critical speed, Fig. 5–19a. We can readily see that for the second mode of vibration, Fig. 5–19b, the system is not in balance. Actually, additional unbalance may be introduced into a system by balancing a rotor for one mode of vibration when its actual mode of vibration is another.

BIBLIOGRAPHY

Den Hartog, J. P. *Mechanical Vibrations*. 4th ed. New York: McGraw-Hill Book Co., Inc., 1956.

Hartman, James B. *Dynamics of Machinery*. New York: McGraw-Hill Book Co., Inc., 1956.

Thomson, William Tyrrell. *Mechanical Vibrations.* 2d ed. Englewood Cliffs, N. J.: Prentice-Hall Inc., 1953.

PROBLEMS

5-1. Using the Rayleigh method, determine the approximate fundamental frequency of a simply supported beam. Assume a deflection in the shape of a trigonometric function. Compare your result with the exact solution which is

$$\omega_n = \pi^2 \sqrt{\frac{EI}{ml^4}}$$

5-2. Determine the approximate fundamental frequency of a simply supported beam when the deflection curve is assumed to be a parabola.

5-3. If the deflection of a beam fixed at both ends is assumed in the shape of a trigonometric function, determine the first natural frequency by means of the Rayleigh method. Compare your result with the exact frequency of

$$\omega_n = 22 \sqrt{\frac{EI}{ml^4}}$$

5-4. If the dynamic deflection curve is assumed to be proportional to the static deflection curve, determine the approximate first natural frequency of a simply supported beam;

$$y_{\text{static}} = \frac{qx}{24EI} (l^3 - 2lx^2 + x^3)$$

5-5. The static deflection curve for a beam fixed at both ends is

$$y_{\text{static}} = \frac{qx^2}{24EI} (l - x)^2$$

By means of the Rayleigh method determine the fundamental frequency.

5-6. A 3-in. standard I beam supports two loads as shown in Fig. P5-6. Determine the approximate first natural frequency. The area moment of inertia of the beam is 2.5 in.[4].

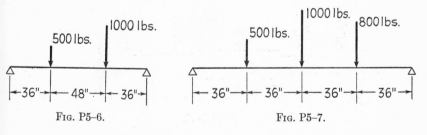

Fig. P5-6.   Fig. P5-7.

5-7. A 4-in. standard I beam supports three loads as shown in Fig. P5-7. Determine the approximate natural frequency of the system if the area moment of inertia is 6.7 in.[4].

5-8. A 2-in.-diameter steel rod is supported so that the load acts at the overhanging end as shown in Fig. P5-8. Determine the approximate fundamental frequency.

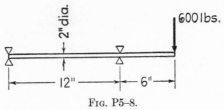

Fig. P5-8.

5-9. A 2-in.-diameter steel shaft is loaded by two forces as shown in Fig. P5-9. Determine the approximate fundamental frequency.

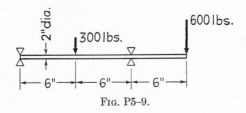

Fig. P5-9.

5-10. By graphical means, determine the first natural frequency of the stepped steel shaft shown in Fig. P5-10. Neglect the weight of the shaft.

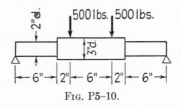

Fig. P5-10.

5-11. Solve Problem 5-10, taking into account the weight of the shaft.

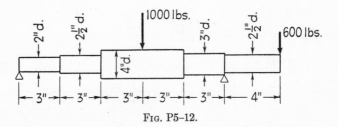

Fig. P5-12.

5-12. By graphical means, determine the approximate fundamental frequency of the stepped steel shaft, loaded as shown in Fig. P5-12. Neglect the weight of the shaft.

5-13. Solve Problem 5–12, taking into account the weight of the shaft.

5-14. Determine the fundamental frequency of the rotor shown in Fig. P5–14. The rotor is steel, 0.283 lb./in.[3].

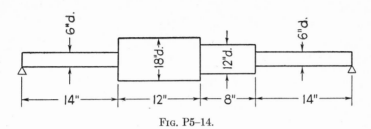

Fɪɢ. P5–14.

5-15. A single-cylinder engine's steel crankshaft with flywheel is shown in Fig. P5–15. Equate the system shown to an equivalent disc-and-shaft system. The specific weight of steel is 0.283 lb./in.[3].

Rod weight 6   lbs.
C.g. of rod from crankpin ....$3\frac{1}{2}$ in.
Rod length 9   in.
Piston weight....................................8.5 lbs.

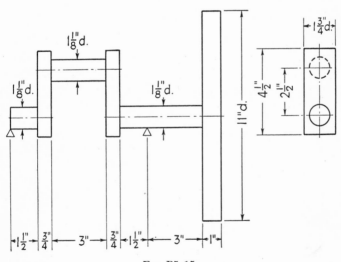

Fɪɢ. P5–15.

5-16. If an electric generator is connected to the flywheel of Problem 5–15 by a $1\frac{1}{2}$ in. diameter steel shaft 8 in. long, determine the first non-trivial natural frequency. The mass moment of inertia of the generator is 4.5 lbs.-in.-sec.[2].

5–17. A diesel-engine crankshaft and flywheel are shown in Fig. P5–17. The physical characteristics of the piston assembly are as follows:

Connecting rod length................................ 24 in.
Connecting rod weight .... 74 lbs.
Distance from c.g. to crankpin .... 9 in.
Weight of piston ....202 lbs.

Convert the above system to an equivalent disc-and-shaft system.

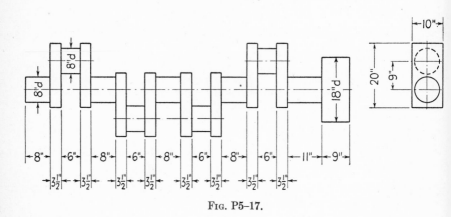

Fig. P5–17.

5–18. If the diesel in Problem 5–17 is connected to a generator by means of a 6 in. × 18 in. shaft between the flywheel and the generator, what is the third natural frequency of the system? The generator has a mass moment of inertia of 94 lbs.-in.-sec.[2].

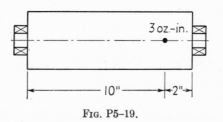

Fig. P5–19.

5–19. A single unbalance of 3 oz.-in. exists in a rotor (Fig. P5–19). Determine the necessary corrections on the end planes for the rotor to be dynamically balanced.

5-20. A rotor is known to have two unbalances as shown in Fig. P5–20. Determine the necessary corrective weights and their position in the end planes if the rotor is to be dynamically balanced.

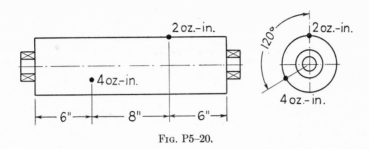

Fig. P5–20.

5-21. A rotor assumes a configuration of $y_0 \sin \pi x/L$ for its first mode of vibration. While rotating in the first-mode configuration, an unbalance of 2 oz.-in. is found at its mid-point. This unbalance is corrected by weights placed at the $L/4$ and $3L/4$ positions on the rotor. The supposedly balanced rotor is then operated at a higher speed so that the second mode of vibration is excited. If the second-mode configuration is $y_0 \sin 2\pi x/L$, determine the corrections necessary at the end planes for the rotor to be dynamically balanced for the second mode. If the corrections are made for the second mode of vibration, will the first mode be dynamically balanced?

CHAPTER 6

THE LAGRANGE EQUATIONS

6-1. Partial Derivative and Partial Differentiation. In the prior chapters we have been able to avoid functions of several variables. By lumping the masses and springs, as was done in Chapters 4 and 5, we were able to set up the differential equations without using partial derivatives. It is not always possible to use an artifice which will separate the variables from each other. In discussing the Lagrange equations and problems of continuous mediums (Chapter 7) we shall have to deal with functions of several variables. The first section of this chapter is therefore devoted to partial derivatives. The following presentation is by no means an exhaustive treatment. Its purpose is to present some of the basic fundamentals, which may serve as a review to those who have had some exposure to this subject, and to offer an invitation to consult a standard advanced calculus text to those who have never met the partial derivative before.[1]

The rules for partial derivatives and partial differentiation may be drawn by analogy from the rules for derivatives and for differentiation of a function of a single variable. Let us consider a function of a single variable x,

$$y = f(x) \tag{6-1}$$

From elementary differential calculus we remember that we define the derivative of y with respect to x as

$$\frac{dy}{dx} = \underset{\Delta x \to 0}{\text{limit}} \frac{f(x + \Delta x) - f(x)}{\Delta x} \tag{6-2}$$

If the limit exists, we can make the difference between the left-hand side and the right-hand side of Eq. (6–2) as small as we desire. This difference can be expressed as

$$\frac{f(x + \Delta x) - f(x)}{\Delta x} - \frac{dy}{dx} = \epsilon \tag{6-3}$$

where $\epsilon \to 0$ as $\Delta x \to 0$.

The concept embodied in Eq. (6–3) can be extended to encompass a function of several variables. For simplicity let us first restrict our discus-

[1] Ivan S. Sokolnikoff, *Advanced Calculus* (New York: McGraw-Hill Book Co., Inc., 1939).

sion to a function of two variables and then extend our results. Let

$$y = f(x_1, x_2) \tag{6-4}$$

We will assume that all the partial derivatives of Eq. (6–4) exist. The assumption that all partial derivatives exist is tantamount to saying that y is a continuous function of the independent variables. We can then obtain the first partial derivatives of y with respect to x_1 by performing the same operations governed by Eq. (6–2), with the additional restriction that we hold x_2 constant during the differentiation. It is also understood that x_2 may take on any permissible value, but that at that value, x_2 remains constant during the operation of differentiation. Then

and

$$\frac{\partial y}{\partial x_1} = \lim_{\Delta x_1 \to 0} \frac{f(x_1 + \Delta x_1, x_2) - f(x_1, x_2)}{\Delta x_1}$$

$$\frac{\partial y}{\partial x_2} = \lim_{\Delta x_2 \to 0} \frac{f(x_1, x_2 + \Delta x_2) - f(x_1, x_2)}{\Delta x_2} \tag{6-5}$$

Rewriting Eq. (6–5) into a form similar to Eq. (6–3), we get

$$\frac{f(x_1 + \Delta x_1, x_2) - f(x_1, x_2)}{\Delta x_1} - \frac{\partial y}{\partial x_1} = \epsilon_1$$

$$\frac{f(x_1, x_2 + \Delta x_2) - f(x_1, x_2)}{\Delta x_2} - \frac{\partial y}{\partial x_2} = \epsilon_2 \tag{6-6}$$

where $\epsilon_1 \to 0$ as $\Delta x_1 \to 0$ and $\epsilon_2 \to 0$ as $\Delta x_2 \to 0$.

Derivatives of higher order can be obtained by repeating the differentiation process.

$$\frac{\partial^2 y}{\partial x_1{}^2} = \frac{\partial}{\partial x_1}\left(\frac{\partial f}{\partial x_1}\right)$$

$$\frac{\partial^2 y}{\partial x_2{}^2} = \frac{\partial}{\partial x_2}\left(\frac{\partial f}{\partial x_2}\right)$$

$$\frac{\partial^2 y}{\partial x_1\, \partial x_2} = \frac{\partial}{\partial x_1}\left(\frac{\partial f}{\partial x_2}\right)$$

$$\frac{\partial^2 y}{\partial x_2\, \partial x_1} = \frac{\partial}{\partial x_2}\left(\frac{\partial f}{\partial x_1}\right) \tag{6-7}$$

If the partial derivatives are continuous functions of x_1 and x_2, then it can be proved that the order of differentiation of the last two equations of Eq. (6–7) may be interchanged. That is,

$$\frac{\partial^2 y}{\partial x_1\, \partial x_2} = \frac{\partial^2 y}{\partial x_2\, \partial x_1} \tag{6-8}$$

Derivatives of order higher than the second derivative may be obtained from the following formulas:

$$\frac{\partial^n y}{\partial x_i{}^n} = \frac{\partial}{\partial x_i}\left(\frac{\partial^{n-1}y}{\partial x_i{}^{n-1}}\right) \tag{6-9}$$

and for the cross derivatives

$$\frac{\partial^n y}{\partial x_i{}^m \, \partial x_j{}^{n-m}} = \frac{\partial}{\partial x_i}\left(\frac{\partial^{n-1}y}{\partial x_i{}^{m-1}\, \partial x_j{}^{n-m}}\right) \tag{6-10}$$

Examples.

1. Find the first partial derivatives when

$$y = x_1 x_2 + 3x_2{}^2$$

Then

$$\frac{\partial y}{\partial x_1} = x_2 \qquad \text{and} \qquad \frac{\partial y}{\partial x_2} = x_1 + 6x_2$$

2. Find all the second partial derivatives when

$$y = \cos\,(2x_1{}^3 + x_2{}^2)$$

Then

$$\frac{\partial y}{\partial x_1} = -6x_1{}^2 \sin\,(2x_1{}^3 + x_2{}^2)$$

$$\frac{\partial^2 y}{\partial x_1{}^2} = -12x_1 \sin\,(2x_1{}^3 + x_2{}^2) - 36x_1{}^4 \cos\,(2x_1{}^3 + x_2{}^2)$$

$$\frac{\partial^2 y}{\partial x_2 \, \partial x_1} = -12x_1{}^2 x_2 \cos\,(2x_1{}^3 + x_2{}^2)$$

and

$$\frac{\partial y}{\partial x_2} = -2x_2 \sin\,(2x_1{}^3 + x_2{}^2)$$

$$\frac{\partial^2 y}{\partial x_2{}^2} = -2 \sin\,(2x_1{}^3 + x_2{}^2) - 4x_2{}^2 \cos\,(2x_1{}^3 + x_2{}^2)$$

$$\frac{\partial^2 y}{\partial x_1 \, \partial x_2} = -12x_1 x_2 \cos\,(2x_1{}^3 + x_2{}^2)$$

Note:

$$\frac{\partial^2 y}{\partial x_2 \, \partial x_1} = \frac{\partial^2 y}{\partial x_1 \, \partial x_2}$$

Let us now find the total differential of $y = f(x_1, x_2)$. If we allow both variables to take on small increments simultaneously, then

$$\Delta y = f(x_1 + \Delta x_1, x_2 + \Delta x_2) - f(x_1, x_2) \qquad (6\text{--}11)$$

We now add and subtract $f(x_1, x_2 + \Delta x_2)$;

$$\Delta y = f(x_1 + \Delta x_1, x_2 + \Delta x_2) - f(x_1, x_2 + \Delta x_2) + f(x_1, x_2 + \Delta x_2) - f(x_1, x_2) \qquad (6\text{--}12)$$

By virtue of the first of Eqs. (6–6) we may write

$$f(x_1 + \Delta x_1, x_2 + \Delta x_2) - f(x_1, x_2 + \Delta x_2) = \frac{\partial f(x_1, x_2 + \Delta x_2)}{\partial x_1} \Delta x_1 + \epsilon_1 \Delta x_1 \qquad (6\text{--}13)$$

However, if we let $\Delta x_2 \to 0$, we get from the R.H.S.

$$\lim_{\Delta x_2 \to 0} \frac{\partial f(x_1, x_2 + \Delta x_2)}{\partial x_1} = \frac{\partial f(x_1, x_2)}{\partial x_1} \qquad (6\text{--}14)$$

which can be written as

$$\frac{\partial f(x_1, x_2 + \Delta x_2)}{\partial x_1} = \frac{\partial y}{\partial x_1} + \epsilon_0 \qquad (6\text{--}15)$$

where $\epsilon_0 \to 0$ as $\Delta x_2 \to 0$. Note that ϵ_1 and Δx_1 are independent of Δx_2. As a consequence of the above we get

$$f(x_1 + \Delta x_1, x_2 + \Delta x_2) - f(x_1, x_2 + \Delta x_2) = \frac{\partial y}{\partial x_1} \Delta x_1 + (\epsilon_1 + \epsilon_0) \Delta x_1 \qquad (6\text{--}16)$$

where $\epsilon_1 \to 0$ as $\Delta x_1 \to 0$ and $\epsilon_0 \to 0$ as $\Delta x_2 \to 0$.

By virtue of the second of Eqs. (6–6),

$$f(x_1, x_2 + \Delta x_2) - f(x_1, x_2) = \frac{\partial y}{\partial x_2} \Delta x_2 + \epsilon_2 \Delta x_2 \qquad (6\text{--}17)$$

We now substitute Eqs. (6–16) and (6–17) into Eq. (6–12). This substitution yields

$$\Delta y = \frac{\partial y}{\partial x_1} \Delta x_1 + \frac{\partial y}{\partial x_2} \Delta x_2 + (\epsilon_1 + \epsilon_0) \Delta x_1 + \epsilon_2 \Delta x_2 \qquad (6\text{--}18)$$

where $\epsilon_1 \to 0$ as $\Delta x_1 \to 0$ and ϵ_0 and ϵ_2 each $\to 0$ as $\Delta x_2 \to 0$. The total differential then becomes

$$dy = \frac{\partial y}{\partial x_1} dx_1 + \frac{\partial y}{\partial x_2} dx_2 \qquad (6\text{--}19)$$

By similar arguments, we may extend Eq. (6–19) to functions of more than two variables:

$$dy = \frac{\partial y}{\partial x_1} dx_1 + \frac{\partial y}{\partial x_2} dx_2 + \cdots + \frac{\partial y}{\partial x_n} dx_n \tag{6-20}$$

where $y = f(x_1, x_2, x_3, \ldots, x_n)$.

If each $x_1, x_2, \ldots, x_n$ is a function of a single variable, say t, we may divide both sides of Eq. (6–20) by dt to get the total derivative of y with respect to t:

$$\frac{dy}{dt} = \frac{\partial y}{\partial x_1} \cdot \frac{dx_1}{dt} + \frac{\partial y}{\partial x_2} \cdot \frac{dx_2}{dt} + \cdots + \frac{\partial y}{\partial x_n} \cdot \frac{dx_n}{dt} \tag{6-21}$$

Without further proof we state that if y is a function of n variables $x_1, x_2, \ldots, x_n$ and each x_i is a function of m variables $t_1, t_2, \ldots, t_m$, then the first partial derivatives of y with respect to the t's are:

$$\frac{\partial y}{\partial t_1} = \frac{\partial y}{\partial x_1} \cdot \frac{\partial x_1}{\partial t_1} + \frac{\partial y}{\partial x_2} \cdot \frac{\partial x_2}{\partial t_1} + \cdots + \frac{\partial y}{\partial x_n} \cdot \frac{\partial x_n}{\partial t_1}$$

$$\frac{\partial y}{\partial t_2} = \frac{\partial y}{\partial x_1} \cdot \frac{\partial x_1}{\partial t_2} + \frac{\partial y}{\partial x_2} \cdot \frac{\partial x_2}{\partial t_2} + \cdots + \frac{\partial y}{\partial x_n} \cdot \frac{\partial x_n}{\partial t_2} \tag{6-22}$$

$$\cdots \cdots \cdots \cdots \cdots \cdots \cdots$$

$$\frac{\partial y}{\partial t_m} = \frac{\partial y}{\partial x_1} \cdot \frac{\partial x_1}{\partial t_m} + \frac{\partial y}{\partial x_2} \cdot \frac{\partial x_2}{\partial t_m} + \cdots + \frac{\partial y}{\partial x_n} \cdot \frac{\partial x_n}{\partial t_m}$$

Examples.

1. Find the total derivative of y with respect to t when

$$y = 2x_1^2 - x_1 x_2 + 3x_2^2 \qquad x_1 = t^2 + 1 \qquad x_2 = t^3 - t$$

$$\frac{dy}{dt} = \frac{\partial y}{\partial x_1} \cdot \frac{dx_1}{dt} + \frac{\partial y}{\partial x_2} \cdot \frac{dx_2}{dt}$$

$$\frac{\partial y}{\partial x_1} = 4x_1 - x_2 \qquad \frac{\partial y}{\partial x_2} = -x_1 + 6x_2$$

$$\frac{dx_1}{dt} = 2t \qquad \frac{dx_2}{dt} = 3t^2 - 1$$

Substituting the values for x_1 and x_2, we get

$$\frac{dy}{dt} = 18t^5 - 5t^4 - 16t^3 + 14t + 1$$

2. Find $\partial y/\partial t_2$ when

$$y = x_1^2 x_2 - x_1 x_2^2 \qquad x_1 = t_1 + t_2 \qquad x_2 = t_1 - t_2$$

$$\frac{\partial y}{\partial t_2} = \frac{\partial y}{\partial x_1} \cdot \frac{\partial x_1}{\partial t_2} + \frac{\partial y}{\partial x_2} \cdot \frac{\partial x_2}{\partial t_2}$$

$$\frac{\partial y}{\partial x_1} = 2x_1x_2 - x_2{}^2 \qquad \frac{\partial y}{\partial x_2} = x_1{}^2 - 2x_1x_2$$

$$\frac{\partial x_1}{\partial t_2} = 1 \qquad \frac{\partial x_2}{\partial t_2} = -1$$

$$\frac{\partial y}{\partial t_2} = (2x_1x_2 - x_2{}^2)(1) + (x_1{}^2 - 2x_1x_2)(-1)$$

$$\frac{\partial y}{\partial t_2} = 4x_1x_2 - x_1{}^2 - x_2{}^2$$

If we substitute the values of x_1 and x_2 in terms of t_1 and t_2, we get

$$\frac{\partial y}{\partial t_2} = 2t_1{}^2 - 6t_2{}^2$$

6–2. Generalized Coordinates. Consider a simple mathematical pendulum, Fig. 6–1, which is oscillating in the x-y plane. At any time t, the position of the pendulum may be defined by the coordinates x_1 and y_1. However, x_1 and y_1 are interdependent. If x_1 is chosen, then y_1 is determined according to the equation:

$$x_1{}^2 + y_1{}^2 = l^2 \qquad (6\text{–}23)$$

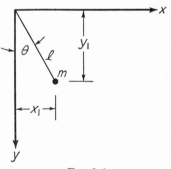

Eq. (6–23) is a constraint on the pendulum based upon the geometry of the equation. In the previous derivation of the equation of motion of the simple pendulum, the angle θ was selected as the coordinate, and this coordinate appeared only in the differential equation. What is implied by this choice of coordinate is that θ completely defines the motion of the pendulum and is independent of any other coordinate. However, the pendulum is still subject to the constraint of Eq. (6–23). That is to say that l is a constant, and this condition must not be violated if the differential equation governing the motion of the simple pendulum is to apply. That is,

$$\ddot{\theta} + \frac{g}{l}\theta = 0$$

FIG. 6–1.

Now consider a double pendulum, Fig. 6–2. The motion of this system can be defined by the angles θ and ϕ. The constraints which govern the motions are:

$$x_1{}^2 + y_1{}^2 = l_1{}^2$$
$$(x_2 - x_1)^2 + (y_2 - y_1)^2 = l_2{}^2 \qquad (6\text{--}24)$$

θ and ϕ completely define the system of the double pendulum. Moreover, an examination shows that θ and ϕ are independent of each other. A change in the angle ϕ does not necessitate a change in the angle θ, or vice

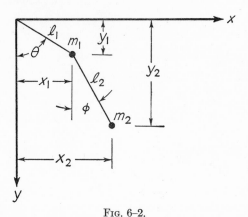

Fig. 6–2.

versa. The coordinates θ and ϕ are referred to as generalized coordinates. The constraints of any system are expressible in terms containing the generalized coordinates. For the system of the double pendulum, the constraints may be expressed by:

$$x_1 = l_1 \sin \theta \qquad\qquad y_1 = l_1 \cos \theta$$
$$x_2 = l_1 \sin \theta + l_2 \sin \phi \qquad y_2 = l_1 \cos \theta + l_2 \cos \phi \qquad (6\text{--}25)$$

Generalized coordinates possess another very important property, namely, that the number of degrees of freedom equals the number of generalized coordinates. For the simple pendulum we have only one generalized coordinate and consequently only one degree of freedom. For the double pendulum we have two generalized coordinates and hence two degrees of freedom. A spherical pendulum, Fig. 6–3, one whose center of mass oscillates with a motion restricted to the surface of a sphere, would have two generalized coordinates and two degrees of freedom. The number of degrees of freedom can also be determined from the number of coordinates necessary to define the equations of constraint. If j equals the number of coordinates and k the number of equations of constraint, then n, the number of degrees of freedom, is given by

$$n = j - k \qquad (6\text{--}26)$$

Thus we can see from Eq. (6–23) that a simple mathematical pendulum has two coordinates and one equation of constraint with the result that the system has only one degree of freedom. From Eqs. (6–24) we see that the double pendulum has two degrees of freedom, since there are four coordinates and two equations of constraint. Often, when we are dealing with

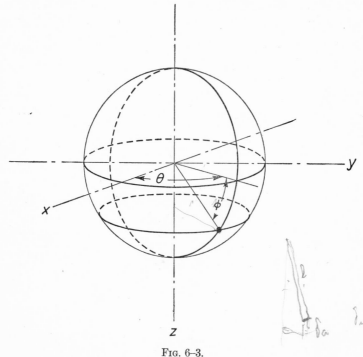

Fig. 6–3.

a fairly complicated problem, the comparison of the number of generalized coordinates with Eq. (6–26) may help prevent an error in defining the equations of constraint or in having too few or too many generalized coordinates.

6–3. Virtual Displacement. A virtual displacement may be defined as a small displacement that is compatible with the constraints of the system. That is to say that, in the case of a spherical pendulum, a small displacement of the center of mass that has its trace on the surface of a sphere of radius l (the pendulum length) will be a virtual displacement.

The principle of virtual displacement states that if a system is in equilibrium, the work done by the forces on all of the virtual displacements is equal to zero. This statement means that the reaction to the force causing the virtual displacement is directed normal to the surface defined by the

equations of constraint, and the work done is therefore equal to zero
Such a condition exists when we are dealing with so-called frictionless
reactions. In the main we will deal with systems which may be considered
to consist of mass points and rigid bodies subjected to geometrical
constraints.

Under the above assumption, it will not be necessary to introduce internal
reactions. We need only concern ourselves with the external reactions
The external reaction of any system will not perform work if it is in a
direction normal to the displacement. When such is the case, the reaction
can be called frictionless. Such is the case for a virtual displacement. The
reactions are normal to the surface of displacement by virtue of the constraints. For a virtual displacement of a spherical pendulum, in a statical
sense, the principle of virtual displacement can be expressed by:

$$X \, \delta x + Y \, \delta y + Z \, \delta z = 0 \tag{6-27}$$

where X, Y, and Z are the components of the forces acting on the mass
in the x, y, and z directions, respectively, and δx, δy, and δz are virtual
displacements in the x, y, and z directions, respectively. The virtual displacement satisfies the geometric constraint $x^2 + y^2 + z^2 = l^2$. Then

$$(x + \delta x)^2 + (y + \delta y)^2 + (z + \delta z)^2 = l^2 \tag{6-28}$$

also satisfies the constraint of the system. If we carry out the operation
as indicated by Eq. (6–28) and neglect terms of higher order in δx, δy, and
δz, since these quantities are small, we get

$$x \, \delta x + y \, \delta y + z \, \delta z = 0 \tag{6-29}$$

We can now draw the conclusion that Eq. (6–29) is a restriction for compatibility for a virtual displacement.

6–4. D'Alembert's Principle. Newton's second law, when applied to a
body of constant mass, states that the force acting on the mass is equal to
the mass times its acceleration. D'Alembert's principle states that a state
of motion may be considered to be in equilibrium if the force and the
inertia force are taken into consideration. If we define the inertia force as
being equal to the mass times the negative acceleration, we can express
D'Alembert's principle as follows:

$$X_i - m_i \ddot{x}_i = 0 \qquad Y_i - m_i \ddot{y}_i = 0 \qquad Z_i - m_i \ddot{z}_i = 0$$

where i takes successive integer values from 1 to n.

If we combine the principle of virtual displacement with D'Alembert's
principle, the differential equation of motion for a constrained system can
be obtained. Consider the case of the spherical pendulum:

$$(X_1 - m_1 \ddot{x}_1) \, \delta x_1 + (Y_1 - m_1 \ddot{y}_1) \, \delta y_1 + (Z_1 - m_1 \ddot{z}_1) \, \delta z_1 = 0 \tag{6-30}$$

Generalizing Eq. (6–30) we get:

$$\sum_{i=1}^{n} [(m_i \ddot{x}_i - X_i) \delta x_i + (m_i \ddot{y}_i - Y_i) \delta y_i + (m_i \ddot{z}_i - Z_i) \delta z_i] = 0 \quad (6\text{–}31)$$

Eq. (6–31) is D'Alembert's equation of motion.

Eq. (6–31) may be best interpreted as a variation of a system, which is in equilibrium, by an arbitrary small amount δ_i which is compatible with the constraints of the system, where δx_i, δy_i, and δz_i are components of δ_i in the x, y, and z directions, respectively.

6–5. Lagrange Equations. Eq. (6–31) may be further simplified by introducing the idea of generalized coordinates. If we let $q_1, q_2, q_3, \ldots q_r$ be the generalized coordinates of a system with r degrees of freedom, then:

$$x_i = x_i(q_1, q_2, \ldots q_r)$$

$$y_i = y_i(q_1, q_2, \ldots q_r) \quad (6\text{–}32)$$

$$z_i = z_i(q_1, q_2, \ldots q_r)$$

where these equations do not imply a dependence upon time or the velocities $\dot{q}_1, \dot{q}_2, \ldots \dot{q}_r$.

The application of Eq. (6–32) to the case of the double pendulum yields the sets of Eqs. (6–25).

As a result of Eq. (6–20), we may express the virtual displacements as:

$$\delta x_i = \sum_{k=1}^{r} \frac{\partial x_i}{\partial q_k} \delta q_k$$

$$\delta y_i = \sum_{k=1}^{r} \frac{\partial y_i}{\partial q_k} \delta q_k \quad (6\text{–}33)$$

$$\delta z_i = \sum_{k=1}^{r} \frac{\partial z_i}{\partial q_k} \delta q_k$$

We now rearrange Eq. (6–31) so that

$$\sum_{i=1}^{n} m_i(\ddot{x}_i \, \delta x_i + \ddot{y}_i \, \delta y_i + \ddot{z}_i \, \delta z_i) = \sum_{i=1}^{n} (X_i \, \delta x_i + Y_i \, \delta y_i + Z_i \, \delta z_i) \quad (6\text{–}34)$$

Consider the R.H.S. of Eq. (6–34). This represents the work done by the forces acting on the virtual displacement, that is,

$$\delta W = \sum_{i=1}^{n} (X_i \, \delta x_i + Y_i \, \delta y_i + Z_i \, \delta z_i) \quad (6\text{–}35)$$

Now we introduce Eq. (6–33), and Eq. (6–35) becomes:

$$\delta W = \sum_{k=1}^{r}\left[\sum_{i=1}^{n}\left(X_i\frac{\partial x_i}{\partial q_k} + Y_i\frac{\partial y_i}{\partial q_k} + Z_i\frac{\partial z_i}{\partial q_k}\right)\right]\delta q_k \qquad (6-36)$$

Let us define the expression within the bracket as a generalized force Q corresponding to the generalized coordinates q_k. That is

$$\sum_{i=1}^{n}\left(X_i\frac{\partial x_i}{\partial q_k} + Y_i\frac{\partial y_i}{\partial q_k} + Z_i\frac{\partial z_i}{\partial q_k}\right) = Q_k \qquad (6-37)$$

Eq. (6–36) now takes the form of:

$$\delta W = \sum_{k=1}^{r} Q_k\,\delta q_k \qquad (6-38)$$

The kinetic energy of the system under discussion is

$$T = \tfrac{1}{2}\sum_{i=1}^{n} m_i(\dot{x}_i{}^2 + \dot{y}_i{}^2 + \dot{z}_i{}^2) \qquad (6-39)$$

Since

$$\frac{\partial T}{\partial \dot{x}_i} = m_i\dot{x}_i, \qquad \frac{\partial T}{\partial \dot{y}_i} = m_i\dot{y}_i, \qquad \text{and} \qquad \frac{\partial T}{\partial \dot{z}_i} = m_i\dot{z}_i \qquad (6-40)$$

then

$$\frac{d}{dt}\left(\frac{\partial T}{\partial \dot{x}_i}\right) = m_i\ddot{x}_i, \qquad \frac{d}{dt}\left(\frac{\partial T}{\partial \dot{y}_i}\right) = m_i\ddot{y}_i, \qquad \text{and} \qquad \frac{d}{dt}\left(\frac{\partial T}{\partial \dot{z}_i}\right) = m_i\ddot{z}_i$$
$$(6-41)$$

We can now substitute the relations of Eq. (6–41) into the L.H.S. of Eq. (6–34). We get for the L.H.S. of Eq. (6–34):

$$\sum_{i=1}^{n}\left[\frac{d}{dt}\left(\frac{\partial T}{\partial \dot{x}_i}\right)\delta x_i + \frac{d}{dt}\left(\frac{\partial T}{\partial \dot{y}_i}\right)\delta y_i + \frac{d}{dt}\left(\frac{\partial T}{\partial \dot{z}_i}\right)\delta z_i\right] \qquad (6-42)$$

Substituting the relations of Eq. (6–33) for δx_i, δy_i and δz_i yields:

$$\sum_{k=1}^{r}\sum_{i=1}^{n}\left[\frac{d}{dt}\left(\frac{\partial T}{\partial \dot{x}_i}\right)\frac{\partial x_i}{\partial q_k} + \frac{d}{dt}\left(\frac{\partial T}{\partial \dot{y}_i}\right)\frac{\partial y_i}{\partial q_k} + \frac{d}{dt}\left(\frac{\partial T}{\partial \dot{z}_i}\right)\frac{\partial z_i}{\partial q_k}\right]\delta q_k \qquad (6-43)$$

To simplify the terms in the bracket, we note that

$$\frac{d}{dt}\left(\frac{\partial T}{\partial \dot{x}_i}\cdot\frac{\partial x_i}{\partial q_k}\right) = \frac{d}{dt}\left(\frac{\partial T}{\partial \dot{x}_i}\right)\frac{\partial x_i}{\partial q_k} + \frac{\partial T}{\partial \dot{x}_i}\cdot\frac{\partial \dot{x}_i}{\partial q_k} \qquad (6-44)$$

or

$$\frac{d}{dt}\left(\frac{\partial T}{\partial \dot{x}_i}\right)\frac{\partial x_i}{\partial q_k} = \frac{d}{dt}\left(\frac{\partial T}{\partial \dot{x}_i}\cdot\frac{\partial x_i}{\partial q_k}\right) - \frac{\partial T}{\partial \dot{x}_i}\cdot\frac{\partial \dot{x}_i}{\partial q_k} \qquad (6-45)$$

In the same manner the other terms in the bracket can be deduced. Substituting these values into Eq. (6–43), we get:

$$\sum_{k=1}^{r} \sum_{i=1}^{n} \left\{ \frac{d}{dt} \left[\frac{\partial T}{\partial \dot{x}_i} \cdot \frac{\partial x_i}{\partial q_k} + \frac{\partial T}{\partial \dot{y}_i} \cdot \frac{\partial y_i}{\partial q_k} + \frac{\partial T}{\partial \dot{z}_i} \cdot \frac{\partial z_i}{\partial q_k} \right] \right.$$
$$\left. - \left[\frac{\partial T}{\partial \dot{x}_i} \cdot \frac{\partial \dot{x}_i}{\partial q_k} + \frac{\partial T}{\partial \dot{y}_i} \cdot \frac{\partial \dot{y}_i}{\partial q_k} + \frac{\partial T}{\partial \dot{z}_i} \cdot \frac{\partial \dot{z}_i}{\partial q_k} \right] \right\} \delta q_k \quad (6\text{–}46)$$

At this point we must establish the fact that $T = T(q_i, \dot{q}_i)$. Consider, if you will, the constraint on a simple pendulum: $x^2 + y^2 = l^2$ and $x = l \sin \theta$; $y = l \cos \theta$, where $q_1 = \theta$. Now

$$\dot{x} = l\dot{\theta} \cos \theta = \dot{x}(q_1, \dot{q}_1) \qquad \dot{y}_i = -l\dot{\theta} \sin \theta = \dot{y}(q_1, \dot{q}_1) \quad (6\text{–}47)$$

Since $T = T_1(\dot{x}, \dot{y})$, then $T = T_2(q_1, \dot{q}_1)$.
Upon generalization, we get:

$$T = T(q_i, \dot{q}_i) \quad (6\text{–}48)$$

It is therefore permissible to take the derivative of T with respect to q_i as well as $\dot{q}_i$. Then, by virtue of Eq. (6–48),

$$\frac{\partial T}{\partial \dot{q}_k} = \sum_{i=1}^{n} \left(\frac{\partial T}{\partial \dot{x}_i} \cdot \frac{\partial \dot{x}_i}{\partial \dot{q}_k} + \frac{\partial T}{\partial \dot{y}_i} \cdot \frac{\partial \dot{y}_i}{\partial \dot{q}_k} + \frac{\partial T}{\partial \dot{z}_i} \cdot \frac{\partial \dot{z}_i}{\partial \dot{q}_k} \right) \quad (6\text{–}49)$$

Consider the total derivative for the function:

$$u = u(q_1, q_2, \cdots q_r) \quad (6\text{–}50)$$

Performing the operations required by Eq. (6–41),

$$\dot{u} = \frac{du}{dt} = \frac{\partial u}{\partial q_1} \cdot \frac{dq_1}{dt} + \frac{\partial u}{\partial q_2} \cdot \frac{dq_2}{dt} + \cdots + \frac{\partial u}{\partial q_r} \cdot \frac{dq_r}{dt} \quad (6\text{–}51)$$

or

$$\dot{u} = \frac{\partial u}{\partial q_1} \cdot \dot{q}_1 + \frac{\partial u}{\partial q_2} \cdot \dot{q}_2 + \cdots + \frac{\partial u}{\partial q_r} \cdot \dot{q}_r \quad (6\text{–}52)$$

Differentiating Eq. (6–52) with respect to $\dot{q}_1, \dot{q}_2, \cdots \dot{q}_r$ in succession, we get:

$$\frac{\partial \dot{u}}{\partial \dot{q}_1} = \frac{\partial u}{\partial q_1}, \qquad \frac{\partial u}{\partial \dot{q}_2} = \frac{\partial u}{\partial q_2}, \qquad \cdots \qquad \frac{\partial u}{\partial \dot{q}_r} = \frac{\partial u}{\partial q_r} \quad (6\text{–}53)$$

or, by generalization,

$$\frac{\partial \dot{x}_i}{\partial \dot{q}_k} = \frac{\partial x_i}{\partial q_k} \quad (6\text{–}54)$$

Substituting the relationship of Eq. (6–54) into Eq. (6–49) yields

$$\frac{\partial T}{\partial \dot{q}_k} = \sum_{i=1}^{n} \left(\frac{\partial T}{\partial \dot{x}_i} \cdot \frac{\partial x_i}{\partial q_k} + \frac{\partial T}{\partial \dot{y}_i} \cdot \frac{\partial y_i}{\partial q_k} + \frac{\partial T}{\partial \dot{z}_i} \cdot \frac{\partial z_i}{\partial q_k} \right) \quad (6\text{–}55)$$

Also, by virtue of relationships given by Eq. (6–47) and Eq. (6–48):

$$\frac{\partial T}{\partial q_k} = \sum_{i=1}^{n} \left(\frac{\partial T}{\partial \dot{x}_i} \cdot \frac{\partial \dot{x}_i}{\partial q_k} + \frac{\partial T}{\partial \dot{y}_i} \cdot \frac{\partial \dot{y}_i}{\partial q_k} + \frac{\partial T}{\partial \dot{z}_i} \cdot \frac{\partial \dot{z}_i}{\partial q_k} \right) \qquad (6\text{--}56)$$

Substituting Eqs. (6–55) and (6–56) into Eq. (6–46) yields:

$$\sum_{k=1}^{r} \left[\frac{d}{dt} \left(\frac{\partial T}{\partial \dot{q}_k} \right) - \frac{\partial T}{\partial q_k} \right] \delta q_k \qquad (6\text{--}57)$$

This is the simplification of the L.H.S. of Eq. (6–34), and, since Eq. (6–38) represents the R.H.S. of Eq. (6–34), we get as a result of the substitution of Eqs. (6–56) and (6–38) into Eq. (6–34):

$$\sum_{k=1}^{r} \left[\frac{d}{dt} \left(\frac{\partial T}{\partial \dot{q}_k} \right) - \frac{\partial T}{\partial q_k} \right] \delta q_k = \sum_{k=1}^{r} Q_k \, \delta q_k \qquad (6\text{--}58)$$

Rearranging Eq. (6–58):

$$\sum_{k=1}^{r} \left[\frac{d}{dt} \left(\frac{\partial T}{\partial \dot{q}_k} \right) - \frac{\partial T}{\partial q_k} - Q_k \right] \delta q_k = 0 \qquad (6\text{--}59)$$

Since δq_k is arbitrary, the term in the bracket must be equal to zero, and Eq. (6–59) becomes:

$$\frac{d}{dt} \left(\frac{\partial T}{\partial \dot{q}_k} \right) - \frac{\partial T}{\partial q_k} = Q_k \qquad (6\text{--}60)$$

Eq. (6–60) is the so-called Lagrange equation of motion as deduced from D'Alembert's equation, Eq. (6–31).

Q_k has been defined as a generalized force. In general, this force may consist of three distinct forces: (1) the spring force or force due to change of potential energy, (2) the force of the damper or dissipative force, (3) the impressed force.

Let us reconsider Eq. (6–37). If we consider that Q_k is formed by three distinct parts as outlined above, we get:

$$X_i = -k_i x_i' - c_i \dot{x}_i' + X_i' \qquad (6\text{--}61)$$

where k_i is the spring constant, c_i is the damping constant, and x_i' and $\dot{x}_i'$ are relative displacements and velocities, respectively. X_i' is the impressed force and may be a function of time. Note should be made of the fact that the displacements and the velocities are relative. In general, the spring and damping forces are dependent upon their relative values; that is, if a spring is attached between m_1 and m_2, the spring force will be $k(x_1 - x_2)$. In the same manner relations similar to Eq. (6–61) are obtainable for Y_i and Z_i. Eq. (6–37) may now be rewritten in the following form:

$$\sum_{i=1}^{n} \left[\left(-k_i x_i' - c_i \dot{x}_i' + X_i' \right) \frac{\partial x_i'}{\partial q_k} + \left(-k_i y_i' - c_i \dot{y}_i' + Y' \right) \frac{\partial y_i'}{\partial q_k} \right.$$
$$\left. + (-k_i z_i' - c_i \dot{z}_i' + Z_i') \frac{\partial z_i'}{\partial q_k} \right] = Q_k \qquad (6\text{–}62)$$

Now the potential energy for spring k_i with a relative displacement of x_i' is:

$$V_{xi} = \sum_{i=1}^{n} \tfrac{1}{2} k_i (x_i')^2$$

and

$$\frac{\partial V_{xi}}{\partial q_k} = \sum_{i=1}^{n} k_i x_i' \frac{\partial x_i'}{\partial q_k} \qquad (6\text{–}63)$$

The energy expended by the damper is:

$$F_{cxi} = \sum_{i=1}^{n} \tfrac{1}{2} c_i (\dot{x}_i')^2$$

and

$$\frac{\partial F_{cxi}}{\partial \dot{q}_k} = \sum_{i=1}^{n} c_i \dot{x}_i' \frac{\partial \dot{x}_i'}{\partial \dot{q}_k} \qquad (6\text{–}64)$$

By virtue of Eq. (6–54),

$$\frac{\partial F_{cxi}}{\partial \dot{q}_k} = \sum_{i=1}^{n} c_i \dot{x}_i' \frac{\partial x_i'}{\partial q_k} \qquad (6\text{–}65)$$

In the same manner similar relations are obtained in y and z directions. By substituting the generalized relations of Eqs. (6–63) and (6–65) into Eq. (6–62) we get:

$$-\frac{\partial V}{\partial q_k} - \frac{\partial F_c}{\partial q_k} + Q_k' = Q_k \qquad (6\text{–}66)$$

where

$$Q_k = \sum_{i=1}^{n} \left(X_i \frac{\partial x_i}{\partial q_k} + Y_i \frac{\partial y_i}{\partial q_k} + Z_i \frac{\partial z_i}{\partial q_k} \right)$$

as before, and

$$Q_k' = \sum_{i=1}^{n} \left(X_i' \frac{\partial x_i'}{\partial q_k} + Y_i' \frac{\partial y_i'}{\partial q_k} + Z_i' \frac{\partial z_i'}{\partial q_k} \right)$$

We must remember that X_i', Y_i', and Z_i' are now the components of the applied external force alone.

The Lagrange equations may now be written as:

$$\frac{d}{dt}\left(\frac{\partial T}{\partial \dot{q}_k}\right) - \frac{\partial T}{\partial q_k} + \frac{\partial V}{\partial q_k} + \frac{\partial F_c}{\partial \dot{q}_k} = Q_k \qquad (6\text{-}67)$$

where now the prime over the Q_k' has been dropped for convenience.

For a conservative system, Eq. (6–67) reduces to the simplified form of:

$$\frac{d}{dt}\left(\frac{\partial T}{\partial \dot{q}_k}\right) - \frac{\partial T}{\partial q_k} + \frac{\partial V}{\partial q_k} = 0 \qquad (6\text{-}68)$$

If we recognize that V is not a function of $\dot{q}_k$, we may further simplify Eq. (6–68) by introducing the Lagrangian function of the system, L, where

$$L = T - V \qquad (6\text{-}69)$$

Eq. (6–68) may be written as:

$$\frac{d}{dt}\left(\frac{\partial L}{\partial \dot{q}_k}\right) - \frac{\partial L}{\partial q_k} = 0 \qquad (6\text{-}70)$$

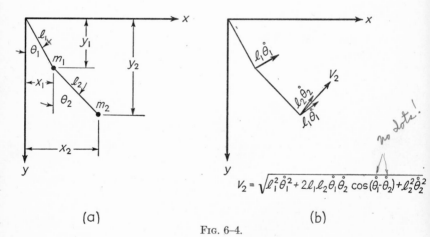

(a)   (b)

Fig. 6–4.

$$V_2 = \sqrt{l_1^2\dot{\theta}_1^2 + 2l_1l_2\dot{\theta}_1\dot{\theta}_2 \cos(\theta_1-\theta_2) + l_2^2\dot{\theta}_2^2}$$

Example. Determine the equations of motion and the natural frequencies of a double pendulum as seen in Fig. 6–4a.

SOLUTION. The equations of constraint are

$$x_1{}^2 + y_1{}^2 = l_1{}^2$$

$$(x_2 - x_1)^2 + (y_2 - y_1)^2 = l_2{}^2$$

Since there are four coordinates and two equations of constraint, we see by means of Eq. (6–26) that there are two generalized coordinates. Let

$q_1 = \theta_1$ and $q_2 = \theta_2$ as sketched. Fig. 6–4b shows the velocity vectors for m_1 and m_2. These were found by the method suggested in Chapter 1. Since $l_2\dot\theta_2$ is the velocity of m_2 relative to m_1, we must remember that $\boldsymbol{v}_2 = \boldsymbol{v}_1 + \boldsymbol{v}_{2/1}$. The resultant for $\boldsymbol{v}_2$ is given in Fig. 6–4b. Another method for determining the kinetic energy is simpler than the straightforward velocity method, especially when the vector geometry is rather complex. As an alternative to the velocity method we shall determine the velocity by means of the configuration of the geometry.

$$x_1 = l_1 \sin \theta_1 \qquad\qquad y_1 = l_1 \cos \theta_1$$

$$x_2 = l_1 \sin \theta_1 + l_2 \sin \theta_2 \qquad y_2 = l_1 \cos \theta_1 + l_2 \cos \theta_2$$

Differentiating the above equations with respect to time, we get

$$\dot x_1 = l_1\dot\theta_1 \cos \theta_1 \qquad\qquad \dot y_1 = -l_1\dot\theta_1 \sin \theta_1$$

$$\dot x_2 = l_1\dot\theta_1 \cos \theta_1 + l_2\dot\theta_2 \cos \theta_2 \qquad \dot y_2 = -l_1\dot\theta_1 \sin \theta_1 - l_2\dot\theta_2 \sin \theta_2$$

Then

$$v_1{}^2 = l_1{}^2\dot\theta_1{}^2$$

$$v_2{}^2 = l_1{}^2\dot\theta_1{}^2 + 2l_1 l_2 \cos (\theta_1 - \theta_2) + l_2{}^2\dot\theta_2{}^2$$

and

$$T = \tfrac{1}{2}m_1 v_1{}^2 + \tfrac{1}{2}m_2 v_2{}^2$$

$$T = \tfrac{1}{2}m_1 l_1{}^2\dot\theta_1{}^2 + \tfrac{1}{2}m_2[l_1{}^2\dot\theta_1{}^2 + 2l_1 l_2\dot\theta_1\dot\theta_2 \cos (\theta_1 - \theta_2) + l_2{}^2\dot\theta_2{}^2]$$

To find the potential energy, let us take as the standard position the static equilibrium position which is along the y axis.

$$V = m_1 g(l_1 - y_1) + m_2 g(l_1 + l_2 - y_2)$$

$$V = m_1 g l_1(1 - \cos \theta_1) + m_2 g[l_1(1 - \cos \theta_1) + l_2(1 - \cos \theta_2)]$$

Since we are dealing with a conservative system, the Lagrange equation is:

$$\frac{d}{dt}\left(\frac{\partial T}{\partial \dot q_k}\right) - \frac{\partial T}{\partial q_k} + \frac{\partial V}{\partial q_k} = 0$$

$$\frac{d}{dt}\left(\frac{\partial T}{\partial \dot q_1}\right) = \frac{d}{dt}[m_1 l_1{}^2\dot\theta_1 + m_2 l_1{}^2\dot\theta_1 + m_2 l_1 l_2\dot\theta_2 \cos (\theta_1 - \theta_2)]$$

$$= (m_1 + m_2)l_1{}^2\ddot\theta_1 + m_2 l_1 l_2\ddot\theta_2 \cos (\theta_1 - \theta_2)$$
$$\qquad\qquad - m_2 l_1 l_2\dot\theta_2(\dot\theta_1 - \dot\theta_2) \sin (\theta_1 - \theta_2)$$

$$\frac{d}{dt}\left(\frac{\partial T}{\partial \dot q_2}\right) = \frac{d}{dt}[m_2 l_1 l_2\dot\theta_1 \cos (\theta_1 - \theta_2) + m_2 l_2{}^2\dot\theta_2{}^2]$$

$$= m_2[l_1 l_2\ddot\theta_1 \cos (\theta_1 - \theta_2) - l_1 l_2\dot\theta_1(\dot\theta_1 - \dot\theta_2) \sin (\theta_1 - \theta_2) + l_2{}^2\ddot\theta_2]$$

$$-\frac{\partial T}{\partial q_1} = m_2 l_1 l_2 \dot\theta_1 \dot\theta_2 \sin (\theta_1 - \theta_2)$$

$$-\frac{\partial T}{\partial q^2} = -m_2 l_1 l_2 \dot\theta_1 \dot\theta_2 \sin (\theta_1 - \theta_2)$$

$$\frac{\partial V}{\partial q_1} = (m_1 + m_2)g l_1 \sin \theta_1$$

$$\frac{\partial V}{\partial q_2} = m_2 g l_2 \sin \theta_2$$

Now we substitute the component parts into the Lagrange equations.

$$(m_1 + m_2)l_1{}^2\ddot\theta_1 + m_2 l_1 l_2 \cos (\theta_1 - \theta_2)\ddot\theta_2 - m_2 l_1 l_2 \dot\theta_1(\dot\theta_1 - \dot\theta_2) \sin (\theta_1 - \theta_2)$$
$$+ m_2 l_1 l_2 \dot\theta_1 \dot\theta_2 \sin (\theta_1 - \theta_2) + (m_1 + m_2)g l_1 \sin \theta_1 = 0 \quad (a)$$

$$m_2 l_1 l_2 \cos (\theta_1 - \theta_2)\ddot\theta_1 - m_2 l_1 l_2 \dot\theta_1(\dot\theta_1 - \dot\theta_2) \sin (\theta_1 - \theta_2)$$
$$+ m_2 l_2{}^2\ddot\theta_2 + m_2 g l_2 \sin \theta_2 = 0 \quad (b)$$

We now linearize Eqs. (a) and (b) by restricting the oscillations to small angles and neglecting quantities that are of order two or higher. Then $\sin \theta \doteqdot \theta$, $\cos (\theta_1 - \theta_2) \doteqdot 1$, and $\dot\theta_1 \dot\theta_2$, $\dot\theta_1{}^2$, $\dot\theta_2{}^2$, etc., may be neglected. The linearized equations are

$$(m_1 + m_2)l_1\ddot\theta_1 + m_2 l_2 \ddot\theta_2 + (m_1 + m_2)g\theta_1 = 0 \quad (c)$$

$$l_1\ddot\theta_1 + l_2\ddot\theta_2 + g\theta_2 = 0 \quad (d)$$

Eqs. (c) and (d) are equations of motion for a double pendulum restricted to small oscillations.

In determining the natural frequencies of the above equations, let us simplify the solution by declaring that $l_2 = 2l_1$ and $m_2 = 2m_1$. Then the differential equations become

$$3l_1\ddot\theta_1 + 4l_1\ddot\theta_2 + 3g\theta_1 = 0$$

$$l_1\ddot\theta_1 + 2l_1\ddot\theta_2 + g\theta_2 = 0$$

We now assume solutions in the form of $\theta_1 = \Theta_1 \cos \omega_n t$, $\theta_2 = \Theta_2 \cos \omega_n t$. The determinant for the characteristic equation becomes

$$|D| \equiv \begin{vmatrix} 3(g - l_1\omega_n{}^2)_1 & -4l_1\omega_n{}^2{}_2 \\ -l_1\omega_n{}^2{}_1 & (g - 2l_1\omega_n{}^2)_2 \end{vmatrix}$$

Then the characteristic equation is

$$3(g - l_1\omega_n{}^2)(g - 2l_1\omega_n{}^2) - 4l_1{}^2\omega_n{}^4 = 0$$

$$\omega_n{}^4 - \frac{9g}{2l_1}\omega_n{}^2 + \frac{3g^2}{2l_1{}^2} = 0$$

$$\omega_n{}^2 = \frac{9g}{4l_1} \mp \frac{\sqrt{81g^2/4l_1{}^2 - 6g^2/l_1{}^2}}{2}$$

$$\omega_n{}^2 = 0.36g/l_1, \; 4.14g/l_1$$

Example. Consider a disc of radius a rotating in the horizontal plane at a constant angular velocity, Ω. Attached to the ends of a diameter of the disc are two rods of length $2l$ and mass m. The rods are attached by pins and are free to oscillate about the pins in the horizontal plane only. The pins are lubricated so that at the pin joints a torsional damping constant of c lbs-in.-sec. exists. If a forcing torque of $M_0 \cos \nu t$ is applied to the disc, determine, first, the equations of motion, and second, the motions of the three elements.

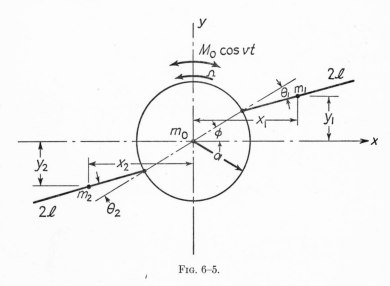

FIG. 6–5.

SOLUTION. The three generalized coordinates are ϕ, θ_1, and θ_2 as depicted in Fig. 6–5.

$$x_0 = 0 \qquad\qquad\qquad y_0 = 0$$

$$x_1 = a \cos \phi + l \cos (\phi + \theta_1) \qquad y_1 = a \sin \phi + l \sin (\phi + \theta_1)$$

$$x_2 = -a \cos \phi - l \cos (\phi + \theta_2) \qquad y_2 = -a \sin \phi - l \sin (\phi + \theta_2)$$

We now differentiate with respect to time the above equations to determine the velocity.

$$\dot{x}_1 = -a\dot\phi \sin \phi - l(\dot\phi + \dot\theta_1) \sin (\phi + \theta_1)$$

$$\dot{y}_1 = a\dot\phi \cos \phi + l(\dot\phi + \dot\theta_1) \cos (\phi + \theta_1)$$

$$\dot{x}_2 = a\dot{\phi} \sin \phi + l(\dot{\phi} + \dot{\theta}_2) \sin (\phi + \theta_2)$$

$$\dot{y}_2 = a\dot{\phi} \cos \phi + l(\dot{\phi} + \dot{\theta}_2) \cos (\phi + \theta_2)$$

Now

$$v_1{}^2 = \dot{x}_1{}^2 + \dot{y}_1{}^2$$

$$v_1{}^2 = a^2\dot{\phi}^2 + l^2(\dot{\phi} + \dot{\theta}_1)^2 + 2al\dot{\phi}(\dot{\phi} + \dot{\theta}_1) \sin \phi \sin (\phi + \theta_1)$$
$$+ 2al\dot{\phi}(\dot{\phi} + \dot{\theta}_1) \cos \phi \cos (\phi + \theta_1)$$

$$v_1{}^2 = a^2\dot{\phi}^2 + l^2(\dot{\phi} + \dot{\theta}_1)^2 + 2al\dot{\phi}(\dot{\phi} + \dot{\theta}_1) \cos \theta_1$$

In like manner,

$$v_2{}^2 = a^2\dot{\phi}^2 + l^2(\dot{\phi} + \dot{\theta}_2{}^2) + 2al\dot{\phi}(\dot{\phi} + \dot{\theta}_2) \cos \theta_2$$

The total kinetic energy is:

$$T = \frac{I_0\dot{\phi}^2}{2} + \frac{I_1\dot{\theta}^2{}_{1abs}}{2} + \frac{m_1v_1{}^2}{2} + \frac{I_2\dot{\theta}^2{}_{2abs}}{2} + \frac{mv_2{}^2}{2}$$

where

$$I_0 = \frac{m_0a^2}{2} \qquad I_1 = I_2 = \frac{4ml^2}{12} = \frac{ml^2}{3}$$

Then

$$T = \frac{m_0a^2}{4}\dot{\phi}^2 + \frac{ml^2}{3}(\dot{\phi}+\dot{\theta}_1)^2 + \frac{m}{2}[a^2\dot{\phi}^2 + l^2(\dot{\phi}+\dot{\theta}_1)^2 + 2al\dot{\phi}(\dot{\phi}+\dot{\theta}_1)\cos\theta_1]$$

$$+ \frac{ml^2}{3}(\dot{\phi}+\dot{\theta}_2)^2 + \frac{m}{2}[a^2\dot{\phi}^2 + l^2(\dot{\phi}+\dot{\theta}_2)^2 + 2al\dot{\phi}(\dot{\phi}+\dot{\theta}_2)\cos\theta_2]$$

$V_0 = V_1 = V_2 = 0$ as a result of placing the disc in the horizontal plane. It is interesting to note that had the disc been placed in the vertical plane, the potential energy would be negligible, since we may assume that the centrifugal field replaces the gravitational field.

$$F_c = \tfrac{1}{2}c(\dot{\theta}_1{}^2 + \dot{\theta}_2{}^2)$$

$$Q_\phi = M_0 \cos vt \qquad Q_{\theta_1} = Q_{\theta_2} = 0$$

The Lagrange equation covering the above problem is

$$\frac{d}{dt}\left(\frac{\partial T}{\partial \dot{q}_k}\right) - \frac{\partial T}{\partial q_k} + \frac{\partial V}{\partial q_k} + \frac{\partial F_c}{\partial \dot{q}_k} = Q_k \qquad (a)$$

Then

$$\frac{d}{dt}\left(\frac{\partial T}{\partial \dot{\phi}}\right) = \frac{d}{dt}\left[\frac{m_0a^2}{2} + \tfrac{2}{3}ml^2(\dot{\phi} + \dot{\theta}_1) + \frac{m}{2}\{2a^2\dot{\phi} + 2l^2(\dot{\phi} + \dot{\theta}_1)\right.$$

$$+ 2al(2\dot{\phi} + \dot{\theta}_1)\cos\theta_1\} + \tfrac{2}{3}ml^2(\dot{\phi} + \dot{\theta}_2) + \frac{m}{2}\{2a^2\dot{\phi}$$

$$\left. + 2l^2(\dot{\phi} + \dot{\theta}_2) + 2al(2\dot{\phi} + \dot{\theta}_2)\cos\theta_2\}\right]$$

$$\frac{d}{dt}\left(\frac{\partial T}{\partial \dot{\phi}}\right) = \left[\frac{m_0 a^2}{2} + m\{\tfrac{10}{3}l^2 + 2a^2 + 2al(\cos\theta_1 + \cos\theta_2)\}\right]\ddot{\phi}$$

$$+ [m\{\tfrac{5}{3}l^2 + al\cos\theta_1\}]\ddot{\theta}_1 + [m\{\tfrac{5}{3}l^2 + al\cos\theta_2\}]\ddot{\theta}_2$$
$$-[mal\{2\dot{\phi} + \dot{\theta}_1\}\dot{\theta}_1]\sin\theta_1 - [mal\{2\dot{\phi} + \dot{\theta}_2\}\dot{\theta}_2]\sin\theta_2$$

$$\frac{d}{dt}\left(\frac{\partial T}{\partial \dot{\theta}_1}\right) = \frac{d}{dt}\left[\frac{2ml^2}{3}(\dot{\phi} + \dot{\theta}_1) + ml^2(\dot{\phi} + \dot{\theta}_1) + mal\dot{\phi}\cos\theta_1\right]$$

$$= [\tfrac{5}{3}ml^2 + mal\cos\theta_1]\ddot{\phi} + \tfrac{5}{3}ml^2\ddot{\theta}_1 - mal\dot{\phi}\dot{\theta}_1\sin\theta_1$$

$$\frac{d}{dt}\left(\frac{\partial T}{\partial \dot{\theta}_2}\right) = [\tfrac{5}{3}ml^2 + mal\cos\theta_2]\ddot{\phi} + \tfrac{5}{3}ml^2\ddot{\theta}_2 - mal\dot{\phi}\dot{\theta}_2\sin\theta_2$$

$$-\frac{\partial T}{\partial \phi} = 0$$

$$-\frac{\partial T}{\partial \theta_1} = mal\dot{\phi}(\dot{\phi} + \dot{\theta}_1)\sin\theta_1$$

$$-\frac{\partial T}{\partial \theta_2} = mal\dot{\phi}(\dot{\phi} + \dot{\theta}_2)\sin\theta_2$$

$$\frac{\partial V}{\partial \phi} = \frac{\partial V}{\partial \theta_1} = \frac{\partial V}{\partial \theta_2} = 0$$

$$\frac{\partial F_c}{\partial \dot{\theta}_1} = c\dot{\theta}_1$$

$$\frac{\partial F_c}{\partial \dot{\theta}_2} = c\dot{\theta}_2$$

$$Q_\phi = M_0 \cos \nu t$$

$$Q_{\theta 1} = Q_{\theta 2} = 0$$

Substituting the proper values into Eq. (a), we get:

$$\left[\frac{m_0 a^2}{2} + m\{\tfrac{10}{3}l^2 + 2a^2 + 2al(\cos\theta_1 + \cos\theta_2)\}\right]\ddot{\phi}$$

$$+ [m\{\tfrac{5}{3}l^2 + al\cos\theta_1\}]\ddot{\theta}_1 + [m\{\tfrac{5}{3}l^2 + al\cos\theta_2\}]\ddot{\theta}_2$$
$$- mal\{2\dot{\phi} + \dot{\theta}_1\}\dot{\theta}_1\sin\theta_1 - mal\{2\dot{\phi} + \dot{\theta}_2\}\dot{\theta}_2\sin\theta_2 = M_0\cos\nu t$$

$$[m\{\tfrac{5}{3}l^2 + al\cos\theta_1\}]\ddot{\phi} + \tfrac{5}{3}ml^2\ddot{\theta}_1 - mal\dot{\phi}\dot{\theta}_1\sin\theta_1$$
$$+ mal\dot{\phi}(\dot{\phi} + \dot{\theta}_1)\sin\theta_1 + c\dot{\theta}_1 = 0$$

$$[m\{\tfrac{5}{3}l^2 + al\cos\theta_2\}]\ddot{\phi} + \tfrac{5}{3}ml^2\ddot{\theta}_2 - mal\dot{\phi}\dot{\theta}_2\sin\theta_2$$
$$+ mal\dot{\phi}(\dot{\phi} + \dot{\theta}_2)\sin\theta_2 + c\dot{\theta}_2 = 0$$

The three above equations are the equations of motion in the system. Since the equations are nonlinear, they will have to be linearized. We will linearize the equations in two steps. The equilibrium position of ϕ is Ωt. We superpose upon the equilibrium position a small angle which will be the oscillation of the disc about the equilibrium position.

Then

$$\phi = \Omega t + \psi$$

where ψ is the small oscillatory angle. The derivatives of ϕ with respect to time are

$$\dot{\phi} = \Omega + \dot{\psi}$$

and

$$\ddot{\phi} = \ddot{\psi}$$

The above relations are now substituted into the equation of motion.

$$\left[\frac{m_0 a^2}{2} + m\{\tfrac{10}{3}l^2 + 2a^2 + 2al(\cos\theta_1 + \cos\theta_2)\}\right]\ddot{\psi}$$
$$+ [m\{\tfrac{5}{3}l^2 + al\cos\theta_1\}]\ddot{\theta}_1 + [m\{\tfrac{5}{3}l^2 + al\cos\theta_2\}]\ddot{\theta}_2$$
$$- mal\{2\Omega + 2\dot{\psi} + \dot{\theta}_1\}\dot{\theta}_1\sin\theta_1$$
$$- mal\{2\Omega + 2\dot{\psi} + \dot{\theta}_2\}\dot{\theta}_2\sin\theta_2 = M_0\cos\nu t$$

$$[m\{\tfrac{5}{3}l^2 + al\cos\theta_1\}]\ddot{\psi} + \tfrac{5}{3}ml^2\ddot{\theta}_1 - mal\{\Omega + \dot{\psi}\}\dot{\theta}_1\sin\theta_1$$
$$+ mal\{\Omega^2 + 2\Omega\dot{\psi} + \dot{\psi}^2 + (\Omega + \dot{\psi})\dot{\theta}_1\}\sin\theta_1 + c\dot{\theta}_1 = 0$$

$$[m\{\tfrac{5}{3}l^2 + al\cos\theta_2\}]\ddot{\psi} + \tfrac{5}{3}ml^2\ddot{\theta}_2 - mal\{\Omega + \dot{\psi}\}\dot{\theta}_2\sin\theta_2$$
$$+ mal\{\Omega^2 + 2\Omega\dot{\psi} + \dot{\psi}^2 + (\Omega + \dot{\psi})\dot{\theta}_2\}\sin\theta_2 + c\dot{\theta}_2 = 0$$

We now take the second step toward the completion of the linearization; namely, we declare that all angles of oscillation are small and that any quantity of order two or higher may be neglected. As a result of the foregoing, $\sin\theta \doteqdot \theta$, $\cos\theta \doteqdot 1$, and $\dot{\psi}\theta$, $\dot{\psi}\dot{\theta}$, $\dot{\psi}^2$, etc., may be neglected.

The equations of motion now are:

$$\left[\frac{m_0 a^2}{2} + m\{\tfrac{10}{3}l^2 + 2a^2 + 4al\}\right]\ddot{\psi} + [m\{\tfrac{5}{3}l^2 + al\}]\ddot{\theta}_1$$
$$+ [m\{\tfrac{5}{3}l^2 + al\}]\ddot{\theta}_2 = M_0\cos\nu t$$
$$[m\{\tfrac{5}{3}l^2 + al\}]\ddot{\psi} + \tfrac{5}{3}ml^2\ddot{\theta}_1 + mal\Omega^2\theta_1 + c\dot{\theta}_1 = 0$$
$$[m\{\tfrac{5}{3}l^2 + al\}]\ddot{\psi} + \tfrac{5}{3}ml^2\ddot{\theta}_2 + mal\Omega^2\theta_2 + c\dot{\theta}_2 = 0$$

The long and laborious but not too mentally taxing procedure for determining the equations of motion has been accomplished. We must now proceed to solve these equations. The method outlined in Section 2–3 becomes quite involved, for it entails dealing with six simultaneous equations. The solution of the above equations can be simplified by transforming the R.H.S. of each equation into the complex form and assuming a solution in complex form. That is, $e^{i\nu t} = \cos \nu t + i \sin \nu t$, where $e^{i\nu t}$ is a single rotating vector which is the result of the two trigonometric terms. Since $M_0 \cos \nu t$ is the real part of $M_0 e^{i\nu t}$, we can replace the rotating vector $M_0 \cos \nu t$ by $M_0 e^{i\nu t}$. In so doing, we must remember that ψ, θ_1, and θ_2 are now complex in form: that is, ψ, θ_1 and θ_2 are in the form of $z = a + ib$. We now assume solutions in the form of

$$\psi = \Psi e^{i\nu t}$$

$$\theta_1 = \Theta_1 e^{i\nu t}$$

$$\theta_2 = \Theta_2 e^{i\nu t}$$

The first and second derivatives with respect to time of the assumed solutions are

$$\dot{\psi} = i\nu\Psi e^{i\nu t} \qquad \ddot{\psi} = -\nu^2\Psi e^{i\nu t}$$

$$\dot{\theta}_1 = i\nu\Theta_1 e^{i\nu t} \qquad \ddot{\theta}_1 = -\nu^2\Theta_1 e^{i\nu t}$$

$$\dot{\theta}_2 = i\nu\Theta_2 e^{i\nu t} \qquad \ddot{\theta}_2 = -\nu^2\Theta_2 e^{i\nu t}$$

Upon substitution of the above, we get

$$\left[\frac{m_0 a^2}{2} + m(\tfrac{10}{3}l^2 + 2a^2 + 4al)\right]\Psi + m(\tfrac{5}{3}l^2 + al)\Theta_1$$
$$+ m(\tfrac{5}{3}l^2 + al)\Theta_2 = -\frac{M_0}{\nu^2}$$

$$m(\tfrac{5}{3}l^2 + al)\nu^2\Psi + \tfrac{5}{3}ml^2\nu^2\Theta_1 - mal\Omega^2\Theta_1 - ic\nu\Theta_1 = 0$$

$$m(\tfrac{5}{3}l^2 + al)\nu^2\Psi + \tfrac{5}{3}ml^2\nu^2\Theta_2 - mal\Omega^2\Theta_2 - ic\nu\Theta_2 = 0$$

We now arrange the equations in a form to facilitate solution by determinates.

Ψ	Θ_1	Θ_2	
$\dfrac{m_0 a^2}{2} + m\{\tfrac{10}{3}l^2 + 2a^2 + 4al\}$	$m\{\tfrac{5}{3}l^2 + al\}$	$m\{\tfrac{5}{3}l^2 + al\}$	$= -\dfrac{M_0}{\nu^2}$
$m\{\tfrac{5}{3}l^2 + al\}\nu^2$	$\{\tfrac{5}{3}ml^2\nu^2 - mal\Omega^2 - i\nu c\}$		$= 0$
$m\{\tfrac{5}{3}l^2 + al\}\nu^2$		$\{\tfrac{5}{3}ml^2\nu^2 - mal\Omega^2 - i\nu c\}$	$= 0$

Upon simplification the determinant becomes:

$$|D| = -\{\tfrac{5}{3}ml^2\nu^2 - mal\Omega^2 - ic\nu\}\,\Delta$$

where

$$\Delta = \left\{ \frac{m_0 m a^2 l}{2} (a\Omega^2 - \tfrac{5}{3}l\nu^2) + 4m^2 l^2 a^2 \left(\Omega^2 - \frac{\nu^2}{3} \right) + 2m^2 al\Omega^2 (\tfrac{5}{3}l^2 + a^2) \right.$$

$$\left. + ic\nu \left[\frac{m_0 a^2}{2} + m(\tfrac{1.0}{3}l^2 + 2a^2 + 4al) \right] \right\}$$

Then

$$\Psi = \frac{- \dfrac{M_0}{\nu^2}[ml(a\Omega^2 - \tfrac{5}{3}l\nu^2) + ic\nu]}{\Delta}$$

$$\Theta_1 = -\frac{M_0 m^2 l^2 (\tfrac{5}{3}l + a)^2}{\Delta}$$

$$\Theta_2 = -\frac{M_0 m^2 l^2 (\tfrac{5}{3}l + a)^2}{\Delta}$$

The three amplitudes are in complex form of

$$z = \frac{a + ib}{c + id}$$

We may transform z as follows:

$$z = \frac{(a + ib)(c - id)}{(c + id)(c - id)} = \frac{ac + bd + i(bc - ad)}{c^2 + d^2} \quad \frac{\angle\tan^{-1}\dfrac{b}{a}}{\angle\tan^{-1}\dfrac{d}{c}}$$

The magnitude of z as a vector is

$$|z| = \sqrt{\frac{(ac + bd)^2 + (bc - ad)^2}{(c^2 + d^2)^2}}$$

$$|z| = \sqrt{\frac{(a^2 + b^2)(c^2 + d^2)}{(c^2 + d^2)^2}}$$

$$|z| = \sqrt{\frac{a^2 + b^2}{c^2 + d^2}}$$

The direction of the vector z is $\alpha_1 - \alpha_2$ where $\alpha_1 = \tan^{-1}(b/a)$ and $\alpha_2 = \tan^{-1} d/c$; then

$$\psi = \frac{- \dfrac{M_0}{\nu^2} \sqrt{m^2 l^2 (a\Omega^2 - \tfrac{5}{3}l\nu^2)^2 + c^2\nu^2} \cos(\nu t + \alpha_1 - \alpha_2)}{\sqrt{\left[m_0 m a^2 l(a\Omega^2 - \tfrac{5}{6}l\nu^2) + 4m^2 l^2 a^2 \left(\Omega^2 - \dfrac{\nu^2}{3} \right) + 2m^2 al\Omega^2 (\tfrac{5}{3}l^2 + a^2) \right]^2 + c^2\nu^2 \left[\dfrac{m_0 a^2}{2} + m(\tfrac{1.0}{3}l^2 + 2a^2 + 4al) \right]^2}}$$

where

$$\alpha_1 = \tan^{-1} \frac{cv}{m^2 l^2 (a\Omega^2 - \frac{5}{3}lv^2)}$$

and

$$\alpha_2 = \tan^{-1} \frac{cv\left[\dfrac{m_0 a^2}{2} + m(\frac{10}{3}l^2 + 2a^2 + 4al)\right]}{m_0 ma^2 l\{a\Omega^2 - \frac{5}{6}lv^2\} + 4m^2 l^2 a^2\left(\Omega^2 - \dfrac{v^2}{3}\right) + m^2 al\Omega^2(\frac{5}{3}l^2 + a^2)}$$

$$\theta_1 = \theta_2 = \frac{-M_0 m^2 l^2 (\frac{5}{3}l + a)^2 \cos(vt - \alpha_2)}{\sqrt{\left[m_0 ma^2 l\{a\Omega^2 - \frac{5}{6}lv^2\} + 4ml^2 a^2\left(\Omega^2 - \dfrac{v^2}{3}\right) + 2m^2 al\Omega^2(\frac{5}{3}l^2 + a^2)\right]^2 + c^2 v^2 \left[\dfrac{m_0 a^2}{2} + 2m(\frac{5}{3}l^2 + a^2 + 2al)\right]^2}}$$

where α_2 is defined above.

The solution of the problem is completed. If the natural frequency of the system is desired, we need only set $|D| \equiv 0$ and solve for v, which will then be the natural frequency.

BIBLIOGRAPHY

BRONWELL, ARTHUR. *Advanced Mathematics in Physics and Engineering.* New York: McGraw-Hill Book Co., Inc., 1953.

CONSTANT, F. WOODBRIDGE. *Theoretical Physics.* Cambridge, Mass.: Addison-Wesley Press, Inc., 1954.

KÁRMÁN, THEODORE VON, and BIOT, MAURICE A. *Mathematical Methods in Engineering.* New York: McGraw-Hill Book Co., Inc., 1940.

MILLER, FREDERIC H. *Partial Differential Equations.* New York: John Wiley & Sons, Inc., 1941.

ROUTH, EDWARD JOHN. *A Treatise on Dynamics of a Particle.* New York: G. E. Stechert & Co., [1898].

SMART, E. HOWARD. *Advanced Dynamics.* Vol. II. London: Macmillan & Co., Ltd., 1951.

TIMOSHENKO, S. *Vibration Problems in Engineering.* 1st ed. Princeton, N. J.: D. Van Nostrand Co., Inc., 1928.

PROBLEMS

6-1. Find all the first and second partial derivatives of $\theta = \sin(3x + y^2)$.

6-2. Find all the first and second partial derivatives of $x = \rho^2 \sin(2\theta - \rho^2)$.

6-3. Find all the first and second partial derivatives of $\theta = \sqrt{x^2 + y^2} + \sin xy$.

6-4. Find the total derivative of z with respect to t; $z = 4x^2 + 3xy - y^2$, $x = t^2 - 1$, $y = t^3 - t$.

6-5. Find the total derivative of θ with respect to t; $\theta = x \cos y + y \cos x$, $x = e^t$, $y = e^{-t}$.

6-6. Find the first partial derivatives of θ with respect to t_1 and t_2. $\theta = \sin xy - x \sin y$, $x = 4t_1^2 + 2t_2$, $y = 3t_1 - t_2^2$.

6-7. Find the first partial derivatives of θ with respect to t_1 and t_2; $\theta = x^3y + 2xy^3$, $x = 2t_1 + t_2$, $y = t_1 - 5t_2$.

6-8. Determine the D.E. of motion for the hinged rods whose masses are m_1 and m_2 and are shown in Fig. P6–8. Determine the equations of motion and the natural frequencies for small angles of oscillation.

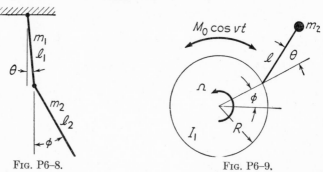

FIG. P6–8.   FIG. P6–9.

6-9. A disc which rotates at a constant angular velocity Ω has an oscillating torque $M_0 \cos \nu t$ acting on it. A simple pendulum of mass m_2 is attached as shown in Fig. P6–9. If the pendulum can oscillate only in the plane of rotation, derive the differential equations of motion for small pendulum oscillations. Show that if $R\Omega^2/l = \nu^2$, the pendulum acts as a vibration-absorber. Any change of potential energy due to the oscillation of the pendulum may be neglected, since the gravitational field is very small compared to the centrifugal field. What limits the practical application of the centrifugal-pendulum absorber?

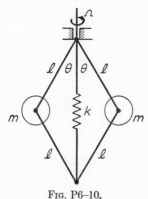

FIG. P6–10.

6-10. Two masses are supported by four weightless rods on a spring as shown in Fig. P6–10. The masses are rotated at a constant angular velocity Ω. If the spring has a length l in its unstretched position, determine the oscillation of the masses. (*Hint:* Let $\theta = \theta_0 + \phi$, where θ_0 is the equilibrium angle for a given Ω, and ϕ is a small perturbation superposed on the equilibrium position. θ_0 may be determined by setting the acceleration equal to zero.)

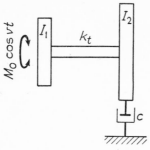

FIG. P6–11.

6–11. Determine the differential equations of motion for the system shown in Fig. P6–11, using the Lagrangian method. Determine the equation of motion for this system if $I_2 = 2I_1$.

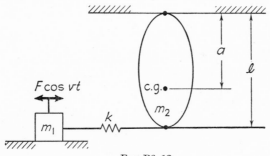

FIG. P6–12.

6–12. A mass m_1 which rests on a frictionless plane is connected to a compound pendulum by means of a spring as shown in Fig. P6–12. The mass m_1 is activated by a force $F \cos \nu t$. Determine the equations of motion for the system if the oscillation of the pendulum is restricted to small angles. The moment of inertia of the pendulum about its center of gravity is $I_{\text{c.g.}} = m_2 r^2$, where r is the radius of gyration.

CHAPTER 7

VIBRATION IN A CONTINUOUS MEDIUM

7-1. Introduction. It is not always possible to simplify a problem by lumping the masses independently of the springs or elastic elements of a system. In nature we find that the mass and the elasticity of a system are distributed in some manner over the entire system. In fact, the mass and the elasticity are inseparable. It is this inseparability that leads us to a new class of problems: vibrations in a continuous medium. We define a continuous medium as one in which the mass and elasticity are distributed, in many cases uniformly, over the entire system. A shaft, a beam, and a string are examples of systems which fall into the category of continuous mediums.

It is true that we can replace a continuous-medium system by an infinite series of lumped masses interconnected by an infinite number of springs. The solution to a problem containing an infinite number of masses and springs would be so cumbersome that the more exact and direct approach of dealing with the continuous system as such is preferred. The mathematics involved in dealing with a continuous system appear to be fairly complicated. The technique, however, for solving the partial differential equations which result from an analysis of a continuous system is not so difficult as will appear at first glance. A single technique will apply to most problems, and the effort necessary to master that technique is well worth while.

7-2. Vibrating String. The lateral vibration of a string is an uninteresting problem from an engineering point of view. It will best serve our purpose, however, to analyze the vibrations of a taut string before passing on to more interesting problems. Via the taut string, we will be able to present the technique for solving a linear partial differential equation.

Fig. 7–1a represents a string in its deflected position. We will assume that the initial tension in the string is sufficiently great so that no appreciable change in tension occurs when the string is in a deflected configuration. To determine the differential equation, we draw a free-body diagram, Fig. 7–1b, of an element Δx in length. Let S be the initial tension in the string. Newton's laws require that the sum of the forces in the vertical direction be equal to mass times the acceleration in vertical direction. Expressed mathematically, we see that

$$S \sin \beta - S \sin \alpha = m \, \Delta x \, \frac{\partial^2 y}{\partial t^2} \tag{7-1}$$

where m is the mass per unit length and $\partial^2 y / \partial t^2$ is the acceleration in the vertical direction. However,

$$\frac{\partial y}{\partial x}\bigg|_{x} = \tan \alpha$$

and $\tag{7-2}$

$$\frac{\partial y}{\partial x}\bigg|_{x+\Delta x} = \tan \beta$$

We now restrict the vibration of string to be of small amplitudes, and as a result,

$$\sin \alpha \fallingdotseq \tan \alpha$$

and $\tag{7-3}$

$$\sin \beta \fallingdotseq \tan \beta$$

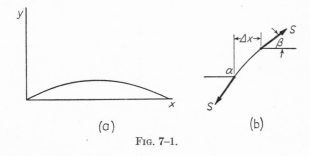

(a)   (b)

FIG. 7–1.

By substituting Eqs. (7–2) and (7–3) into Eq. (7–1), we get

$$\frac{\partial^2 y}{\partial t^2} = \frac{S}{m} \left[\frac{\dfrac{\partial y}{\partial x}\bigg|_{x+\Delta x} - \dfrac{\partial y}{\partial x}\bigg|_{x}}{\Delta x} \right] \tag{7-4}$$

If we now let Δx approach zero in the limit, the term contained in the bracket becomes $\partial^2 y / \partial x^2$. Eq. (7–1) may now be written as

$$\frac{\partial^2 y}{\partial t^2} = a^2 \frac{\partial^2 y}{\partial x^2} \tag{7-5}$$

where

$$a^2 = \frac{S}{m}$$

A special meaning can be imposed upon a. Since S is the force acting in the string and m is the mass per unit length, we can state that

$$a = \sqrt{\frac{S}{m}} = \sqrt{\frac{\sigma A}{\rho A}} \qquad (7\text{-}6)$$

where σ = stress
ρ = mass density
A = cross-sectional area of string.

Since $\sigma = E\epsilon$, where E is the Young's modulus, and ϵ is the unit strain, then

$$a = \sqrt{\frac{E}{\rho}} \sqrt{\epsilon} \qquad (7\text{-}7)$$

It can be shown that the speed of sound, c, in a particular medium is

$$c = \sqrt{\frac{E}{\rho}} \qquad (7\text{-}8)$$

We then may write that

$$a = c\sqrt{\epsilon} \qquad (7\text{-}9)$$

Since ϵ is a dimensionless quantity, a has the dimensions of velocity. The physical interpretation of a is that its contribution to the vibration will be governed by the velocity of sound propagation of the particular medium times the square root of the strain initially imposed upon the string.

Eq. (7-5) is the basic differential equation for the vibration of a taut string. There are many approaches to solving a partial differential equation of the above type. We will try to solve Eq. (7-5) by finding a particular solution. For a particular solution, it is necessary that we have four boundary conditions. Therefore, we must define our problem in a more specific fashion than we have. Let us select the initial displacement conditions as a sinusoidal of amplitude y_0. The four boundary conditions then are

$(a) \qquad y(0,t) = 0 \qquad\qquad (b) \qquad\qquad y(L,t) = 0$

$(c) \qquad y(x,0) = y_0 \sin \dfrac{\pi x}{L} \qquad (d) \qquad \dfrac{\partial y}{\partial t}\bigg|_{t=0} = 0$ $\qquad (7\text{-}10)$

Conditions (a) and (b) result from the fact that the ends of the string are firmly fastened to the ground. The initial displacement is given by (c), and (d) governs the condition so that initially the velocity is zero.

The method that we shall use is known as separating variables. This method will not always yield a solution, but it is general enough to warrant trying for a first solution. We assume a solution in the form of a product of quantities each of which is a function of one of the independent variables:

$$y(x,t) = X(x) \cdot T(t) \qquad (7\text{--}11)$$

where $X(x)$ and $T(t)$ are each functions of a single variable x or t as noted. We now differentiate Eq. (7–11) with respect to x and to t, respectively, until we have the same order of derivatives as we have in Eq. (7–5). That is

$$\frac{\partial^2 y}{\partial x^2} = T(t)\frac{\partial^2 X}{\partial x^2}$$

and $\qquad\qquad\qquad\qquad\qquad\qquad\qquad\qquad\qquad\qquad\qquad (7\text{--}12)$

$$\frac{\partial^2 y}{\partial t^2} = X(x)\frac{\partial^2 T}{\partial t^2}$$

Substituting the derivatives into Eq. (7–5), we get

$$XT'' = a^2 TX'' \qquad (7\text{--}13)$$

where the primes denote the order of differentiation. Since X and T are independent of each other, we may rearrange Eq. (7–13) so that the variables are separated:

$$\frac{T''}{a^2 T} = \frac{X''}{X} \qquad (7\text{--}14)$$

Upon examining Eq. (7–14) we can draw the conclusion that since $X(x)$ and $T(t)$ are independent of each other, then both the R.H.S. and the L.H.S. of the equation must be equal to a constant, say $-\lambda^2$. Then

$$\frac{T''}{a^2 T} = \frac{X''}{X} = -\lambda^2 \qquad (7\text{--}15)$$

The choice of the negative λ^2 is a bit of farsightedness on our part and will be explained shortly. Eq. (7–13) can now be written as two ordinary differential equations:

$$X'' + \lambda^2 X = 0$$

and $\qquad\qquad\qquad\qquad\qquad\qquad\qquad\qquad\qquad\qquad\qquad (7\text{--}16)$

$$T'' + a^2\lambda^2 T = 0$$

It now becomes apparent why negative λ^2 was selected. Eqs. (7–16) will both yield trigonometric functions as solutions. We can expect, since we are dealing with a vibratory problem, at least one branch of the solution to be of trigonometric form (the branch which is a function of time will always be trigonometric). Had a positive λ^2 been chosen, the solution would have been completely in hyperbolic form, and such a form would be inadmissible.

The solution to Eqs. (7–16) can be written by inspection. Both are second-order ordinary differential equations without a damping term. Now the assumed form of Eq. (7–11) can be completed:

$$y(x,t) = (C_1 \sin \lambda x + C_2 \cos \lambda x)(C_3 \sin a\lambda t + C_4 \cos a\lambda t) \quad (7\text{–}17)$$

There are four constants which agree with the required number, since the order of all the derivatives in Eq. (7–5) totals to four. Our foresight in providing four boundary conditions allows us to evaluate these constants. We can now see that there is a valid solution for our system by means of the separation of variable method.

Boundary condition (a) gives us

$$0 = C_2[C_3 \sin a\lambda t + C_4 \cos a\lambda t] \quad (7\text{–}18)$$

whence $C_2 = 0$.

Applying condition (b), we get

$$0 = C_1 \sin \lambda L[C_3 \sin a\lambda t + C_4 \cos a\lambda t] \quad (7\text{–}19)$$

We cannot set $C_1 = 0$, which will obviously satisfy Eq. (7–19), for then we will have the trivial solution for a stationary string. However, we can let

$$0 = \sin \lambda L \quad (7\text{–}20)$$

Since λ is an unknown constant, we can see that Eq. (7–20) will be satisfied if

$$\lambda L = n\pi \qquad n = 0, 1, 2, 3, \ldots \quad (7\text{–}21)$$

Our equation now becomes

$$y(x,t) = \sin \frac{n\pi x}{L}\left[C_5 \sin \frac{n\pi a}{L} t + C_6 \cos \frac{n\pi a}{L} t \right] \quad (7\text{–}22)$$

where C_5 and C_6 have now absorbed the constant C_1.

We now apply boundary condition (d). We find that

$$0 = C_5 \frac{n\pi a}{L} \sin \frac{n\pi x}{L} \quad (7\text{–}23)$$

Therefore, $C_5 = 0$. Our equation is now

$$y(x,t) = C_6 \sin \frac{n\pi x}{L} \cos \frac{n\pi at}{L} \quad (7\text{–}24)$$

The last boundary condition is (c). Upon applying it, we find that

$$y_0 \sin \frac{\pi x}{L} = C_6 \sin \frac{n\pi x}{L} \quad (7\text{–}25)$$

It is quite obvious that Eq. (7–25) can be satisfied if $n = 1$ and $C_6 = y_0$.

The solution to our problem now is

$$y(x,t) = y_0 \sin \frac{\pi x}{L} \cos \frac{\pi a t}{L} \qquad (7\text{--}26)$$

where $a = c\sqrt{\epsilon}$.

The form of the vibration as represented by Eq. (7–26) may be considered to be a sine wave with a varying amplitude of $y_0 \cos a\pi t/L$. By using the trigonometric identity for $\sin \alpha \cos \beta$, we can rewrite Eq. (7–26) in another form:

$$y(x,t) = \tfrac{1}{2}y_0 \left[\sin \frac{\pi}{L}(x + at) + \sin \frac{\pi}{L}(x - at) \right] \qquad (7\text{--}27)$$

The form of Eq. (7–27) gives a different picture of the vibration of a string than does the interpretation of the vibration from Eq. (7–26). From Eq. (7–27), we can see that the vibration consists of two wave motions, one moving from the right, the other from the left. These waves are sinusoidal in form. We can best see this action by considering a fixed point x_0. Then the displacement $y]_{x_0}$ is dependent upon a; that is, y_0 will change at a rate governed by a. We remember that a is dependent only upon the initial tension and the density of the string, Eq. (7–6). At $x_0 = 0$ we can see that the two waves are equal but have opposite signs, since $y(0,t) = 0$. The same is also true at $x = L$. Since the waves are traveling pulses, at the ends they reflect in the opposite direction.

The initial deflection of the string was judiciously selected in the form of a sine wave. This solution of initial deformation made it possible to evaluate the constant C_6 by elementary mathematics. In general, C_6 has to be evaluated by a trigonometric series. Let us reconsider the string problem, when the boundary conditions are more general. We will let the boundary conditions as given by Eq. (7–10) remain unchanged except for condition (c). To keep our discussion quite general, let the new boundary condition be

$$(c') \qquad y(x,0) = f(x) \qquad (7\text{--}28)$$

Eq. (7–24) is still a valid equation for our new problem. If we now apply condition (c') we find that

$$f(x) = C_6 \sin \frac{n\pi x}{L} \qquad (7\text{--}29)$$

where n is an integer and may take values of $n = 0, 1, 2, 3, \ldots$. To evaluate C_6 it will be necessary to resort to a Fourier series solution.[1]

A function, $f(x)$, which is single-valued and is continuous, except for a finite number of discontinuities, in an interval of length, $-L$ to L, may

[1] Ruel V. Churchill, *Fourier Series and Boundary Value Problems* (New York: McGraw-Hill Book Co., Inc., 1941).

be represented by a convergent Fourier series. A Fourier series is a trigonometric series, which we define as

$$f(x) = \frac{a_0}{2} + \sum_{n=1}^{\infty} \left(a_n \cos \frac{n\pi x}{L} + b_n \sin \frac{n\pi x}{L} \right) \qquad (7\text{–}30)$$

We can readily show that

$$\int_{-L}^{L} \sin \frac{n\pi x}{L} \, dx = 0 \qquad n \neq 0$$

$$\int_{-L}^{L} \cos \frac{n\pi x}{L} \, dx = 0 \qquad n \neq 0$$

$$\int_{-L}^{L} \sin \frac{m\pi x}{L} \cos \frac{n\pi x}{L} = 0$$

$$\int_{-L}^{L} \sin \frac{m\pi x}{L} \sin \frac{n\pi x}{L} = 0 \qquad m \neq n$$

$$\int_{-L}^{L} \cos \frac{m\pi x}{L} \cos \frac{n\pi x}{L} = 0 \qquad m \neq n$$

$$\int_{-L}^{L} \sin^2 \frac{n\pi x}{L} = L \qquad n \neq 0$$

$$\int_{-L}^{L} \cos^2 \frac{n\pi x}{L} = L \qquad n \neq 0 \qquad (7\text{–}31)$$

Since the Fourier series is convergent, the trigonometric series as given by
Eq. (7–30) may be integrated term for term. Then

$$\int_{-L}^{L} f(x) \, dx = \int_{-L}^{L} \frac{a_0}{2} \, dx + \int_{-L}^{L} a_1 \cos \frac{\pi x}{L} \, dx + \int_{-L}^{L} a_2 \cos \frac{2\pi x}{L} \, dx + \cdots$$

$$+ \int_{-L}^{L} b_1 \sin \frac{\pi x}{L} \, dx + \int_{-L}^{L} b_2 \sin \frac{2\pi x}{L} \, dx + \cdots$$

$$(7\text{–}32)$$

If we now multiply both sides of Eq. (7–32) by $\cos n\pi x/L$ and then integrate, by virtue of Eqs. (7–31), we find that

$$\int_{-L}^{L} f(x) \cos \frac{n\pi x}{L} \, dx = a_n L$$

$$n = 0, 1, 2, 3, \ldots \qquad (7\text{–}33)$$

We repeat the process except that we now multiply by $\sin n\pi x/L$. The results of these integrations are

$$\int_{-L}^{L} f(x) \sin \frac{n\pi x}{L} \, dx = b_n L$$

$$n = 1, 2, 3, \ldots$$

(7-34)

We can evaluate the constants a_n and b_n from Eqs. (7-33) and (7-34). The constants are given by the equations

$$a_0 = \frac{1}{L} \int_{-L}^{L} f(x) \, dx$$

$$a_n = \frac{1}{L} \int_{-L}^{L} f(x) \cos \frac{n\pi x}{L} \, dx$$

$$b_n = \frac{1}{L} \int_{-L}^{L} f(x) \sin \frac{n\pi x}{L} \, dx$$

$$n = 1, 2, 3, \ldots$$

(7-35)

The representation of a function by a Fourier series is in effect a periodic representation. In our case, the period chosen is the length $2L$. The solution of a period of $2L$ rather than L is based upon the manner in which the Fourier series was first developed. Fourier developed the series for the period 2π and, in keeping with this period, our development is based upon $2L$. However, there is an advantage in expressing the period as $2L$, for if we select the length of the string as being L, we can then resort to a half-range series which will be valid for $0 < x < L$. The advantage of the half-range series lies in the fact that we may select a sine or cosine series to express our function.

Consider a function $f(x)$, as sketched in Fig. 7-2a, valid for $0 < x < L$. We may extend the function as sketched in Fig. 7-2b so that the new function can be expressed by a Fourier series over the interval $-L$ to L. The Fourier series representing the function as sketched in Fig. 7-2b is still valid for the original part of the interval, namely, $0 < x < L$. It is permissible, therefore, to add to the original function a hypothetical portion so that the $2L$ interval can be satisfied. Since the construction of the hypothetical portion of the function is optional, we can construct it as sketched in Fig. 7-2c if we wish. There is a difference between the functions sketched in Fig. 7-2b and Fig. 7-2c. The former is an odd function and the latter is an even function. A function is said to be odd if

$$f(-x) \equiv -f(x)$$

(7-36)

and a function is said to be even if

$$f(-x) \equiv f(x)$$

(7-37)

By inspection we can see that Fig. 7–2b is governed by Eq. (7–36), while Fig. 7–2c is satisfied by Eq. (7–37). Without any further proof (demonstration of this fact will be left for the student to do as an exercise), we

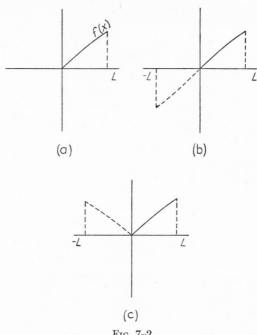

FIG. 7–2.

will say that an odd function, when represented by a Fourier series, is expressed in terms of the sines only and an even function by the cosine terms only. Formalizing the above, we can write: When an odd or even function is expressed by a Fourier series over the interval from $-L$ to L, the coefficients of the series are:

for odd series,

$$b_n = \frac{2}{L} \int_0^L f(x) \sin \frac{n\pi x}{L}$$

$$a_n = 0 \tag{7–38}$$

for even series,

$$a_n = \frac{2}{L} \int_0^L f(x) \cos \frac{n\pi x}{L}$$

$$b_n = 0 \tag{7–39}$$

We may now use Eqs. (7–38) and (7–39) for the half-range series, with the validity being restricted to $0 < x < L$. The selection of the sine or cosine series is optional; however, one note of caution about the selection of the series should be made. The function $f(x)$ was originally defined to allow for finite discontinuities. At such a discontinuity the value of the Fourier series will be the mean value. Consider a function $f(x) = x + 1$, valid for $0 < x < L$. This function is sketched in Fig. 7–3a as an odd function and in Fig. 7–3b as an even function. At $x = 0$ the value of $f(x)$

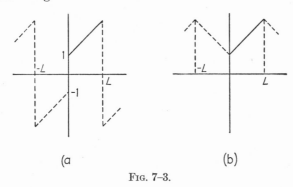

(a   (b)

Fig. 7–3.

for the odd function is zero, while for the even function, the value of $f(x) = 1$. We can see that there is an advantage in representing this function as an even one. We can also see that we get a correct value for $x = L$ for the even function, while this is not so for the odd.

We are now prepared to resume our discussion of the vibrating string. Let us now evaluate the constant C_6 of Eq. (7–29)

$$C_{6n} = \frac{2}{L} \int_0^L f(x) \sin \frac{n\pi x}{L} \, dx \qquad (7\text{–}40)$$

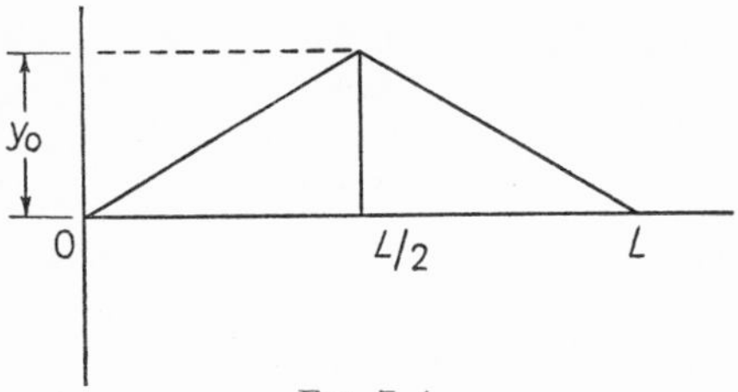

Fig. 7–4.

Let us now define $f(x)$ as being the result of the string being plucked at the center, as shown in Fig. 7–4. Then

$$f(x) = 2y_0 \frac{x}{L} \qquad\qquad 0 \le x \le \frac{L}{2}$$

$$f(x) = 2y_0 \left(1 - \frac{x}{L}\right) \qquad \frac{L}{2} \le x \le L \qquad (7\text{–}41)$$

Evaluating Eq. (7–40), we get

$$C_{6n} = \frac{2}{L} \int_0^{L/2} 2y_0 \frac{x}{L} \sin \frac{n\pi x}{L} \, dx + \frac{2}{L} \int_{L/2}^L 2y_0 \left(1 - \frac{x}{L}\right) \sin \frac{n\pi x}{L} \, dx \quad (7\text{–}42)$$

$$C_{6n} = \frac{8y_0}{n^2 \pi^2} \sin \frac{n\pi}{2}$$

$$n = 1, 3, 5, \ldots$$

or   (7–43)

$$C_{6n} = \frac{8y_0(-1)^n}{(2n + 1)^2 \pi^2}$$

$$n = 0, 1, 2, 3, \ldots$$

We now substitute the value for C_{6n} into Eq. (7–24) for the answer to the vibration of a plucked string. Upon such a substitution, we get

$$y(x,t) = \frac{8y_0}{\pi^2} \sum_{n=0}^{\infty} \frac{(-1)^n}{(2n + 1)^2} \sin \frac{(2n + 1)\pi}{L} x \cos \frac{(2n + 1)\pi a}{L} t \quad (7\text{–}44)$$

The vibration of the plucked string consists of all the odd harmonics; that is, the vibration contains all the modes of vibration which are odd. The even modes of vibration are absent. Eq. (7–44) can be written to show the wave motion as follows:

$$y(x,t) = \frac{4y_0}{\pi^2} \sum_{n=0}^{\infty} \frac{(-1)^n}{(2n + 1)^2} \left[\sin \left\{ \frac{(2n + 1)\pi}{L} (x + at) \right\} \right.$$

$$\left. + \sin \left\{ \frac{(2n + 1)\pi}{L} (x - at) \right\} \right] \quad (7\text{–}45)$$

In the above case, we have an infinite number of traveling waves which make up the motion.

7–3. Lateral Vibration of a Beam or Shaft. The equations of motion for a beam and a shaft are identical in form. The solution of the differential equation for one will suffice for the other. The fact that in one case the inertia force is due to harmonic motion and in the other to a centrifugal force does not alter the condition that the acceleration is the second derivative of the displacement with respect to time. It is, therefore, only the definition of the displacement that is different. The displacement of the beam is lateral as shown in Fig. 7–5, while the displacement of the shaft is depicted in Fig. 7–6. We will therefore derive the equation of motion for a beam, bearing in mind that the derivation is also applicable to a shaft.

Consider a beam uniformly loaded by q lbs./unit length. The load represents the weight per unit length of the beam. It may also include any uniform load that is being carried by the beam. We will restrict the beam to be carrying its own weight only. In this way we will be able to find the natural frequencies of the beam itself without the influence of the load. If the additional load being carried is uniform, however, then there

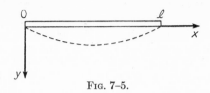

FIG. 7–5.

is no difficulty in extending our analysis to include the load. The sketch of the beam in Fig. 7–5 shows no visible means of support for the beam. We leave the manner in which the beam is supported unrestricted at this point so that the equations we derive will be general. The manner in

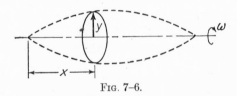

FIG. 7–6.

which the beam is supported will be reflected in the boundary conditions used to evaluate the constants. It can be readily seen that the deflection y resulting from the vibration of a beam is a function of two independent variables: x, a position variable, and t, a time variable. We then have a general relationship

$$y = f(x,t)$$

For equilibrium of a particle section of the beam

$$q = ma \tag{7–46}$$

where q = load per unit length
    m = mass per unit length
    a = acceleration

Since

$$q = \frac{\partial^2}{\partial x^2}\left(EI(x)\frac{\partial^2 y}{\partial x^2}\right) \tag{5–18}$$

and

$$a = -\frac{\partial^2 y}{\partial t^2}$$

the equation of motion becomes

$$\frac{\partial^2}{\partial x^2}\left(EI(x)\frac{\partial^2 y}{\partial x^2}\right) = -m\frac{\partial^2 y}{\partial t^2} \tag{7-47}$$

Let us restrict our analysis to a beam of constant cross-section. Then

$$\frac{\partial^2 y}{\partial t^2} + \frac{EI}{m}\frac{\partial^4 y}{\partial x^4} = 0 \tag{7-48}$$

or

$$\frac{\partial^2 y}{\partial t^2} + a^2\frac{\partial^4 y}{\partial x^4} = 0 \tag{7-49}$$

where

$$a^2 = \frac{EI}{m}$$

Eq. (7–49) is the D.E. of motion for a beam or shaft of uniform cross-section. We now assume a solution in the form of

$$y = X(x)\cdot T(t) \tag{7-50}$$

where X and T are functions of x and t, respectively. Differentiating Eq. (7–50) with respect to x and to t the proper number of times, we find

$$\frac{\partial^4 y}{\partial x^4} = T\frac{\partial^4 X}{\partial x^4}$$

and $\tag{7-51}$

$$\frac{\partial^2 y}{\partial t^2} = X\frac{\partial^2 T}{\partial t^2}$$

Substituting the derivatives, Eqs. (7–51), into Eq. (7–49), we get

$$X\frac{\partial^2 T}{\partial t^2} + a^2 T\frac{\partial^4 X}{\partial x^4} = 0 \tag{7-52}$$

Dividing by XT and rearranging, we get

$$\frac{1}{T}\frac{\partial^2 T}{\partial t^2} = -\frac{a^2}{X}\frac{\partial^4 X}{\partial x^4} \tag{7-53}$$

Eq. (7–49) now has been converted into Eq. (7–53), in which the independent variables are now separable. It becomes obvious that since the L.H.S. and R.H.S. of Eq. (7–53) are equal, each side must be equal to some common constant, say $-\omega^2$. Then we may write Eq. (7–53) in the following form:

$$\frac{1}{T}\frac{d^2 T}{dt^2} = -\frac{a^2}{X}\frac{d^4 X}{dx^4} = -\omega^2 \tag{7-54}$$

Eq. (7–54) now may be separated into two independent equations in T and X:

$$\frac{d^2 T}{dt^2} + \omega^2 T = 0 \qquad (7\text{–}55)$$

and

$$\frac{d^4 X}{dx^4} - k^4 X = 0 \qquad (7\text{–}56)$$

where

$$k^4 = \frac{\omega^2}{a^2} = \frac{m\omega^2}{EI}$$

The solution to Eq. (7–55) is well known to us, and we write

$$T(t) = A \cos (\omega t - \phi) \qquad (7\text{–}57)$$

Eq. (7–56) is a fourth-order, homogeneous, ordinary differential equation. The procedure for solving the above equation is identical with the procedure outlined in Chapter 2 for solving a second-order homogeneous equation, Section 2–2. Let us assume a solution in the form of

$$X = e^{rx} \qquad (7\text{–}58)$$

Then the auxiliary equation is

$$r^4 - k^4 = 0 \qquad (7\text{–}59)$$

The auxiliary equation yields four roots:

$$r = k, \quad -k, \quad ik, \quad -ik, \qquad (7\text{–}60)$$

where $i = \sqrt{-1}$.

Then the solution to Eq. (7–56) is

$$X = C_1 e^{kx} + C_2 e^{-kx} + C_3 e^{ikx} + C_4 e^{-ikx} \qquad (7\text{–}61)$$

Eqs. (2–12) and (2–13) define the hyperbolic cosine and the hyperbolic sine. They are repeated here for the convenience of the reader. kx has replaced u which is used in Eq. (2–12);

$$\cosh kx = \frac{e^{kx} + e^{-kx}}{2} \qquad \sinh kx = \frac{e^{kx} - e^{-kx}}{2} \qquad (7\text{–}62)$$

$$e^{kx} = \cosh kx + \sinh kx$$
$$e^{-kx} = \cosh kx - \sinh kx \qquad (7\text{–}63)$$

Then

$$C_1 e^{kx} + C_2 e^{-kx} = (C_1 + C_2) \cosh kx + (C_1 - C_2) \sinh kx \qquad (7\text{–}64)$$

$$C_1 e^{kx} + C_2 e^{-kx} = C_1' \cosh kx + C_2' \sinh kx$$

where $C_1' = C_1 + C_2$ and $C_2' = C_1 - C_2$.

By means of the Euler's relations, defined by Eqs. (2–23) and (2–24), we get

$$C_3 e^{ikx} + C_4 e^{-ikx} = C_3' \cos kx + C_4' \sin kx \qquad (7\text{–}65)$$

where $C_3' = C_3 + C_4$ and $C_4' = i(C_3 - C_4)$.

Note: Hereafter, the primes will be dropped as a matter of convenience.

Eq. (7–61) may be written in the following form:

$$X = C_1 \cosh kx + C_2 \sinh kx + C_3 \cos kx + C_4 \sin kx \qquad (7\text{–}66)$$

The solution to the differential equation of motion is now complete and is

$$y(x,t) = [C_1 \cosh kx + C_2 \sinh kx + C_3 \cos kx + C_4 \sin kx] \cos (\omega t - \phi) \qquad (7\text{–}67)$$

where the constant A is now absorbed into the C coefficients.

Eq. (7–67) is the general solution for a beam or a shaft. For a particular solution of a special case of end supports, we need only to evaluate the constants. Let us consider a beam which is simply supported. This case also covers a rotating shaft which is supported at the ends by self-aligning ball bearings. The boundary conditions are:

$$(a) \quad y(0,t) = 0 \qquad\qquad (b) \quad y(l,t) = 0$$

$$(c) \quad \text{when } y(0,t) \qquad M_0 = 0, \quad \text{and} \quad \left.\frac{\partial^2 y}{\partial x^2}\right|_{x=0} = 0 \qquad (7\text{–}68)$$

$$(d) \quad \text{when } y(l,t) \qquad M_l = 0, \quad \text{and} \quad \left.\frac{\partial^2 y}{\partial x^2}\right|_{x=l} = 0$$

where M is the bending moment at the respective ends of the beam.

From condition (a), we find

$$0 = (C_1 + C_3) \cos (\omega t - \phi)$$

Since $\cos \omega t$ cannot be zero for all t, then

$$C_1 + C_3 = 0$$

Applying condition (c), we get

$$0 = k^2 C_1 - k^2 C_3$$

We now deduce that

$$C_1 = C_3 = 0$$

Eq. (7–67) now reduces to

$$y(x,t) = (C_2 \sinh kx + C_4 \sin kx) \cos (\omega t - \phi) \qquad (7\text{–}69)$$

Using the remaining two boundary conditions (b) and (d), we find a pair of simultaneous equations:

$$0 = (C_2 \sinh kl + C_4 \sin kl) \cos (\omega t - \phi)$$

and $$(7\text{-}70)$$

$$0 = (C_2 \sinh kl - C_4 \sin kl) \cos (\omega t - \phi)$$

For the non-trivial solution, we find that the above equations can be satisfied if

$$\sinh kl \sin kl = 0 \qquad (7\text{-}71)$$

However Eq. (7–71) can be satisfied only if

$$\sin kl = 0 \qquad (7\text{-}72)$$

The conditions of Eq. (7–72) will occur if

$$kl = n\pi \qquad (7\text{-}73)$$

where n is an integer, 0, 1, 2, ... Then

$$k^4 = \frac{n^4\pi^4}{l^4} = \frac{m\omega^2}{EI}$$

and $$(7\text{-}74)$$

$$\omega = \frac{n^2\pi^2}{l^2} \sqrt{\frac{EI}{m}}$$

where $n = 0, 1, 2, 3, \ldots$

Having satisfied Eq. (7–72), we can now investigate the values of C_2 and C_4. Substituting Eq. (7–72) into either of the simultaneous Eqs. (7–70), we find that $C_2 = 0$. Our original solution has now been reduced to

$$y(x,t) = C_4 \sin \frac{n\pi x}{l} \cos \left(\frac{n^2\pi^2}{l^2} \sqrt{\frac{EI}{m}} \, t - \phi \right)$$

where $n = 0, 1, 2, \ldots$. $$(7\text{-}75)$$

Our original boundary conditions were four in number. However, our original Eq. (7–67) had five constants. Therefore, we are left with the constant C_4. We can evaluate C_4 only if the original displacement at $t = 0$ is known. Since we are really interested in the natural frequencies of the beam, which has been given by ω, C_4 is of little interest. We may determine C_4 by means of a Fourier series when the boundary condition

$$y(x,0) = f(x) \qquad (7\text{-}76)$$

is known.

Eq. (7–74) yields the natural frequencies of the beam. Since we have an elastic material, there will be an infinite number of degrees of freedom with the resulting infinite number of natural frequencies. For each natural frequency there will be a mode of vibration. The modes of vibration are given by $C_4 \sin n\pi x/l$. When discussing the vibration of a rotating shaft, we refer to the natural frequency as the critical speed, ω_{cr}. A shaft does not vibrate in the same sense as does a beam. The elements of the whirling of a shaft that interest us are the configuration of the elastic curve and the amplitude of that configuration. The mode or configuration of a rotating shaft is also given by $C_4 \sin n\pi x/l$.

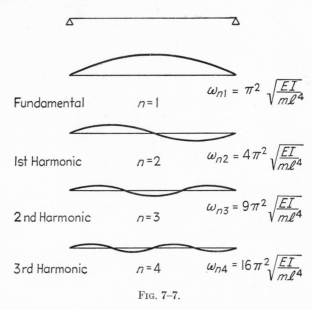

$$\omega_{n1} = \pi^2 \sqrt{\frac{EI}{m\ell^4}}$$

Fundamental $n = 1$

$$\omega_{n2} = 4\pi^2 \sqrt{\frac{EI}{m\ell^4}}$$

1st Harmonic $n = 2$

$$\omega_{n3} = 9\pi^2 \sqrt{\frac{EI}{m\ell^4}}$$

2nd Harmonic $n = 3$

$$\omega_{n4} = 16\pi^2 \sqrt{\frac{EI}{m\ell^4}}$$

3rd Harmonic $n = 4$

FIG. 7-7.

When a beam or shaft is forced at one of the natural frequencies or critical speeds, then the member is in resonance and the amplitudes are excessive. Fig. 7–7 depicts some of the various normal modes of vibration for a simply supported beam or shaft.

As a further demonstration of the evaluation of boundary conditions which may be applied to Eq. (7–67), we take the case of a beam clamped at both ends. This solution may also serve for the case of a rotating shaft with stiff journal bearings at each end.

In order to simplify the evaluation of the boundary conditions, let us take advantage of the symmetry of the deflection of the beam. To do this, we place the origin of the coordinate system at the mid-point of the beam. Then

$$y_{+x} = y_{-x} \qquad\qquad (7\text{-}77)$$

Eq. (7–67) now has to be replaced by two equations, one valid for x positive, the other valid for x negative. Then

$$y_{+x} = [C_1 \cosh kx + C_2 \sinh kx + C_3 \cos kx + C_4 \sin kx] \cos (\omega t - \phi)$$
$$(7\text{-}78)$$

$$y_{-x} = [C_1 \cosh kx - C_2 \sinh kx + C_3 \cos kx - C_4 \sin kx] \cos (\omega t - \phi)$$
$$(7\text{--}79)$$

Note: The $\sin (-x) = -\sin x$, $\sinh (-x) = -\sinh x$, $\cos (-x) = \cos x$, and $\cosh (-x) = \cosh x$.

We now subtract Eq. (7–79) from Eq. (7–78), remembering that $y_{+x} = y_{-x}$. Then

$$0 = (C_2 \sinh kx + C_4 \sin kx) \tag{7--80}$$

Since Eq. (7–80) must be valid for $-l/2 \le x \le l/2$, then $C_2 = C_4 = 0$. As a consequence,

$$y_{+x} = (C_1 \cosh kx + C_3 \cos kx) \cos (\omega t - \phi) \tag{7--81}$$

By taking advantage of the symmetry of the problem, we have eliminated two of the four constants. This same device could have been used for the simply supported beam as well. We now need to find only two boundary conditions to satisfy Eq. (7–81). We choose

(a) $$y \left(\pm \frac{l}{2}, t \right) = 0$$

(b) $$\text{at } y \left(\pm \frac{l}{2}, t \right); \theta = 0 \quad \text{and} \quad \frac{\partial y}{\partial x}\bigg|_{x=\pm l/2} = 0. \tag{7--82}$$

Applying the above boundary conditions yields

$$0 = C_1 \cosh \frac{kl}{2} + C_3 \cos \frac{kl}{2}$$
$$\tag{7--83}$$
$$0 = C_1 \sinh \frac{kl}{2} - C_3 \sin \frac{kl}{2}$$

Setting the $|D| = 0$, we find

$$\sinh \frac{kl}{2} \cos \frac{kl}{2} + \cosh \frac{kl}{2} \sin \frac{kl}{2} = 0 \tag{7--84}$$

which simplifies to

$$\tan \frac{kl}{2} = -\tanh \frac{kl}{2} \tag{7--85}$$

We may evaluate Eq. (7–85) by trial-and-error methods or by plotting the curves of $\tan kl/2$ and $-\tanh kl/2$. The latter method is shown in Fig. 7–8. We find that Eq. (7–85) is satisfied when $kl/2 = 0, 2.365, 3.927, 5.498, 7.069, 8.640, \ldots$. Then

$$\omega = 22.4 \sqrt{\frac{EI}{ml^4}}, \quad 61.7 \sqrt{\frac{EI}{ml^4}}, \quad 121 \sqrt{\frac{EI}{ml^4}}, \quad 200 \sqrt{\frac{EI}{ml^4}}, \quad 298 \sqrt{\frac{EI}{ml^4}}$$

These are the first five natural frequencies if we discount the trivial frequency $\omega = 0$.

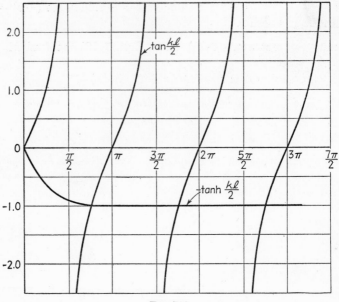

Fig. 7–8.

To complete the equation for the elastic curve, we can eliminate one of the constants in Eq. (7–81). From the first of Eqs. (7–83), we get

$$C_1 = -C_3 \frac{\cos \dfrac{kl}{2}}{\cosh \dfrac{kl}{2}}$$

Then

$$y(x,t) = C_3 \left(\cos kx - \frac{\cos \dfrac{kl}{2} \cosh kx}{\cosh \dfrac{kl}{2}} \right) \cos (\omega t - \phi)$$

$$y(x,t) = C_3 \left(\frac{\cosh \dfrac{kl}{2} \cos kx - \cos \dfrac{kl}{2} \cosh kx}{\cosh \dfrac{kl}{2}} \right) \cos (\omega t - \phi)$$

$$(7\text{–}86)$$

When the boundary condition $y(x,0)$ is known, C_3 can be evaluated by using a Fourier-series representation.

The configuration of a few of the modes of vibration for the clamped beam is sketched in Fig. 7–9.

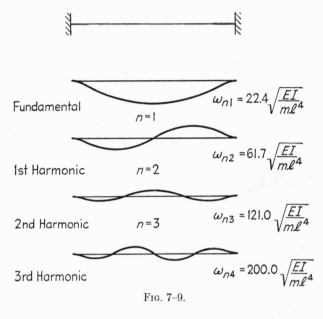

Fundamental $n=1$ $\omega_{n1} = 22.4\sqrt{\dfrac{EI}{m\ell^4}}$

1st Harmonic $n=2$ $\omega_{n2} = 61.7\sqrt{\dfrac{EI}{m\ell^4}}$

2nd Harmonic $n=3$ $\omega_{n3} = 121.0\sqrt{\dfrac{EI}{m\ell^4}}$

3rd Harmonic $\omega_{n4} = 200.0\sqrt{\dfrac{EI}{m\ell^4}}$

Fig. 7–9.

7–4. Torsional Vibration of a Circular Shaft. In the discussion of the torsional vibration of a shaft, we will restrict ourselves to a shaft of constant circular cross-section. The particle of a shaft, Fig. 7–10, has acting

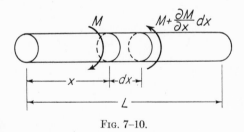

Fig. 7–10.

on the left end a moment M and on the right end, which is a distance dx away, $M + (\partial M/\partial x)\, dx$: from elementary torsion theory, we know that

$$M = GI_P \frac{\partial \theta}{\partial x} \tag{7-87}$$

and therefore

$$\frac{\partial M}{\partial x} = GI_P \frac{\partial^2 \theta}{\partial x^2} \tag{7-88}$$

where G = shear modulus of elasticity

I_P = area, polar moment of inertia

θ = angle of twist of cross-section at x

Dynamic equilibrium during torsional vibration requires that

$$I \frac{\partial^2 \theta}{\partial t^2} = M + \frac{\partial M}{\partial x} dx - M \qquad (7\text{-}89)$$

where I is the mass moment of inertia and is equal to $mI_P\, dx$, where m is the mass per unit length. In view of the relationship of Eq. (7–88), we find that

$$\frac{\partial^2 \theta}{\partial t^2} = a^2 \frac{\partial^2 \theta}{\partial x^2} \qquad (7\text{-}90)$$

where $a^2 = G/m$.

Eq. (7–90) is identical in form with the differential equation of a vibrating string and therefore the general solution, Eq. (7–17), is applicable. The solution to Eq. (7–90) is

$$\theta(x,t) = (C_1 \sin \lambda x + C_2 \cos \lambda x)(C_3 \sin a\lambda t + C_4 \cos a\lambda t) \qquad (7\text{-}91)$$

The general solution for a torsional vibrating shaft is given by Eq. (7–91). We now must consider a specific problem to evaluate the constants. Fig. 7–11 pictures a shaft, fixed at one end and with a disc I attached to the

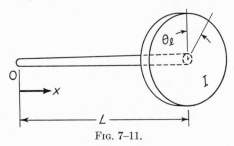

FIG. 7–11.

free end. Initially the disc is displaced by an angle θ_l and then released. Our task is to evaluate the constants of Eq. (7–91), given the boundary conditions of the above problem. We must look for four boundary conditions, since we have four constants.

(a)
$$\theta(0,t) = 0$$

(b)
$$GI_P \left(\frac{\partial \theta}{\partial x}\right)_{x=L} = -I \left(\frac{\partial^2 \theta}{\partial t^2}\right)_{x=L}$$

(c)
$$\theta_{t=0} = f_1(x) = \frac{\theta_l x}{l} \qquad (7\text{-}92)$$

(d)
$$\left.\frac{\partial \theta}{\partial t}\right|_{t=0} = f_2(x) = 0$$

The boundary conditions chosen may need some explanation. Condition (a) stems from the fact that at $x = 0$, the shaft is fixed and no angle of twist can develop. Equilibrium conditions at $x = L$ require that the inertia forces of the disc be balanced by the torque, and (b) recites these conditions. We have an initial displacement at the disc of θ_l, and since Hooke's law is in effect, we reflect the initial conditions by (c) and (d).

From (a) we find that $C_2 = 0$, and Eq. (7–91) now becomes

$$\theta(x,t) = (C_1 \sin \lambda x)(C_3 \sin a\lambda t + C_4 \cos a\lambda t) \tag{7–93}$$

In order to satisfy condition (b), we first find

$$\frac{\partial \theta}{\partial x} = C_1\lambda \cos \lambda x (C_3 \sin a\lambda t + C_4 \cos a\lambda t)$$

and $\tag{7–94}$

$$\frac{\partial^2 \theta}{\partial t^2} = -\lambda^2 C_1 \sin \lambda x (C_3 \sin a\lambda t + C_4 \cos a\lambda t)$$

Substituting Eq. (7–94) into (b), we get

$$GI_P C_1 \lambda \cos \lambda L = I\lambda^2 C_1 \sin \lambda L$$

Then

$$\lambda = \frac{GI_P}{I} \cot \lambda L \tag{7–95}$$

The determination of λ may be by trial and error or by the method used to plot Fig. 7–8. Let λ_n be the roots of the transcendental Eq. (7–95).

We now use condition (d), whence

$$0 = C_3 a\lambda_n C_1 \sin \lambda_n x \tag{7–96}$$

Then $C_3 = 0$. The equation is now reduced to

$$\theta(x,t) = C_{5n} \sin \lambda_n x \cdot \cos a\lambda_n t \tag{7–97}$$

where $C_{5n} = C_1 C_4$. We may now evaluate C_{5n} from condition (c), which when applied yields

$$\frac{\theta_l x}{L} = C_{5n} \sin \lambda_n x \tag{7–98}$$

By means of the Fourier half-range odd series,

$$a_n = 0 \qquad b_n = \frac{2}{L} \int_0^L \frac{\theta_l x}{L} \sin \lambda_n x \, dx \tag{7–99}$$

Then

$$b_n = \frac{2\theta_l}{L^2}\left[\frac{1}{\lambda_n^2}\sin \lambda_n L - \frac{L}{\lambda_n}\cos \lambda_n L\right] \tag{7–100}$$

From Eq. (7–95) we find that

$$\cos \lambda_n L = \frac{\lambda_n I}{G I_P} \sin \lambda_n L \qquad (7\text{–}101)$$

By substituting Eq. (7–101) into Eq. (7–100),

$$b_n = \frac{2\theta_l}{L^2} \left[\frac{1}{\lambda_n{}^2} - \frac{LI}{G I_P} \right] \sin \lambda_n L \qquad (7\text{–}102)$$

The solution now is

$$\theta(x,t) = \frac{2\theta_l}{L^2} \sum_{n=1}^{\infty} \left[\frac{1}{\lambda_n{}^2} - \frac{LI}{G I_P} \right] \sin \lambda_n L \sin \lambda_n x \cos a\lambda_n t \qquad (7\text{–}103)$$

7–5. Longitudinal Vibrations of a Bar. A bar which has been initially compressed will vibrate in the longitudinal direction upon release of the forces which cause the compression. The motion of vibration is not unlike that of a vibrating string. The displacement, however, is along the longitudinal axis, instead of transversely as is the case of the vibrating string

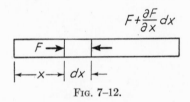

$$F + \frac{\partial F}{\partial x} dx$$

FIG. 7–12.

discussed in Section 7–2. As with the other analyses in this chapter, let us derive and solve the differential equation of motion without any restrictions due to boundary or initial conditions.

Dynamic equilibrium of a particle of the bar, Fig. 7–12, requires that

$$F + \frac{\partial F}{\partial x} dx - F = m \, dx \, \frac{\partial^2 u}{\partial^2 t} \qquad (7\text{–}104)$$

where F = force, which may be tensile or compressive

m = mass per unit length of bar

u = the longitudinal displacement

From Hooke's law we know that

$$\frac{F}{A} = E\epsilon = E \frac{\partial u}{\partial x} \qquad (7\text{–}105)$$

where $\partial u/\partial x$ is defined as the unit strain.

Then

$$\frac{\partial F}{\partial x} = A E \frac{\partial^2 u}{\partial x^2} \qquad (7\text{–}106)$$

Substituting Eq. (7–106) into Eq. (7–104) yields

$$\frac{\partial^2 u}{\partial t^2} = a^2 \frac{\partial^2 u}{\partial x^2} \tag{7–107}$$

where $a^2 = AE/m$. Since $m = \rho A$, where ρ is density per unit volume and A the cross-sectional area, then

$$a = c = \sqrt{\frac{E}{\rho}} \tag{7–108}$$

where c is the speed of sound in the bar.

Eq. (7–107) is identical in form to the D.E. of the vibrating string, Eq. (7–5), and therefore the solution will be

$$u(x,t) = (C_1 \sin \lambda x + C_2 \cos \lambda x)(C_3 \sin c\lambda t + C_4 \cos c\lambda t) \tag{7–109}$$

Let us now first consider a free-free bar; that is, both ends of the bar are free during the vibration. We let the initial displacement be governed by compressive forces which are suddenly released. The boundary conditions are

(a)
$$\epsilon(0,t) = \frac{\partial u}{\partial x}\bigg|_{x=0} = 0$$

(b)
$$\epsilon(L,t) = \frac{\partial u}{\partial x}\bigg|_{x=L} = 0 \tag{7–110}$$

(c)
$$u(x,0) = f_1(x) = \frac{\epsilon_0 L}{2} - \epsilon_0 x$$

where ϵ_0 is the unit strain at time $t = 0$,

(d)
$$\frac{\partial u}{\partial t}\bigg|_{t=0} = f_2(x) = 0$$

Conditions (a) and (b) result from the free ends of the bar, since no strain can be sustained at the free ends. The compressive forces cause an initial displacement in terms of ϵ_0, and this condition is reflected in (c). The velocity at $t = 0$ is everywhere zero and is so given by (d).

From condition (a), we get $0 = C_1\lambda(C_3 \sin c\lambda t + C_4 \cos c\lambda t)$, and therefore $C_1 = 0$. Applying (b), we find

$$0 = -C_2\lambda \sin \lambda L(C_3 \sin c\lambda t + C_4 \cos c\lambda t),$$

which can be satisfied if $\sin \lambda L = 0$. Then

$$\lambda = \frac{n\pi}{L}$$

where $n = 1, 2, 3 \ldots$. Our original equation is now reduced to

$$u(x,t) = \cos \frac{n\pi x}{L} \left(C_5 \sin \frac{n\pi c}{L} t + C_6 \cos \frac{n\pi c}{L} t \right) \tag{7-111}$$

From (d), we find

$$0 = \frac{n\pi c}{L} C_5 \cos \frac{n\pi x}{L}$$

which results in $C_5 = 0$. Then the equation of motion is now

$$u(x,t) = C_6 \cos \frac{n\pi x}{L} \cos \frac{n\pi c}{L} t \tag{7-112}$$

The constant C_6 is now evaluated by means of a Fourier series, where

$$a_n = \frac{2}{L} \int_0^L \left(\frac{\epsilon_0 L}{2} - \epsilon_0 x \right) \cos \frac{n\pi x}{L} \, dx, \qquad b_n = 0 \tag{7-113}$$

Upon integration, we find

$$a_n = \frac{2\epsilon_0 L}{n^2 \pi^2} (1 - \cos n\pi) \tag{7-114}$$

$$n = 0, 1, 2, 3, \ldots$$

which may be written as

$$a_n = \frac{4\epsilon_0 L}{(2n - 1)^2 \pi^2}$$

$$n = 1, 2, 3, \ldots$$

The solution finally is

$$u(x,t) = \frac{4\epsilon_0 L}{\pi^2} \sum_{n=1}^{\infty} \frac{1}{(2n - 1)^2} \cos \frac{(2n - 1)\pi x}{L} \cos \frac{(2n - 1)\pi ct}{L} \tag{7-115}$$

Eq. (7-115) may be rewritten to emphasize the wave motion in the bar:

$$u(x,t) = \frac{2\epsilon_0 L}{\pi^2} \sum_{n=1}^{\infty} \frac{1}{(2n - 1)^2} \left[\cos \frac{(2n - 1)\pi}{L} (ct + x) \right.$$

$$\left. + \cos \frac{(2n - 1)\pi}{L} (ct - x) \right] \tag{7-116}$$

The wave motion will be such that when it reaches a free end the wave will be reflected with an opposite sign. That is, a compression wave reaching a free end will be reflected as a tension wave. A discussion of wave motion in solids can be found in a monograph by H. Kolsky.[2]

[2] H. Kolsky, *Stress Waves in Solids* (New York: Oxford University Press, 1953).

We will consider next a rod with one end fixed, Fig. 7–13. A force P is suddenly affixed to the free end. If the duration of the time during

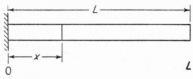

FIG. 7–13.

which the force is applied is a very short period, then we can reasonably approximate the initial conditions due to the force as imparting an initial displacement to the bar of $\epsilon_0 x$, where

$$\epsilon_0 = P/AE \qquad (7\text{–}117)$$

The boundary conditions for the above case may be written as

(a) $$u(0,t) = 0$$

(b) $$\epsilon(L,t) = \frac{\partial u}{\partial x}\bigg|_{x=L} = 0$$

(c) $$u(x,0) = f_1(x) = \epsilon_0 x$$

(d) $$\frac{\partial u}{\partial t}\bigg|_{t=0} = f_2(x) = 0$$

Applying (a) to Eq. (7–109), we find that $C_2 = 0$. From (b), we see that $\cos \lambda L = 0$. Therefore

$$\lambda = \frac{n\pi}{2L} \qquad n = 1, 3, 5, \ldots$$

and Eq. (7–109) is now

$$u(x,t) = \sin\frac{n\pi x}{2L}\left(C_5 \sin\frac{n\pi c}{2L}t + C_6 \cos\frac{n\pi c}{2L}t\right) \qquad (7\text{–}118)$$

From boundary condition (d),

$$0 = \frac{n\pi c}{2L}\cdot\frac{\sin n\pi x}{2L}C_5$$

therefore $C_5 = 0$. Then

$$u(x,t) = C_6 \sin\frac{n\pi x}{2L}\cos\frac{n\pi c}{2L}t \qquad (7\text{–}119)$$

Boundary condition (c) can be satisfied by the Fourier-series coefficients

$$b_n = \frac{2}{L}\int_0^L \epsilon_0 x \sin\frac{n\pi x}{2L} \qquad n \text{ odd} \qquad (7\text{–}120)$$

Then

$$b_n = \frac{8\epsilon_0 L}{n^2 \pi^2} \sin \frac{n\pi x}{2L} \qquad n \text{ odd}$$

or

$$b_n = \frac{8\epsilon_0 L}{\pi^2 (2n-1)^2} \sin \frac{(2n-1)\pi x}{2L} \qquad n = 1, 2, 3, \cdots$$

The equation of motion now can be written as

$$u(x,t) = \frac{8\epsilon_0 L}{\pi^2} \sum_{n=1}^{\infty} \frac{1}{(2n-1)^2} \sin \frac{(2n-1)\pi x}{2L} \cos \frac{(2n-1)\pi c}{2L} t \quad (7\text{--}121)$$

7-6. Duhamel's Integral. As an aid to the solution of the longitudinal vibrations due to certain types of forcing functions, Duhamel's[3] integral will now be introduced. The types of forcing functions that will be represented by Duhamel's integral will be in the main suddenly applied. We will approach the development of Duhamel's integral through the mediums of "indicial admittance" and "response to a unit impulse."

a. Indicial Admittance. Consider a single mass attached to a spring. Initially the system is at rest at $t = 0$, but at $t = 0^+$ a unit force acts upon the system and remains in action for $t > 0$. We will represent this unit force as $1(t)$, signifying that the unit force is a function of time. The D.E. of motion is

$$m\ddot{x} + kx = 1(t) \qquad (7\text{--}122)$$

The general solution to Eq. (7–122) is

$$x(t) = A' \cos \sqrt{\frac{k}{m}} t + B' \sin \sqrt{\frac{k}{m}} t + \frac{1}{k} \qquad (7\text{--}123)$$

The boundary conditions are:

$$\text{for } t = 0, \qquad x = 0, \qquad \text{and} \qquad \dot{x} = 0 \qquad (7\text{--}124)$$

From Eq. (7–124), we find that $A' = -(1/k)$ and $B' = 0$. Then

$$x(t) = \frac{1}{k}\left(1 - \cos \sqrt{\frac{k}{m}} t\right) \qquad (7\text{--}125)$$

The displacement $x(t)$ due to a unit force $1(t)$ is called the "indicial admittance" of the system, and we may write Eq. (7–125) as

$$A(t) = \frac{1}{k}\left(1 - \cos \sqrt{\frac{k}{m}} t\right) 1(t)$$

where $1(t)$ is symbolic of the applied unit force.

[3] Theodore von Kármán and Maurice A. Biot, *Mathematical Methods in Engineering* (New York: McGraw-Hill Book Co., Inc., 1940).

b. Response to a Unit Impulse. We now study the effect of a unit impulse upon the spring and mass system. The relationship of impulse-momentum is given by Eq. (1–43), and therefore

$$m\dot{x} = \int F\,dt = 1(t) \qquad \text{for } t = 0^+ \qquad (7\text{--}126)$$

Eq. (7–126) becomes one of our boundary conditions, which are then

$$t = 0, \qquad x = 0, \qquad \text{and} \qquad m\dot{x} = 1(t) \qquad (7\text{--}127)$$

We will assume that during time Δt the effect of the impulse upon the spring is negligible. Our differential equation is

$$m\ddot{x} + kx = 0 \qquad (7\text{--}128)$$

and its solution is

$$x(t) = A' \cos \sqrt{\frac{k}{m}}\,t + B' \sin \sqrt{\frac{k}{m}}\,t \qquad (7\text{--}129)$$

From our boundary conditions, we find

$$A' = 0 \qquad \text{and} \qquad B' = \frac{1}{\sqrt{mk}}$$

Then

$$x(t) = \frac{1}{\sqrt{mk}} \sin \sqrt{\frac{k}{m}}\,t \qquad (7\text{--}130)$$

Eq. (7–130) is called the "response to a unit impulse" and is symbolized by

$$h(t) = \left(\frac{1}{\sqrt{mk}} \sin \sqrt{\frac{k}{m}}\,t \right) 1(t) \qquad (7\text{--}131)$$

In general it can be shown that

$$h(t) = \frac{dA}{dt} \qquad (7\text{--}132)$$

In the system we have used as an example, this may be demonstrated as follows:

$$h(t) = \frac{dA}{dt}$$

$$\frac{1}{\sqrt{mk}} \sin \sqrt{\frac{k}{m}}\,t = \frac{d}{dt}\left[\frac{1}{k}\left(1 - \cos \sqrt{\frac{k}{m}}\,t \right) \right] = \frac{1}{\sqrt{mk}} \sin \sqrt{\frac{k}{m}}\,t$$

No rigorous proof of Eq. (7–132) will be attempted here. Such a proof is beyond the scope of this text.

c. Duhamel's Integral. The concepts of indicial admittance and response to a unit impulse may be used to obtain the response to a force $F(\tau)$ which is a function of time. It is permissible to superpose the two types of responses to a linear system. However, we must add another restriction to our differential equation. The coefficients must be constants, since the response of $F(\tau)$ will be assumed to be a function of the elapsed time $(t - \tau)$. That is, the impulse will be applied at time τ and observed at time t.

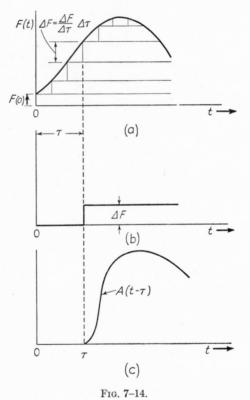

Fig. 7–14.

Still considering a spring-and-mass system, we apply a force $F(\tau)$, at time τ. We approximate the action of $F(\tau)$ by steps of ΔF at equal time intervals 0, $\Delta\tau$, $2\Delta\tau$, etc., Fig. 7–14a. Fig. 7–14c represents the admittance during the time interval $(t - \tau)$. If we represent the force $F(\tau)$ at $\tau < 0$ as $F(0)$ we can apply our concept of indicial admittance to the system, to yield

$$x(t) = F(0)A(t) + \sum_{\tau = \Delta\tau}^{t} \frac{\Delta F}{\Delta\tau} \Delta\tau\, A(t - \tau) \qquad (7\text{–}133)$$

We let $\Delta\tau \to 0$ as a limit, then

$$\underset{\Delta\tau \to 0}{\lfloor x(t)} = F(0)A(t) + \int_0^t \frac{dF}{d\tau} A(t - \tau)\, d\tau \qquad (7\text{--}134)$$

Eq. (7–134) is known as Duhamel's integral. However, if we integrate Eq. (7–134) by parts, we find

$$x(t) = F(t)A(0) + \int_0^t F(\tau)\dot{A}(t - \tau)\, d\tau \qquad (7\text{--}135)$$

where $\dot{A} = dA/d\tau$. Now $\dot{A}(t - \tau) = h(t - \tau)$, and if we assume that $F(\tau)$ for $\tau < 0$ is zero, then $A(0) = 0$. Using the above two conditions, we may write Duhamel's integral as

$$x(t) = \int_0^t F(\tau)h(t - \tau)\, d\tau \qquad (7\text{--}136)$$

Let us now apply a periodic force $F_0 \cos \omega_n t$ to our spring-and-mass system. We represent $F(\tau)$ by $F(\tau) = (F_0 \cos \omega_n \tau)1(\tau)$. Since

$$x(t) = \int_0^t F_0(\tau)h(t - \tau)\, d\tau$$

and

$$h(t - \tau) = \frac{1}{\sqrt{mk}} \sin \omega_n(t - \tau)\, d\tau$$

we find

$$x(t) = \frac{F_0}{\sqrt{mk}} \int_0^t \cos \omega_n \tau \sin \omega_n(t - \tau)\, d\tau \qquad (7\text{--}137)$$

We may rewrite Eq. (7–137) as

$$x(t) = \frac{F_0}{2\sqrt{mk}} \int_0^t [\sin \omega_n t - \sin \omega_n(2\tau - t)]\, d\tau \qquad (7\text{--}138)$$

Let us first evaluate

$$\int_0^t \sin \omega_n(2\tau - t)\, d\tau$$

Let $(2\tau - t) = u$. Then $d\tau = \dfrac{du}{2}\cdot$ Making the above substitution,

$$\int_0^t \sin \omega_n(2\tau - t)\, d\tau = \tfrac{1}{2} \int_{-t}^t \sin \omega_n u\, du$$

$$= \frac{1}{2w_n} \left| \cos \omega_n u \right|_{-t}^{t} = 0$$

Then Eq. (7–138) may be evaluated as follows:

$$x(t) = \frac{F_0}{2\sqrt{mk}} \int_0^t \sin \omega_n t \, d\tau$$

$$= \frac{F_0}{2\sqrt{mk}} t \sin \omega_n t \qquad (7\text{–}139)$$

Eq. (7–139) is in agreement with Eq. (3–81) which represents a spring-mass system being forced at resonant frequency.

7-7. Forced Vibrations. We will use a slightly different approach in solving the forced vibration of a bar from the one used for the free vibration. First we will derive the equation of motion for a bar in longitudinal vibrations by means of the Lagrange equations; then, by applying the concepts of Duhamel's integral, we will modify the differential equation.

By way of demonstrating the method to be used, let us confine ourselves to a bar with one fixed end. We will select as our generalized coordinates the amplitudes of the normal modes of vibration. That is,

$$u = \sum_{n=1}^{\infty} q_n \sin \frac{n\pi}{2L} x \qquad (7\text{–}140)$$

where q_n are the generalized coordinates. The potential energy due to tension and compression is

$$V = \frac{AE}{2} \int_0^L \epsilon^2 \, dx = \frac{AE}{2} \int_0^L \left(\frac{\partial u}{\partial x}\right)^2 dx$$

$$V = \frac{AE\pi^2}{8L^2} \int_0^L \sum_{n=1}^{\infty} \left(nq_n \cos \frac{n\pi}{2L} x\right)^2 dx \qquad (7\text{–}141)$$

By virtue of Eq. (7–31), we need only integrate the terms containing the $\cos^2 (n\pi/2L)x$. Then

$$V = \frac{AE}{8} \frac{\pi^2}{L^2} \int_0^L n^2 q_n{}^2 \cos^2 \frac{n\pi}{2L} x \, dx \qquad (7\text{–}142)$$

Upon integration of Eq. (7–142), we get

$$V = \frac{AE\pi^2}{16L} \sum_{n=1}^{\infty} n^2 q_n{}^2 \qquad (7\text{–}143)$$

In like manner, we compute the kinetic energy to be

$$T = \frac{\rho A}{2} \int_0^L \left(\frac{\partial u}{\partial t}\right)^2 dx = \frac{\rho A L}{4} \sum_{n=1}^{\infty} \dot{q}_n{}^2 \qquad (7\text{–}144)$$

The general Lagrange equation is

$$\frac{d}{dt}\left(\frac{\partial T}{\partial \dot{q}_n}\right) - \frac{\partial T}{\partial q_n} + \frac{\partial V}{\partial q_n} = Q_n \qquad (7\text{--}145)$$

Then

$$\frac{d}{dt}\left(\frac{\partial T}{\partial \dot{q}_n}\right) = \frac{d}{dt}\left(\frac{\rho AL}{2}\sum_{n=1}^{\infty}\dot{q}_n\right) = \frac{\rho AL}{2}\sum_{n=1}^{\infty}\ddot{q}_n$$

$$\frac{\partial T}{\partial q_n} = 0$$

and

$$\frac{\partial V}{\partial q_n} = \frac{AE\pi^2}{8L}\sum_{n=1}^{\infty}n^2 q_n{}^2 \qquad (7\text{--}146)$$

The D.E. of motion for a single mode of vibration is

$$\frac{\rho AL}{2}\ddot{q}_n + \frac{AE\pi^2 n^2}{8L}q_n = Q_n \qquad (7\text{--}147)$$

For the moment let Q_n be replaced by a unit force $1(t)$. Then

$$\ddot{q}_n + \frac{E\pi^2 n^2}{4L^2\rho}q_n = \frac{2}{\rho AL}1(t) \qquad (7\text{--}148)$$

The solution then is

$$q_n = A_n{}' \sin\frac{n\pi c}{2L}t + B_n{}' \cos\frac{n\pi c}{2L}t + \frac{8L}{A\rho n^2\pi^2 c^2} \qquad (7\text{--}149)$$

where $c = \sqrt{E/\rho}$

To determine the value of the coefficients A' and B', we use as boundary conditions:

$$u(x,0) = 0$$

$$\left.\frac{\partial u}{\partial t}\right|_{t=0} = 0$$

Then

$$A_n{}' = 0 \qquad \text{and} \qquad B_n{}' = -\frac{8}{n^2\pi^2\rho A c^2}$$

and

$$A(t) = \sum_{n=1}^{\infty}\frac{8L}{n^2\pi^2\rho A c^2}\left(1 - \cos\frac{n\pi c}{2L}t\right)1(t) \qquad (7\text{--}150)$$

The response to a unit impulse is

$$\frac{dA}{d\tau} = h(t-\tau) = \sum_{n=1}^{\infty}\frac{4}{n\pi\rho A c}\sin\frac{n\pi c}{2L}(t-\tau) \qquad (7\text{--}151)$$

As a result of the foregoing,

$$q_n = \sum_{n=1}^{\infty} \frac{4}{n\pi\rho A c} \int_0^t F(\tau) \sin \frac{n\pi c}{2L} (t - \tau) \, d\tau \qquad (7\text{--}152)$$

Eq. (7–152) is a general solution for q_n of the longitudinal vibration of a bar with one fixed end with a forcing function $F(\tau)$ on the other.

First let us consider the forcing function to be a suddenly applied constant force P_0. Then

$$q_n = \sum_{n=1}^{\infty} \frac{4P_0}{n\pi\rho A c} \int_0^t \sin \frac{n\pi c}{2L} (t - \tau) \, d\tau$$

or $\qquad (7\text{--}153)$

$$q_n = \sum_{n=1}^{\infty} \frac{4P_0}{n\pi\rho A c} \int_0^t \left[\sin \frac{n\pi}{2L} t \cos \frac{n\pi}{2L} \tau - \cos \frac{n\pi}{2L} t \sin \frac{n\pi}{2L} \tau \right] d\tau$$

$$q_n = \sum_{n=1}^{\infty} \frac{8LP_0}{n^2\pi^2\rho A c^2} \left(1 - \cos \frac{n\pi c}{2L} t \right) \qquad (7\text{--}154)$$

Eq. (7–154) may now be substituted into Eq. (7–140) for the complete solution of a fixed end beam with a suddenly applied constant load P_0 at the free end.

Next we take the case when

$$F(\tau) = P_0 \sin \nu\tau \qquad (7\text{--}155)$$

Substituting for $F(\tau)$, we get

$$q_n = \sum_{n=1}^{\infty} \frac{4P_0}{n\pi\rho A c} \int_0^t \sin \nu\tau \sin \frac{n\pi c}{2L} (t - \tau) \, d\tau \qquad (7\text{--}156)$$

Eq. (7–156) may be rewritten as

$$q_n = \sum_{n=1}^{\infty} \frac{4P_0}{n\pi\rho A c} \left[\sin \frac{n\pi c}{2L} t \int_0^t \sin \nu\tau \cos \frac{n\pi c}{2L} \tau \, d\tau \right.$$

$$\left. - \cos \frac{n\pi c}{2L} t \int_0^t \sin \nu\tau \sin \frac{n\pi c}{2L} \tau \, d\tau \right] \qquad (7\text{--}157)$$

$$q_n = \sum_{n=1}^{\infty} \frac{4P_0}{n\pi\rho A c} \left[-\frac{1}{2} \sin \frac{n\pi c}{2L} t \left| \frac{\cos \left(\nu - \frac{n\pi c}{2L} \right) \tau}{\nu - \frac{n\pi c}{2L}} - \frac{\sin \left(\nu + \frac{n\pi c}{2L} \right) \tau}{\nu + \frac{n\pi c}{2L}} \right|_{}^{t} \right.$$

$$\left. -\frac{1}{2} \cos \frac{n\pi c}{2L} \left| \frac{\sin \left(\nu - \frac{n\pi c}{2L} \right) \tau}{\nu - \frac{n\pi c}{2L}} - \frac{\sin \left(\nu + \frac{n\pi c}{2L} \right) \tau}{\nu + \frac{n\pi c}{2L}} \right|_0^t \right] \qquad (7\text{--}158)$$

valid for $\nu \neq n\pi c/2L$.

$$
q_n = -\sum_{n=1}^{\infty} \frac{2P_0}{n\pi\rho Ac} \left[\sin\frac{n\pi c}{2L}t \left\{ \frac{\cos\left(\nu - \frac{n\pi c}{2L}\right)t}{\nu - \frac{n\pi c}{2L}} + \frac{\cos\left(\nu + \frac{n\pi c}{2L}\right)t}{\nu + \frac{n\pi c}{2L}} \right\} \right.
$$

$$
+ \cos\frac{n\pi c}{2L}t \left\{ \frac{\sin\left(\nu - \frac{n\pi c}{2L}\right)t}{\nu - \frac{n\pi c}{2L}} - \frac{\sin\left(\nu + \frac{n\pi c}{2L}\right)t}{\nu + \frac{n\pi c}{2L}} \right\}
$$

$$
\left. - \left\{ \frac{1}{\nu - \frac{n\pi c}{2L}} + \frac{1}{\nu + \frac{n\pi c}{2L}} \right\} \sin\frac{n\pi c}{2L}t \right] \tag{7–159}
$$

Equation (7–159) may be written as

$$
q_n = \frac{4P_0\nu}{\pi\rho Ac} \sum_{n=1}^{\infty} \frac{1}{n} \left(\frac{1}{\nu^2 - \frac{n^2\pi^2 c^2}{4L^2}} \right) \left[\sin\frac{n\pi c}{2L}t - \sin\nu t \right] \tag{7–160}
$$

Eq. (7–160) is now substituted into Eq. (7–140) for the complete solution, which is

$$
u(x,t) = \frac{4P_0\nu}{\pi\rho Ac} \sum_{n=1}^{\infty} \frac{1}{n} \left(\frac{1}{\nu^2 - \frac{n^2\pi^2 c^2}{4L^2}} \right) \sin\frac{n\pi}{2L}x \left[\sin\frac{n\pi c}{2L}t - \sin\nu t \right] \tag{7–161}
$$

Though the method discussed in this section has been applied only to a bar with one end fixed, there is no reason why bars with other end conditions may not be treated in the same manner. In fact the method is sufficiently general so that it can be applied to any of the problems discussed in this chapter.

BIBLIOGRAPHY

HANSEN, H. M., and CHENEA, PAUL F. *Mechanics of Vibration.* New York: John Wiley & Sons, Inc., 1952.

McLACHLAN, N. W. *Theory of Vibrations.* New York: Dover Publications, 1951.

TIMOSHENKO, S. *Vibration Problems in Engineering.* Princeton, N. J.: D. Van Nostrand Co., Inc., 1928.

PROBLEMS

7-1. Determine the resultant motion when a taut string is plucked at $x = L/3$ with an amplitude of y_0.

7-2. A taut string is initially set in motion by giving each point along the string an initial velocity of v_0. Determine the equation of motion for the string.

7-3. Give a physical explanation of why the even harmonics vanish when a string is plucked at the center. (*Hint:* Examine the nodal points of even harmonics.)

7-4. Determine the characteristic equation from which the natural frequencies of lateral vibration can be deduced for a beam of constant cross-section of which one end is built in, the other simply supported. (This is the case of a shaft with one journal and one ball bearing.)

7-5. Determine the natural frequency of the lateral vibration of a free-free beam (moment and shear are equal to zero at each end). To simplify the calculations, let β_i represent the roots of the characteristic equation from which the natural frequencies are determined.

7-6. Determine the natural frequencies and equation of motion of the lateral vibration of a beam of constant cross-section, one end of which is built in, the other end is free. Let β_i represent the roots of the characteristic equation.

7-7. Determine the characteristic equation for the natural frequency of the lateral vibration for a beam of uniform cross-section supported as shown in Fig. P7-7.

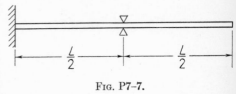

FIG. P7-7.

7-8. Determine the characteristic equation and then the natural frequencies for the torsional vibration for a round shaft of uniform cross-section when the ends are free-free.

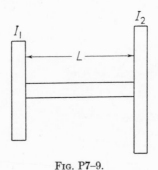

FIG. P7-9.

7-9. Find the characteristic equation for the natural frequencies of the torsional vibration of a circular shaft which has a disc at each end, the mass moments of inertia of which are I_1 and I_2.

7–10. Determine the equation of motion for the longitudinal vibration of a bar of uniform cross-section with the ends built in (Fig. P7–10). At time equal to zero there is a strain in the bar due to a load acting at the center. In one half of the bar, the strain is positive; in the other, negative. The load is suddenly removed, and a longitudinal vibration results.

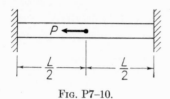

FIG. P7–10.

7–11. A force of P_0 is suddenly applied to the free end of a bar, the other end of which is fixed. The force remains in contact with the end of the bar during the time t_0 and then is removed, that is

$$F(\tau) = \frac{P_0,\ 0^+ \leq t \leq t_0}{0,\ t > t_0}$$

Determine the longitudinal vibration of the bar.

7–12. A circular cross-section shaft with one end fixed is acted upon by a moment M_0 suddenly applied at the free end. Determine the torsional equation of motion of the shaft.

7–13. Determine the general solution for the longitudinal vibration for a free-free bar for a function $F(\tau)$ by applying a unit force $1(t)$. (*Hint:* let

$$u = \sum_{n=1}^{\infty} q_n \cos \frac{n\pi x}{L} \cdot \bigg)$$

CHAPTER 8

MISCELLANEOUS TOPICS

8-1. Electrical-Mechanical Analogy. Kirchhoff's law, which states that the algebraic sum of the voltage drops around a circuit is zero, is analogous to Newton's second law of motion as expressed by D'Alembert's principle. For one reason or another, mechanical engineers seem to be more at home with electrical parameters than with mechanical. This preference may in part be due to the engineering student's introduction to electrical circuits long before he is introduced to topics of advanced dynamics. It may also in part be due to the fact that the electrical engineers have devised methods of solving circuit problems without the use of differential equations. Be this as it may, because of this reputed preference, it is necessary to discuss the analogous situation between electrical circuits and mechanical vibration systems.

The task before us will not be to outline the solution of electrical circuit problems, but to show the correspondence between electrical and mechanical parameters and also to establish that the differential equations of both systems are of identical form. At the outset, let us restrict our discussion to systems in which the electromotive force is analogous to the mechanical force. There is another concept wherein the current is analogous to the mechanical force. There is much to be said concerning these two systems. However, lack of space prevents us from giving a full discussion to each system. We will therefore confine our discussions to the emf system.

The electrical parameters are L, C, R, and $e(t)$, which, respectively, are inductance, capacitance, resistance, and voltage. The voltages across each of these parameters are:

Across capacitance: $\dashv\vdash$, $e_c = \dfrac{1}{C} \displaystyle\int i\, dt = \dfrac{1}{C} q$

Across inductance: $\sim\!\ell\ell\ell\!\sim$, $e_L = L\dfrac{di}{dt} = L\dfrac{d^2q}{dt^2}$

Across resistance: $\sim\!\!\bigwedge\!\!\sim$, $e_R = iR = R\dfrac{dq}{dt}$ (8-1)

where i is the current and q the charge. The relationship between i and

232

q is given by

$$\int i \, dt = q$$

or

$$i = \frac{dq}{dt}$$

(8–2)

(a)   (b)

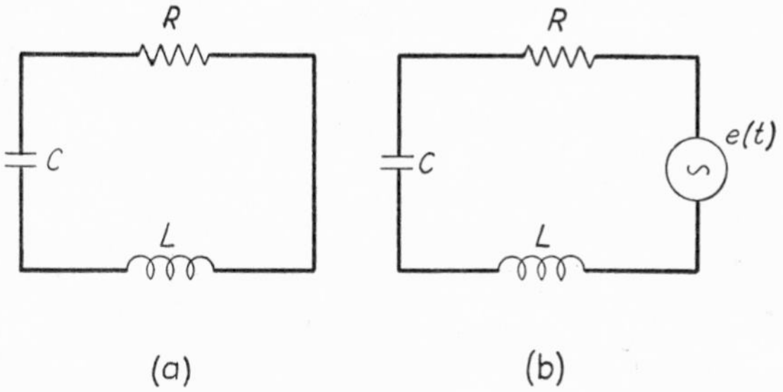

FIG. 8–1.

Let us now put the L, C, and R components into series in a closed circuit, Fig. 8–1a. To satisfy Kirchhoff's law, we sum the voltage drops across the L, C, and R elements, setting the sum equal to zero. Then

$$L\frac{d^2q}{dt^2} + R\frac{dq}{dt} + \frac{1}{C} q = 0$$

(8–3)

Compare Eq. (8–3) to the D.E. of a free single-degree vibrating system with damping, namely,

$$m\ddot{x} + c\dot{x} + kx = 0$$

or

$$I\ddot{\theta} + c\dot{\theta} + k_t\theta = 0$$

(8–4)

We draw the conclusion that

x or θ corresponds to q

m or I corresponds to L

c corresponds to R

(8–5)

k or k_t corresponds to $\dfrac{1}{C}$

As a result of the first of the above correspondences, we relate the time derivatives of x or θ to the derivatives of q: that is,

$\dot{x}$ or $\dot{\theta}$ corresponds to $\dot{q}$

and

(8–6)

$\ddot{x}$ or $\ddot{\theta}$ corresponds to $\ddot{q}$

To complete our analogy, let us insert an emf source in our L, C, and R circuit, Fig. 8–1b. Since the voltage source is opposing the voltage drops in the circuit, we may write the D.E. for the circuit as

$$L\ddot{q} + R\dot{q} + \frac{1}{C} q = e(t) \tag{8-7}$$

which corresponds to the mechanical system differential equations

$$m\ddot{x} + c\dot{x} + kx = F(t)$$

or $\tag{8-8}$

$$I\ddot{\theta} + c\dot{\theta} + k_t\theta = M(t)$$

$e(t)$ corresponds to $F(t)$ or $M(t)$ and may be a constant or a function of time.

The conversion from mechanical to electrical systems may best be explained by several examples. Fig. 8–2 contains several diagrams of conversions. The simple L, C, and R circuit represented by Eq. (8–3) and its mechanical equivalent are drawn in Fig. 8–2a. We notice that the spring and damper are in parallel while their electrical equivalents are connected in series. We can make the statement that parallel mechanical circuits are represented as series electrical circuits. If we remember that the force acting on a parallel mechanical system is the sum of the forces through each of the parallel elements, then it is quite obvious that we must connect the electrical system in series. A series electrical connection gives us individual voltage drops across each element, while a parallel electrical system has the same voltage drop across each element. The same reasoning is applied to series mechanical systems which are converted to parallel electrical circuits. Perhaps the easiest way to draw the electrical circuit is to remember that the electrical circuit must be a closed loop. In that way we can see that we must feed through all three elements of Fig. 8–2a to close the circuit.

Fig. 8–2b is a two-mass–three-spring mechanical system with a forcing function acting on m_1. Since k_1 and k_2 are in parallel, they convert to series condensers. We now can see that the two springs, the mass m_1, and $F(t)$ are all represented in a series electrical diagram which still is not a closed loop. We close the loop by inserting C_3 which represents k_3. Since m_2 is attached to k_3, we put C_3 and L_2 in a closed series loop. Our electrical diagram is now complete. We note that C_1 and C_2 are in parallel with C_3, which corresponds with k_1 and k_2 being in series with k_3.

Fig. 8–2c represents a fairly complicated damped system. We convert to an electrical circuit in the same manner as outlined above. The three springs which are in series become three condensers in parallel. The dampers are in parallel, therefore they are in series in each of the two electrical loops and are represented by R_1 and R_2. The masses are inserted in series in their respective series circuit and $F(t)$ acting on m_2 becomes $e(t)$ con-

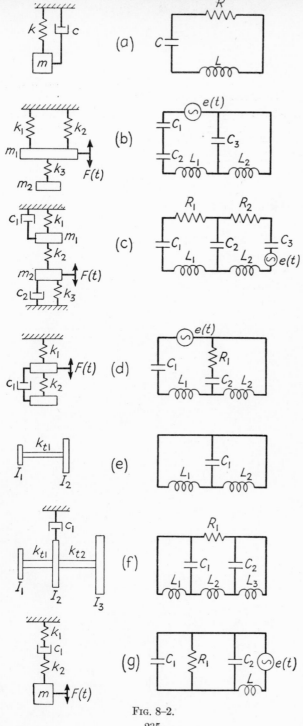

(a)

(b)

(c)

(d)

(e)

(f)

(g)

Fig. 8–2.

235

nected in series with L_2. We again note that we have two loops in the electrical circuit, with C_2 now being the common connector between the loops.

The justification of the conversions for the remaining systems of Fig. 8–2 is left to the reader. The conversions may be verified by proceeding in a manner similar to the other diagrams.

The method whereby electrical circuits are solved will not be dealt with in this text. In its place we will discuss, in Section 8–2, the mobility method, which is in effect applying electrical circuit solution techniques directly to mechanical parameters.

Since the equations for both the mechanical and electrical systems are of identical form, an experimental determination of an electrical circuit will give results which are proportional to the mechanical. Not too many years ago analogous electrical circuits were used for determining mechanical vibration systems. However, with introduction of the analogue computers, the interest in analogous electrical circuits has nearly vanished. This much should be said about analogous circuits: the problem is one of similitude and is best approached through the means of dimensional analysis.[1,2] Because of the general use of the analogue computer, which will be discussed in Section 8–3, we omit any discussion of similitude and the subsequent experimental determination of mechanical vibrations by analogous electrical circuits.

8–2. Mobility Method. As an alternative to solving vibration problems by way of the electrical-mechanical analogy, F. A. Firestone[3] in 1938 proposed a mobility concept. In Firestone's proposal, he likens the mobility of mechanical or acoustical systems to the admittance, which is the reciprocal of impedance, of electrical circuits. Mobility is defined by Firestone as

$$Z = \frac{V}{F}$$

where Z is the mobility, V is the velocity, and F is the force. With time, other authors have given other definitions to mobility. W. T. Thomson,[4] who uses the term "mechanical impedance" instead of mobility, defines impedance as

$$Z_{\text{mech}} = \frac{F}{V} \tag{8–9}$$

---

[1] P. W. Bridgman, *Dimensional Analysis* (New Haven: Yale University Press, 1931).

[2] Glenn Murphy, *Similitude in Engineering* (New York: The Ronald Press Co., 1950).

[3] F. A. Firestone, "The Mobility Method of Computing the Vibration of Linear Mechanical and Acoustical Systems: Mechanical-Electrical Analogies," *Journal of Applied Physics*, 9 (June, 1938), 373.

[4] William Tyrrell Thomson, *Mechanical Vibrations*, 2d ed. (Englewood Cliffs, N. J.: Prentice-Hall, Inc., 1953).

Thomson's definition is analogous to electrical impedance. Hansen and Chenea[5] have an entirely different definition. They define mobility as

$$z = \frac{1}{a} \qquad (8\text{-}10)$$

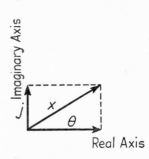

FIG. 8–3.

where a is the amplitude of displacement. The Hansen and Chenea definition will be used in this text because of its straightforward simplicity of approach.

Since the solution of vibration problems by the mobility method will use the techniques used in solving electrical circuits, we shall first review the concepts of complex algebra. Let us draw a displacement vector x, Fig. 8–3, on the complex plane. The real and imaginary axes (j will denote the imaginary axis) are as marked. Then the displacement vector may be written as

$$x = A + jB = \sqrt{A^2 + B^2}\,(\cos\theta + j\sin\theta) \qquad (8\text{-}11)$$

From Euler's relations, Eq. (2–23), we see that

$$e^{j\theta} = \cos\theta + j\sin\theta \qquad (8\text{-}12)$$

The displacement vector may now be written as

$$x = \sqrt{A^2 + B^2}\,e^{j\theta} \qquad (8\text{-}13)$$

where $\theta = \tan^{-1}B/A$.

We must keep track of the signs of both A and B in order to determine in which quadrant θ falls. If we write that

$$x = X_0 e^{j\nu t} \qquad (8\text{-}14)$$

where $X_0 = \sqrt{A^2 + B^2}$ and $\theta = \nu t$, we find by differentiation that

$$\dot{x} = j\nu X_0 e^{j\nu t}$$

and
$$\qquad (8\text{-}15)$$
$$\ddot{x} = -\nu^2 X_0 e^{j\nu t}$$

Let us also recall that a harmonic forcing function can be represented by

$$F = F_0 e^{j\nu t} \qquad (8\text{-}16)$$

where F is the harmonic function, F_0 is the amplitude, and ν is the forcing frequency.

[5] H. M. Hansen and Paul F. Chenea, *Mechanics of Vibration* (New York: John Wiley & Sons, Inc., 1952).

Complex quantities are subject to certain rules of complex algebra. They are:

(1) *Addition*:

$$(A + jB) + (C + jD) = (A + C) + j(B + D)$$

The real quantities and the imaginary quantities are added separately.

(2) *Subtraction*:

$$(A + jB) - (C + jD) = (A - C) + j(B - D)$$

The process of subtraction is the same as the process of addition where we add a negative quantity.

(3) *Multiplication*:

$$(A+jB)(C+jD)=AC+jAD+jBC+j^2BD=(AC-BD)+j(AD+BC).$$

(4) *Division*:

$$\frac{A + jB}{C + jD} = \frac{(A + jB)(C - jD)}{(C + jD)(C - jD)}$$

$$= \frac{(AC + BD) + j(BC - AD)}{C^2 + D^2}$$

The conjugate of $(C + jD)$ is $(C - jD)$, and the complex number times its conjugate yields a real number.

(5) *Multiplication and division in polar form:*

$$X_1 e^{j\nu_1 t} \cdot X_2 e^{j\nu_2 t} = X_1 X_2 e^{j(\nu_1 + \nu_2)t}$$

and

$$\frac{X_1 e^{j\nu_1 t}}{X_2 e^{j\nu_2 t}} = \frac{X_1}{X_2} e^{j(\nu_1 - \nu_2)t}$$

We are now prepared to proceed with a discussion of the mobility concept. Let us determine the mobility across each of the elements of a vibrating system; namely, the spring, damper, and mass.

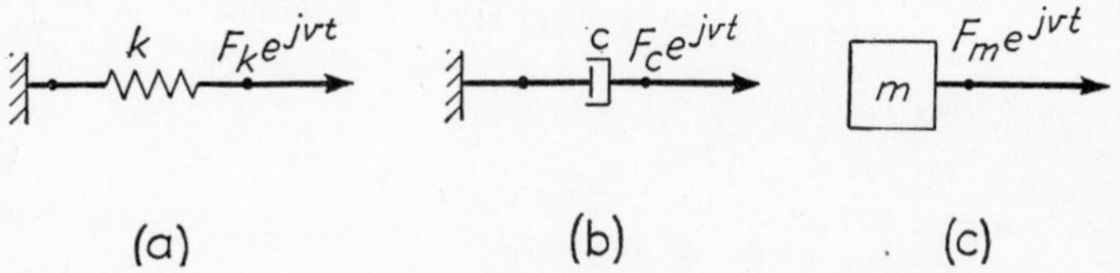

(a)   (b)   (c)

FIG. 8–4.

a. *Spring mobility.* We apply a force $F_k e^{j\nu t}$ to the free terminal of a spring, Fig. 8–4a, the other terminal being fixed. If we define

$$X_k = \text{total displacement due to } F_k e^{j\nu t}$$

and

$$x_k = \text{unit displacement due to } e^{j\nu t}$$

(8–17)

then the total force acting on the spring in terms of displacement is

$$F_k e^{j\nu t} = k X_k$$

or (8–18)

$$X_k = \frac{1}{k} F_k e^{j\nu t}$$

For a unit force we get

$$x_k = \frac{1}{k} e^{j\nu t} = a_k e^{j\nu t} \tag{8–19}$$

where $a_k = 1/k$ and is considered to be the amplitude of the unit displacement. We must remember that all of the displacements, velocities, and accelerations are vector quantities. By substituting the definition of mobility, Eq. (8–10), we get

$$x_k = \frac{1}{z_k} e^{j\nu t} \tag{8–20}$$

where

$$z_k = \frac{1}{a_k}$$

It is obvious that

$$z_k = k \tag{8–21}$$

and that the mobility is a measure of the stiffness of the spring. Differentiation with respect to time of Eq. (8–20) gives us the velocity and acceleration across the terminals of the spring:

$$\dot{x}_k = \frac{j\nu e^{j\nu t}}{z_k}$$

and (8–22)

$$\ddot{x}_k = -\frac{\nu^2 e^{j\nu t}}{z_k}$$

b. *Damper Mobility.* Fig. 8–4b is a schema of a force $F_c e^{j\nu t}$ acting at one terminal of a damper with the other end fixed. Then

$$F_c e^{j\nu t} = c\dot{X}_c$$

or (8–23)

$$\dot{X}_c = \frac{F_c}{c} e^{j\nu t}$$

where $\dot{X}_c$ is the velocity of the displacement across the terminals of the dashpot due to the force. For a unit force

$$\dot{x}_c = \frac{1}{c} e^{j\nu t} \tag{8–24}$$

Then

$$x_c = \frac{1}{c} \int e^{j\nu t} = \frac{1}{j\nu c} e^{j\nu t} \qquad (8\text{--}25)$$

If we let

$$a_c = \frac{1}{j\nu c} \qquad (8\text{--}26)$$

then $x_c = a_c e^{j\nu t}$.

The mobility is then defined as

$$z_c = \frac{1}{a_c} = j\nu c \qquad (8\text{--}27)$$

and is a measure of the frequency times the damping strength. The higher the frequency or the stronger the damping, the greater will the damper resistance be.

The acceleration across the dashpot terminals can be computed as

$$\ddot{x}_c = \frac{j\nu}{c} e^{j\nu t} \qquad (8\text{--}28)$$

c. *Mass Mobility.* Fig. 8–4c is a mass resting on a frictionless plane, which is being acted upon by a force $F_m e^{j\nu t}$. Then

$$F_m e^{j\nu t} = m\ddot{X}_m$$

$$\qquad (8\text{--}29)$$

or

$$X_m = \frac{F_m}{m} e^{j\nu t}$$

where X_m is the displacement of the mass due to the force $F_m e^{j\nu t}$. We now integrate Eq. (8–29) twice to yield the velocity and the displacement. For a unit force,

$$\dot{x}_m = \frac{1}{j\nu m} e^{j\nu t} \qquad (8\text{--}30)$$

and

$$x_m = -\frac{1}{\nu^2 m} e^{j\nu t} \qquad (8\text{--}31)$$

where x_m is the displacement due to a unit force. We write

$$x_m = a_m e^{j\nu t} \qquad (8\text{--}32)$$

where

$$a_m = -\frac{1}{\nu^2 m}$$

Then

$$z_m = \frac{1}{a_m} = -\nu^2 m \qquad (8\text{--}33)$$

The mobility of the mass is a measure of the mass times the square of the velocity and is a measure of resistance to the acceleration.

Having determined the individual mobilities for the spring, damper, and mass, our next task is to apply the method to a system with these

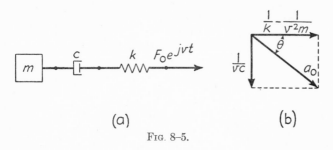

(a)   (b)

FIG. 8–5.

elements interconnected. Let us first consider a system which is so connected that all the elements are in series, Fig. 8–5a. Since the system is in series,

$$F_0 = F_k = F_c = F_m \tag{8–34}$$

The total displacement per unit load will be the sum of the individual displacements; that is

$$a_0 = a_k + a_c + a_m$$

or in general   (8–35)

$$a_{0 \text{ series}} = \sum a$$

We can deduce from the latter of Eqs. (8–35) that in general

$$z_{0 \text{ series}} = \frac{1}{\sum a} = \frac{1}{\sum \dfrac{1}{z}} \tag{8–36}$$

Then the displacement per unit load for the system sketched in Fig. 8–5a is

$$a_0 = \frac{1}{k} + \frac{1}{jvc} - \frac{1}{v^2 m}$$

$$a_0 = \left(\frac{1}{k} - \frac{1}{v^2 m}\right) - \frac{j}{vc} \tag{8–37}$$

We must remember that a_0 is a vector and therefore it is made up of two vectorial components, one along the real axis, the value of which is $(1/k) - (1/v^2 m)$, the other along the imaginary axis, $-1/vc$. These vectors are plotted in Fig. 8–5b. The resultant displacement is

$$a_0 = \sqrt{\left(\frac{1}{k} - \frac{1}{v^2 m}\right)^2 - \left(\frac{1}{vc}\right)^2} \, \underline{|\theta} \qquad (8\text{–}38)$$

where

$$\theta = \tan^{-1} \frac{-\dfrac{1}{vc}}{\dfrac{1}{k} - \dfrac{1}{v^2 m}}$$

$$A_0 = F_0 a_0 \qquad (8\text{–}39)$$

where A_0 is the total amplitude due to the force $F_0 e^{jvt}$.

If we are dealing with a free vibration then we set F_0 equal to zero. Then

$$\frac{A_0}{a_0} = 0$$

To find the natural frequency we set

$$\frac{1}{a_0} = z_0 = 0$$

which will yield the characteristic equation.

Let us now consider a system which has its spring, damper, and mass arranged in parallel, Fig. 8–6a. To allay any doubt as to whether the sys-

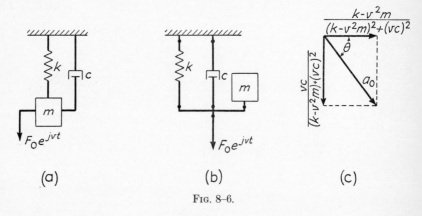

(a)   (b)   (c)

Fig. 8–6.

tem is in parallel, let us rearrange the system as is shown in Fig. 8–6b. It can be readily seen from the second arrangement that the displacements of k, c, and m are all the same. Therefore the system is in a parallel arrangement. Then

$$a_{0\,\text{parallel}} = a_k = a_c = a_m \qquad (8\text{–}40)$$

$$A_0 = F_k a_k = F_c a_c = F_m a_m \qquad (8\text{–}41)$$

and

$$A_0 = \frac{F_0}{z_0} = \frac{F_k}{z_k} = \frac{F_c}{z_c} = \frac{F_m}{z_m} \qquad (8\text{-}42)$$

Now

$$F_0 = F_k + F_c + F_m \qquad (8\text{-}43)$$

Then

$$A_0 z_0 = A_0 z_k + A_0 z_c + A_0 z_m$$

or $\qquad (8\text{-}44)$

$$z_0 = z_k + z_c + z_m$$

In general, for systems whose elements are connected in parallel, we can say that

$$z_{0 \text{ parallel}} = \sum z \qquad (8\text{-}45)$$

For the system at hand, we get

$$z_0 = k + j\nu c - \nu^2 m = (k - \nu^2 m) + j\nu c \qquad (8\text{-}46)$$

Then

$$a_0 = \frac{1}{(k - \nu^2 m) + j\nu c} = \frac{(k - \nu^2 m) - j\nu c}{(k - \nu^2 m)^2 + (\nu c)^2}$$

or $\qquad (8\text{-}47)$

$$A_0 = \frac{F_0(k - \nu^2 m) - j\nu c}{(k - \nu^2 m)^2 + (\nu c)^2}$$

We find the vector a_0 in Fig. 8-6c, where

$$a_0 = \sqrt{\frac{(k - \nu^2 m)^2 + (\nu c)^2}{[(k - \nu^2 m)^2 - (\nu c)^2]^2}} \underline{|\theta}$$

$$a_0 = \frac{1}{\sqrt{(k - \nu^2 m)^2 - (\nu c)^2}} \underline{|\theta} \qquad (8\text{-}48)$$

where

$$\theta = \tan^{-1} \frac{-\nu c}{k - \nu^2 m}$$

The total amplitude A_0, then, is

$$A_0 = \frac{F_0}{\sqrt{(k - \nu^2 m)^2 + (\nu c)^2}} \qquad (8\text{-}49)$$

If F_0 is equal to zero, we find the natural frequency by setting the denominator of either Eq. (8-48) or Eq. (8-49) equal to zero, which will yield the characteristic equation. We can also find the natural frequency by setting $z_0 = 0$, Eq. (8-46), which will give us the characteristic equation in complex form.

Example. Consider a system as sketched in Fig. 8–7a. Determine the amplitude of the mass.

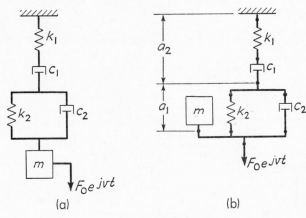

Fig. 8–7.

SOLUTION. We rearrange the system as shown in Fig. 8–7b. It is now clear that one part of the system is in parallel, the other part is in series, and the two parts are connected in series. Since the part which is in parallel is identical with the parallel problem just solved, we can write referring to Eq. (8–47),

$$a_1 = \frac{1}{k_2 - \nu^2 m + j\nu c_2}$$

Now the total unit force displacement is $a_0 = a_1 + a_2$. We see that

$$a_2 = \frac{1}{k_1} + \frac{1}{j\nu c_1}$$

Then $a_0 = \dfrac{1}{k_1} + \dfrac{1}{j\nu c_1} + \dfrac{1}{(k_2 - \nu^2 m) + j\nu c_2}$

$$= \frac{1}{k_1} - \frac{j}{\nu c_1} + \frac{(k_2 - \nu^2 m) - j\nu c_2}{(k_2 - \nu^2 m)^2 + \nu^2 c_2{}^2}$$

$$= \frac{1}{k_1} + \frac{k_2 - \nu^2 m}{(k_2 - \nu^2 m)^2 + \nu^2 c_2{}^2} - j\left[\frac{1}{\nu c_1} + \frac{c_2}{(k_2 - \nu^2 m)^2 + \nu^2 c_2{}^2}\right]$$

$$= \frac{1}{(k_2 - \nu^2 m)^2 + \nu^2 c_2{}^2}\left\{\frac{(k_2 - \nu^2 m)^2 + \nu^2 c_2{}^2 + k_1(k_2 - \nu^2 m)}{k_1}\right.$$

$$\left. - j\left[\frac{(k_2 - \nu^2 m)^2 + \nu^2(c_2{}^2 + c_1 c_2)}{\nu c_1}\right]\right\}$$

$$A_0 = \frac{F_0}{(k - v^2m)^2 + v^2c_2{}^2} \left\{ \left[\frac{(k_2 - v^2m)^2 + v^2c_2{}^2 + k_1(k_2 - v^2m)}{k_1} \right]^2 \right.$$
$$\left. + \left[\frac{(k_2 - v^2m)^2 + v^2(c_2{}^2 + c_1c_2)}{vc_1} \right]^2 \right\}^{1/2} \underline{|\theta}$$

where

$$\theta = \tan^{-1} = \frac{-k_1[(k_2 - v^2m)^2 + v^2(c_2{}^2 + c_1c_2)]}{vc_1[(k_2 - v^2m)^2 + v^2c_2{}^2 + k_1(k_2 - v^2m)]}$$

Though the mobility method has been explained only in terms of linear springs and masses, it is equally applicable to shafts and discs. It is an aid, however, to represent schematically the shaft and disc system as springs and masses so that the amplitudes and the mobilities become more apparent.

A note of caution concludes this discussion of the mobility method. The mobilities for the several vibration elements were derived by using a force of F_0e^{jvt}. Since the force is sinusoidal by nature, a system which is acted upon by any other type of force does not respond to mobility analysis.

8–3. Analogue Computers. One of the recent advances in the study of mechanical vibration problems has come about through the introduction of the analogue computer. In the sense that we are about to discuss the analogue computer, we should really refer to this piece of equipment as a differential analyzer. The equipment is basically assembled from a number of high-gain electronic amplifiers. The mathematical properties of the amplifiers are threefold: (a) multiplication, (b) integration, and (c) summing.

First let us consider the heart of the computer; namely, the amplifier. A high-gain amplifier of the order of ten to forty thousand should be used. The voltage output should be about 100 volts or less. The stability of the amplifier, that is, its lack of drift, should be fairly high. The required stability is a function of the accuracy desired or necessary to solve a given problem. There is no need to study the make-up of the amplifier; for our purpose we can consider it to be a black box which performs according to its label.

a. Multiplication. Fig. 8–8 is a schematic representation of the use of the amplifier as a multiplier. The amplifier is represented by a triangular block with the apex of the block representing the output. Since the output voltage of the amplifier is 100 volts or less, the input voltage e_0 is extremely small. The source current i_1 will always pass through a large resistor R_1, so that the amplifier input current i_0 is so small that it is negligible. Then, summing the currents we find:

$$i_1 + i_2 \doteqdot 0 \tag{8–50}$$

Now

$$i_1 = \frac{e_1}{R_1} \qquad \text{and} \qquad i_2 = \frac{e_2}{R_2} \qquad (8\text{-}51)$$

Then

$$\frac{e_1}{R_1} + \frac{e_2}{R_2} \doteqdot 0 \qquad (8\text{-}52)$$

whence

$$e_2 \doteqdot -\frac{R_2}{R_1} e_1 \qquad (8\text{-}53)$$

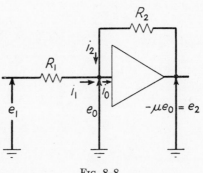

FIG. 8-8.

We now see that if we feed back from the output of the amplifier through a resistance R_2, the output voltage is governed by the ratio of the feedback resistance to the input resistance. The multiplying constant is negative. If $R_2 = R_1$, then we have a sign-changer. Both the multiplier and the sign-changer are useful components of the analogue computer.

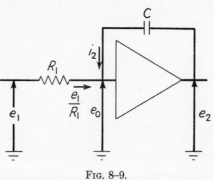

FIG. 8-9.

    b. Integration. If we replace resistor R_2 in Fig. 8-8 by a condenser, we have converted the amplifier into an integrator. This is shown in Fig. 8-9, where now the feedback is done through a condenser. Summing the currents at the input, we find

$$\frac{e_1}{R_1} + i_2 \doteqdot 0 \tag{8-54}$$

Now

$$C = \frac{q}{V} = \frac{\displaystyle\int_{t_1}^{t_2} i_2 \, dt}{e_2} \tag{8-55}$$

and

$$i_2 \doteqdot -\frac{e_1}{R_1} \tag{8-56}$$

Then

$$e_2 C \doteqdot -\int_{t_1=0}^{t_2} \frac{e_1}{R_1} \, dt$$

or $\qquad\qquad (8\text{--}57)$

$$e_2 \doteqdot -\frac{1}{CR_1} \int_0^{t_2} e_1 \, dt$$

We now can see that e_2 is the result of an integration. Hence the amplifier, when feedback is through a condenser, becomes a negative integrator.

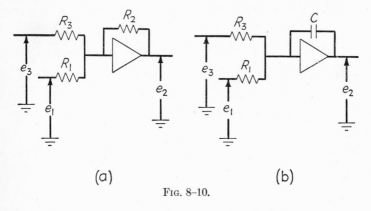

(a) (b)

FIG. 8–10.

c. *Summing.* Fig. 8–10a is the schematic of a summarizer. It is quite apparent from the foregoing that

$$e_2 \doteqdot -\frac{R_2}{R_1} e_1 - \frac{R_2}{R_3} e_3 \tag{8-58}$$

which shows that e_2 is the negative sum of e_1 and e_3. The summarizer need not be limited only to two inputs. Fig. 8–10b is an integrator summarizer and is governed by

$$e_2 \doteqdot -\int_{t_1=0}^{t_2} \left(\frac{e_1}{CR_1} + \frac{e_3}{CR_3} \right) dt \tag{8-59}$$

Let us assemble the elements described above so that they will analyse a differential equation. Let us consider first the harmonic equation which may be written in the following form:

$$\ddot{y} + \lambda^2 y = 0 \qquad (8\text{-}60)$$

Rearranging Eq. (8-60), we write

$$\ddot{y} = -\lambda^2 y \qquad (8\text{-}61)$$

The quantity to be integrated twice is $\ddot{y}$. We therefore let the input to amplifier ①, Fig. 8-11, be $-\lambda^2 y$. For the moment we do not worry about

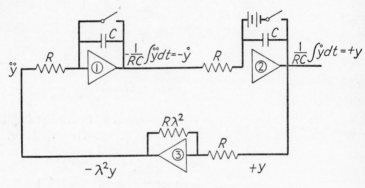

Fig. 8-11.

the source of $-\lambda^2 y$. The output of ① will be $-\dot{y}$, which is the result of the first integration. The constant of integration $1/RC$, is set equal to one by letting RC have a value of one; or we change the time scale to

$$t' = \frac{t}{RC} \qquad (8\text{-}62)$$

where t is the true time and t' the new time. Increasing R slows down the output. We now repeat the process at amplifier ②. The input is now $-\dot{y}$ and the output will be $+y$. We feed $+y$ through a multiplier so that we get at the output end of amplifier ③, $-\lambda^2 y$. We now have the source for our $\ddot{y}$, which results from connecting ③ to ①. In order to start our problem, we must set up the initial conditions. If the initial displacement of the system is y_0, we impress a voltage across amplifier ② while shorting out the condenser at ①. Opening the switches at ① and ② simultaneously releases the mass, and our vibration problem begins. The voltage source, or initial conditions, are usually a built-in feature of the computer. The required output y may be recorded on a recorder or seen on an oscilloscope. If more than one channel is available on the recorder, we may record $-\dot{y}$ and/or $\ddot{y}$ simultaneously with y.

Let us now consider a damped forced vibration which may be represented by the following equation:

$$\ddot{y} + \zeta\dot{y} + \lambda^2 y = \frac{F}{m}\cos \nu t \tag{8-63}$$

We rewrite Eq. (8-63) so that our input at the first amplifier is seen to be

$$\ddot{y} = -\zeta\dot{y} - \lambda^2 y + \frac{F}{m}\cos \nu t \tag{8-64}$$

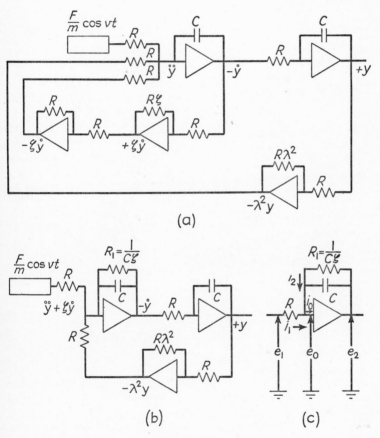

Fig. 8-12.

Fig. 8-12a is the schematic hookup for solving Eq. (8-63). $\ddot{y}$ is found as in the previous problem, except that we add from an outside source $F/m \cos \nu t$. This quantity can be obtained from a cosine generator, the amplitude of which is F/m and the frequency ν. A simpler circuit involving only three amplifiers will accomplish the feat performed by the five amplifiers of

Fig. 8–12a. The three-amplifier circuit is shown in Fig. 8–12b. We feed back at the first amplifier through a condenser and a resistor ($R_1 = C/\zeta$) connected in parallel to the input instead of just a condenser, as is done in Fig. 8–12a. Let us analyse the new circuit to see if we are accomplishing our task.

Let us rewrite Eq. (8–64) so that

$$\ddot{y} + \zeta\dot{y} = -\lambda^2 y + \frac{F}{m}\cos \nu t \qquad (8\text{–}65)$$

From the circuit diagram, we see that the input to the first amplifier is the R.H.S. of Eq. (8–65). Our proof of the circuit will rest on the fact that e_1 must be shown to be proportional to $\ddot{y} + \zeta\dot{y}$. Let us isolate the first amplifier, Fig. 8–12c. Now

$$i_1 \fallingdotseq -i_2 \qquad (8\text{–}66)$$

$$i_1 = \frac{e_1}{R} \qquad \text{and} \qquad i_2 = \frac{e_2 - e_0}{R_1} + C\frac{d}{dt}(e_2 - e_0)$$

It can be shown that e_0 can be considered negligible. However, such a proof requires the knowledge of the impedance of the amplifier. We will assume, without proof, that e_0 is negligible. Then

$$\frac{e_1}{R} \fallingdotseq -\left(\frac{e_2}{R_1} + C\dot{e}_2\right) \qquad (8\text{–}67)$$

Rearranging Eq. (8–67), we have

$$-\dot{e}_2 - \frac{e_2}{R_1 C} \fallingdotseq \frac{e_1}{RC} \qquad (8\text{–}68)$$

Now $e_2 = -\dot{y}$ and $R_1 = 1/C\zeta$; then

$$\ddot{y} + \zeta\dot{y} \fallingdotseq -\frac{e_1}{RC} \qquad (8\text{–}69)$$

Since RC is either unity or it is absorbed into the time scale, we have shown that the input to the amplifier is as required. Therefore circuits (a) and (b) of Fig. 8–12 are equivalent circuits, with (b) being the preferred one.

As our last circuit example, let us consider two simultaneous differential equations, in particular the case of the free vibration of two masses and two springs, Fig. 8–13a. The differential equations governing this system are

$$\begin{aligned} m_1\ddot{x}_1 + (k_1 + k_2)x_1 - k_2 x_2 &= 0 \\ m_2\ddot{x}_2 + k_2 x_2 - k_1 x_1 &= 0 \end{aligned} \qquad (8\text{–}70)$$

We rewrite these equations as

$$\ddot{x}_1 = -\frac{k_1 + k_2}{m_1} x_1 + \frac{k_2}{m_1} x_2$$

$$\ddot{x}_2 = -\frac{k_2}{m_2} x_2 + \frac{k_1}{m_2} x_1$$

(8–71)

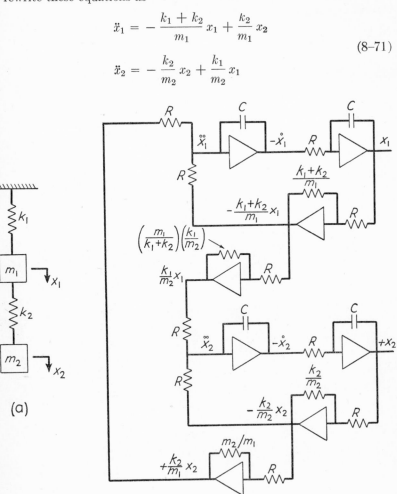

FIG. 8–13.

The wiring diagram is given in Fig. 8–13b. Eight amplifiers are necessary to accomplish this circuit. There are essentially two circuits which are cross-connected to take care of the coupling action. The only limitation to the solution of simultaneous equations is the number of amplifiers which are available.

There are many commercial analogue computers on the market today. Essentially they are collections of amplifiers. Many of the computers have built-in condensers and resistors so that the components are marked as integrators and sign-changers. There is nothing to be gained here by trying to discuss the different computers that are available today. However, one word of comment should be made on the fact that many of the computers are so designed as to be able to handle nonlinear as well as linear vibration problems. The solution to nonlinear differential equations may be accomplished by a servomechanism which will multiply a function by itself so that the function squared may be entered into the amplifiers. In fact, the servomechanism can be made to multiply the squared function by the function so that we have a cubed function, etc. There is another device known as a function-fitter which approximates a nonlinear function by small line segments which are interconnected by parabolic lines, thereby giving a fairly smooth function which reasonably approximates the original nonlinear function.

All of the above discussion has been given not in any attempt to make computer experts but to acquaint the reader with the basic fundamentals which are involved in the analogue computer.

BIBLIOGRAPHY

HAGELBARGER, D. W., HOWE, C. E., and HOWE, R. M. *Investigation of the Utility of an Electronic Analog Computer in Engineering Problems.* Aeronautical Research Center, Engineering Research Institute, University of Michigan, April 1, 1949.

OLSON, HARRY F. *Dynamical Analogies.* Princeton, N. J.: D. Van Nostrand Co., Inc., 1943.

PROBLEMS

8-1. Draw the analogous electrical circuit for the system shown in Fig. P8–1.

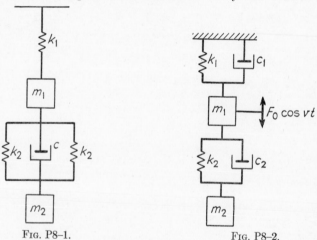

FIG. P8–1.   FIG. P8–2.

8-2. Draw the analogous electrical circuit for the system shown in Fig. P8–2.

8-3. Draw the analogous electrical circuit for the torsional system shown in Fig. P8–3.

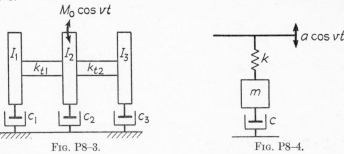

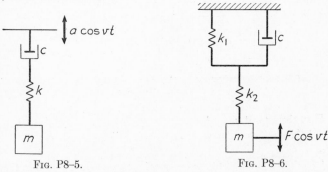

FIG. P8–3. FIG. P8–4.

8-4. Determine the amplitude of the mass for the system shown in Fig. P8–4, using the mobility method.

8-5. By means of the mobility method, determine the amplitude of the mass for the system shown in Fig. P8–5.

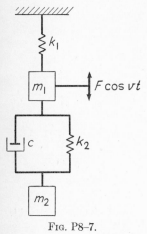

FIG. P8–5. FIG. P8–6.

8-6. Determine the amplitude of the mass for the system shown in Fig. P8–6, by means of the mobility method.

8-7. Determine the amplitude of the mass m_1 for the system shown in Fig. P8–7, by means of the mobility method.

8-8. Determine the amplitude of the mass for the system shown in Fig. P8–8.

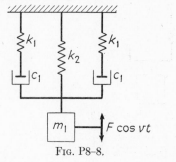

FIG. P8–7. FIG. P8–8.

8-9. Determine the amplitude of vibration for each of the discs in the system shown in Fig. P8-9. Use the mobility method.

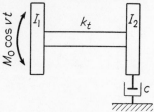

FIG. P8-9.

8-10. Do Problem 3-43 by means of the mobility method.

8-11. Do Problem 3-45 by means of the mobility method.

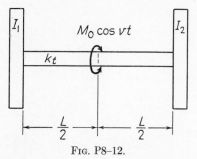

FIG. P8-12.

8-12. Find the amplitude of the disc when a torque $M_0 \cos vt$ is applied to the mid-point of the shaft as shown in Fig. P8-12. The total spring constant of the shaft is k_t.

8-13. Draw the analogue computer circuit for the system shown in Fig. P8-13. (This is the diagram for a damped vibration-absorber.)

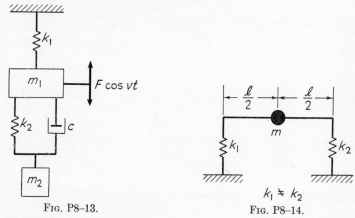

FIG. P8-13.

FIG. P8-14.

8-14. Draw the analogue computer circuit for the system shown in Fig. P8-14. The bar supporting the mass has a negligible weight.

ANSWERS TO PROBLEMS

1-1. $\dot{\rho} = 56.6$ ft./sec., $\ddot{\rho} = 14.14$ ft./sec.^{2}

1-2. $\dot{\rho} = 50$ in./sec., $\ddot{\rho} = 48$ in./sec.^{2}

1-3. $\dot{\theta} = \frac{3}{16}$ radian/sec., $\ddot{\theta} = -\frac{3}{16}$ radian/sec.^{2}

1-4. $v = 3$ ft./sec., $a = 3$ ft./sec.^{2}

1-11. 10.37 ft. above low water

1-16. $mv = -x_0 \sin kt$

1-17. $\ddot{\theta} + \left(\dfrac{k}{m} + \dfrac{2g}{l} \right) \sin \theta = 0$

2-1. $x = \dfrac{v_0}{\omega_{nd}} e^{-(c/2m)t} \sin \omega_{nd} t$

2-5. $\theta = \dfrac{\Omega}{\omega_n} \sin \sqrt{\dfrac{2g}{3(R + r)}}\, t$

2-6. $x = \frac{1}{2} \cos \sqrt{\dfrac{g}{l}}\, t$

3-1. $\theta = \theta_0 \cos \sqrt{\dfrac{4W}{3g} \left(\dfrac{a + r}{r} \right)^2}\, t$

3-4. $\tau = 0.943$ sec.

3-7. $I_{\text{c.g.}} = 2.03$ lbs.-in.-sec.^{2}

3-8. $\omega_n = \sqrt{\dfrac{kr^2}{I_0 + \dfrac{W}{g} R^2}}$

3-10. $\omega_n = \dfrac{2}{3} \sqrt{\dfrac{2k_t}{I}}$

3-12. $\omega_n = 61.3$ radians/sec., $\omega_n = 72.7$ radians/sec.

3-15. $\omega_{nd} = \sqrt{\dfrac{k}{m} - \left(\dfrac{c}{8m} \right)^2}$

3-17. $x = -0.463$ in.

3-21. $\theta_\mu = \dfrac{M_0 \cos \nu t}{k_t (1 - \beta^2)}$

3-22. $x_\mu = \dfrac{F}{k} \mu \cos (\nu t - \psi)$

255

3-26. $x = \left(\dfrac{v_0}{\omega_n} + \dfrac{Ft}{c_c}\right) \sin \omega_n t$

3-27. $x = \dfrac{F}{c_c}\left[t \cos \omega_n t - \dfrac{1}{\omega_n} \sin \omega_n t\right]$

3-29. $x = 6.58 \times 10^{-3}$ in.

3-32. $\zeta = \frac{1}{15}$

3-33. $x = \dfrac{m_p r \nu^2}{k(1 - \beta^2)} \cos \nu t$

3-36. (a) T.R. = 0.297, (b) T.R. = 0.0233

3-40. (a) $x = 0.0745$ in., (b) 0.1048

3-43. $x = 0.1714$ in.

3-45. $x = 1.208$ in.

3-46. $\nu \geq {\omega_n}^2 \sqrt{\dfrac{100 + \alpha}{\alpha}}$

3-50. $c_e = \dfrac{8bF\mu\nu}{3\pi k}$

4-2. $D = 2r\sqrt{\dfrac{G}{E}}$

4-4. ${\omega_n}_{1,2}{}^2 = \dfrac{k}{2}\left[\left(\dfrac{2}{m} + \dfrac{5l^2}{9I}\right) \pm \sqrt{\left(\dfrac{2}{m} + \dfrac{5l^2}{9I}\right)^2 - \dfrac{4l^2}{mI}}\right]$

4-9. ${\omega_n}_{1,2}{}^2 = \dfrac{\left(\dfrac{g}{l_1} + \dfrac{k}{m_1 l_1}\right) + \left(\dfrac{g}{l_2} + \dfrac{k}{m_2 l_2}\right)}{2}$

$$\pm \sqrt{\left[\left(\dfrac{g}{l_1} + \dfrac{k}{m_1 l_1}\right) + \left(\dfrac{g}{l_2} + \dfrac{k}{m_2 l_2}\right)\right]^2 - \dfrac{4g}{l_1 l_2}\left[g + \dfrac{k}{m_1} + \dfrac{k}{m_2}\right]}$$

4-10. ${\omega_n}_{1,2}{}^2 = 0, \sqrt{\dfrac{2}{3}k\left(\dfrac{m_1 + m_2}{m_1 m_2}\right)}$

4-11. ${\omega_n}_{1,2}{}^2 = 0$, 13.9 radians/sec.

4-12. $\theta_1 = \dfrac{k_{t2} M_0 \cos \nu t}{\Delta}$, $\theta_2 = \dfrac{(k_{t1} + k_{t2} - I_1 \nu^2) M_0 \cos \nu t}{\Delta}$,

where $\Delta = (k_{t1} + k_{t2} - I_1 \nu^2)(k_{t2} - I_2 \nu^2) - {k_{t2}}^2$

4-16. ${\omega_n}^2 = 4.06$, 18.35, radians/sec.

5-2. Assumed parabola $Ax^2 + Bx + Cy + D = 0$, whence $\omega_n = 3.46\sqrt{\dfrac{EI}{ml^4}}$;

method fails because end moments are not satisfied.

5-4. $\omega_n = 9.86\sqrt{\dfrac{EI}{mL^4}}$

5–6. $\omega_n = 27.1$ rad./sec.

5–10. $\omega_n = 389$ rad./sec.

5–19. L.H. end 0.5 oz.-in.
R.H. end 2.5 oz.-in.

6–1. $\dfrac{\partial\theta}{\partial y} = 2y\cos(3x + y^2); \dfrac{\partial\theta}{\partial x} = 3\cos(3x + y^2)$

$\dfrac{\partial^2\theta}{\partial y^2} = 2\cos(3x + y^2) - 4y^2\sin(3x + y^2); \dfrac{\partial^2\theta}{\partial x^2} = -9\sin(3x + y^2)$

$\dfrac{\partial^2\theta}{\partial y\partial x} = \dfrac{\partial^2\theta}{\partial x\partial y} = -6y\sin(3x + y^2)$

6–4. $\dfrac{dz}{dt} = -6t^5 + 15t^4 + 24t^3 - 18t^2 - 18t + 3$

6–7. $\dfrac{\partial\theta}{\partial t_1} = x^3 + 6x^2y + 6xy^2 + 4y^3$

$\dfrac{\partial\theta}{\partial t_2} = -5x^3 + 3x^2y - 30xy^2 + 2y^3$

6–8. $\left(\dfrac{m_1l_1{}^2}{3} + m_2l_1{}^2\right)\ddot\theta + \dfrac{m_2l_1l_2}{2}[\cos(\phi - \theta)]\ddot\phi +$

$\qquad\qquad \dfrac{m_2l_1l_2}{2}\dot\phi^2\sin(\phi - \theta) + gl_1\left(\dfrac{m_1}{2} + m_2\right)\sin\theta = 0,$

$\tfrac{2}{3}l_2{}^2\ddot\phi + l_1l_2[\cos(\phi - \theta)]\ddot\theta + l_1l_2\dot\phi^2\sin(\phi - \theta) + gl_2\sin\phi = 0$

6–12. $x = \dfrac{F[m_2ga + kl^2 - (a^2 + \mathbf{r}^2)m_2\nu^2]}{\Delta}\cos\nu t$

$\qquad \theta = \dfrac{Fkl}{\Delta}\cos\nu t,$

where

$$\Delta = \nu^4 - \dfrac{m_1m_2ga + m_1kl^2 - k(a^2 + \mathbf{r}^2)}{m_1m_2(a^2 + \mathbf{r}^2)}\nu^2 + \dfrac{kga}{m_1(a^2 + \mathbf{r}^2)}$$

7–1. $y = \dfrac{9y_0}{\pi^3}\displaystyle\sum_{n=1}^{\infty}\dfrac{1}{n^2}\sin\dfrac{n\pi}{3}\sin\dfrac{n\pi x}{L}\cos\dfrac{n\pi at}{L}$

7–2. $y = \dfrac{4v_0L}{\pi^2 a}\displaystyle\sum_{n=1}^{\infty}\dfrac{1}{(2n-1)^2}\sin\dfrac{(2n-1)\pi x}{L}\sin\dfrac{(2n-1)\pi at}{L}$

7–5. $\omega_n = \beta_i{}^2\sqrt{\dfrac{EI}{m}}$

where β_i are the roots of the transcendental equation $\cos kl\cosh kl = 1$

7–8. $\sin\lambda L = 0$, whence $\omega_n = \dfrac{n\pi}{L}\sqrt{\dfrac{G}{\rho}}$

7–10. $u = \dfrac{2PL}{AE\pi^2} \displaystyle\sum_{n=1}^{\infty} (-1)^{n-1} \dfrac{1}{(2n-1)^2} \sin \dfrac{(2n-1)\pi x}{L} \cos \dfrac{(2n-1)\pi ct}{L}$

8–7. $A_{m_1} = \dfrac{F[(k_2 - m_2\nu^2) + jc\nu]}{[(k_1 - m_1\nu^2)(k_2 - m_2\nu^2) - k_2 m_2\nu^2] + j\nu c[k_1 - (m_1 + m_2)\nu^2]}$

8–8. $A_0 = \dfrac{F(k_1 + j\nu c)}{k_1(k_2 - m\nu^2) + j\nu c(2k_1 + k_2 - m\nu^2)}$

8–11. $A_m = \dfrac{2(1 + j)}{(-2.11 + j)}$

INDEX